Machining of Composite Materials II

Proceedings of
ASM 1993 Materials Congress
Materials Week '93
October 17-21, 1993
Pittsburgh, Pennsylvania

Co-Sponsored by
ASM International® and
The Minerals, Metals and Materials Society

Edited by
T.S. Srivatsan, C.T. Lane and D.M. Bowden

Published by
ASM International®
Materials Park, Ohio 44073-0002

ASM
INTERNATIONAL

**The Materials
Information Society**

Library of Congress Cataloging Card Number: 93-074804
ISBN: 0-0-87170-489-7
SAN: 204-7586

ASM International®
Materials Park, OH 44073-0002

Printed in the United States of America

ORGANIZING COMMITTEE

T. S. Srivatsan
The University of Akron
Akron, Ohio

D. M. Bowden
McDonnell Douglas Aerospace
St. Louis, Missouri

C. T. Lane
Duralcan USA
San Diego, California

SESSION CHAIRMEN

D. Bhattacharyya
University of Auckland
Auckland, New Zealand

C. L. Lane
Duralcan USA
San Diego, California

H. Y. Puw
National Tsing Hua University
Hsinchu, Taiwan, ROC

D. Schuocker
Technical University of Vienna
Vienna, Austria

T. M. Yue
Hong Kong Polytechnic
Hong Kong

A. M. Gadalla
Texas A & M University
College Station, Texas

C. May
Lanxide Corporation
Newark, Delaware

S. K. Poon
Hong Kong Polytechnic
Hong Kong

I. Shareef
Bradley University
Peoria, Illinois

Preface

This volume is a collection of papers presented at the symposium "Machining of Composite Materials II," during ASM Materials Week '93 held 18-21 October in Pittsburgh, PA. This symposium, sponsored by the Machining Committee of the Materials Shaping Technology Division of ASM International, served as a forum for discussing a variety of machining methods being developed for use with advanced composite materials. A total of 20 papers covering a wide range of materials and machining techniques were presented in three sessions entitled:

Machining of Metal-Matrix Composites
Machining of Polymer- and Ceramic-Matrix Composites
Machining Technology

This proceedings is a companion volume to "Machining of Composite Materials," a collection of papers presented during the 1992 ASM Materials Week held in Chicago, Illinois. Together, these volumes present the latest information available on the machining processes that are critical to producing useful products from advanced composite materials.

We are grateful to the authors of this volume, and to their supporting institutions, for their participation in this symposium. Special thanks are extended to the staff of ASM International.

We anticipate that this collection of papers, together with its companion volumes will provide useful information to those involved with the manufacturing of composite materials and the products that they make possible.

Dr. T. S. Srivatsan
Department of Mechanical Engineering
The University of Akron
Akron, Ohio 44325-3903, USA
Phone: 216\972-6196

Dr. D. M. Bowden
McDonnell Douglas Aerospace
New Aircraft and Missle Products
P.O. Box 516/MC 1064900
St. Louis, Missouri 63166, USA
Phone: 314\232-1859

Mr. C. T. Lane
Duralcan USA
10505 Roselle Street
San Diego, California 92121, USA
Phone: 619\597-1212

Table of Contents

Machining of Metal-Matrix Composites

Machining of Polymer- and Ceramic-Matrix Composites

Machining Technology

CUTTING OF TITANIUM MATRIX COMPOSITE LAMINATES

D. M. Bowden
McDonnell Douglas Aerospace
New Aircraft & Missile Products
Saint Louis, MO 63166 USA

Abstract

Thin gage titanium matrix composite (TMC) laminates have been cut using a variety of techniques, including shearing, diamond saw cutting, electrical discharge machining (EDM), and abrasive water jet (AWJ) machining. A qualitative assessment of cut surface quality has been made using scanning electron microscopy (SEM). EDM and AWJ machining produce the best cut surface quality, with minimal damage to the laminate. However, AWJ produces good cut quality without a heat affected zone, and represents the method of choice for cutting TMC laminates. Other cutting methods may be used, however, with secondary finishing operations.

TITANIUM MATRIX COMPOSITE (TMC) MATERIALS provide the opportunity to extend the operating temperature range of titanium alloys in advanced aerospace products. Continuous reinforcing silicon carbide fibers can significantly increase strength and stiffness of structural titanium alloys at elevated temperatures. TMC laminates are typically produced using a foil/fiber approach, shown schematically in Figure 1, in which alternating layers of matrix alloy foil and reinforcing fiber mat are stacked in the desired architecture, and the resulting layup is consolidated to full density by hot isostatic pressing (HIP). Temperatures on the order of 900-1000°C and pressures from 100-200 MPa are typically used to fabricate TMC laminates. The HIP pressure is applied to the layup by a steel bag welded to the tool landing which presses the laminate against the hard steel tool. This hard tooling approach yields a composite part with good surface quality and shape control. A typical composite microstructure is illustrated by the optical micrograph of a 3-ply [0/90/0] laminate shown in Figure 2.

In order to fully utilize TMC materials, machining methods must be developed to cut and drill laminates for assembly into useful product forms. Cutting and drilling operations must be performed economically and with minimal damage to the laminate. In this paper, the results of a preliminary study of the applicability of a variety of cutting methods to TMC structure fabrication will be reviewed. The results presented focus on machined surface quality and the extent of material damage induced by the various cutting processes.

Experimental Procedures

The materials utilized in this investigation are thin gage TMC laminates fabricated using a variety of matrix alloys, including the beta alloy Ti-15Mo-2.7Nb-0.2Si-3Al, and the alpha-beta alloy Ti-6Al-4V (in weight percent). The fibers utilized include the Textron SCS-6 and SCS-9 silicon carbide fibers. These fibers are chemically similar, with SiC deposited onto a carbon core, and differ only in diameter (142 μm (0.0056 in) for SCS-6 and 82 μm (0.0032 in) for SCS-9).

Various TMC specimens were cut by conventional shearing, diamond saw cutting, electrical discharge machining (EDM), and abrasive water jet (AWJ) machining. In most cases, the exact cutting parameters used in preparing specimens are proprietary. However, since our purpose is to compare the cut surface quality produced by the various techniques, a relative quality assessment may still be made without specific knowledge of the optimized process parameters. The results of this assessment are presented in the following section.

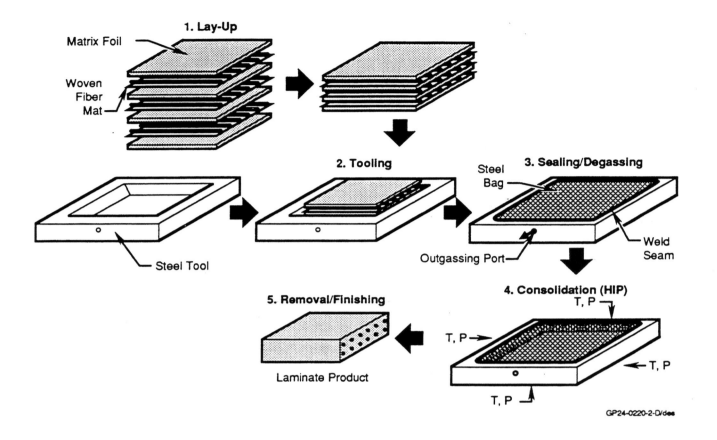

Figure 1. Schematic of Foil/Fiber Approach to Fabrication of Titanium Matrix Composite (TMC) Laminates.

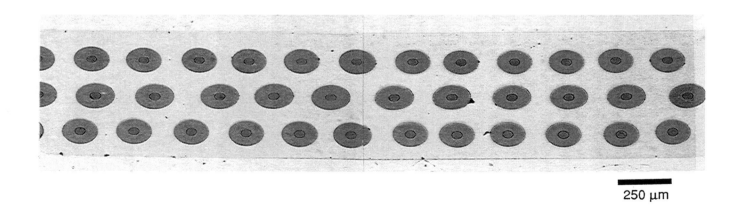

250 µm

Figure 2. Optical Micrograph of Silicon Carbide Fiber Reinforced Ti-6Al-4V Laminate.

Results and Discussion

Conventional Methods. Traditional cutting methods such as shearing produce rough edges with significant fiber damage, as illustrated in the SEM micrographs of the cut surface of a 3-ply TMC laminate shown in Figure 3. This laminate has a ductile beta titanium alloy matrix, which shears with no matrix cracking. It appears that the cutting blade "rides up" over the hard SiC fibers to some extent, since the matrix surface topography exhibits high points around the fibers and low points in between fibers (Figure 3(a)).

Fibers fail by brittle cleavage fracture, and the 90° cross-ply fibers lying parallel to the cut surface are broken and missing in sections. Figure 3(b) shows details of the damage done to the transverse fibers. Cleavage fracture of a 0° fiber lying perpendicular to the shear cut surface is shown in Figure 3(c). The micrograph of Figure 3(d) shows smearing of the ductile matrix in the shear direction.

While conventional shearing may serve as a simple and economical method to rough cut thin gage TMC laminates subject to further finishing operations, other methods would be required to cut thicker laminates or to improve cut surface quality and minimize material damage. The surface topography of

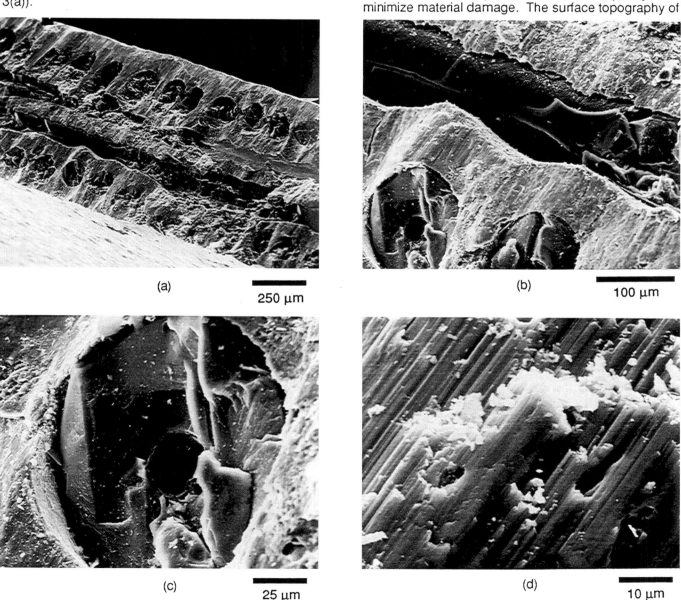

(a) 250 μm

(b) 100 μm

(c) 25 μm

(d) 10 μm

Figure 3. Cut Surface Characteristics of Sheared 3-Ply Silicon Carbide/Beta Titanium Alloy Composite Laminate, (a) General Surface Topography, (b) Transverse 90° Fiber Damage, (c) 0° Fiber Fracture by Cleavage, (d) Matrix Shear Surface.

a diamond saw cut laminate utilizing the beta alloy matrix with the SCS-6 SiC fiber is shown in the SEM micrographs of Figure 4. While the matrix surface quality is good, some fiber damage does occur. Again, fibers fail by brittle cleavage fracture, to a depth on the order of 30 μm below the cut surface. The high magnification micrograph of Figure 4(b) shows ductile matrix debris covering a portion of a fiber.

While diamond saw cutting produces a cut surface with improved quality, fiber damage is not eliminated. In order to minimize material damage, nontraditional cutting methods which apply no forces directly to the workpiece must be used.

Electrical Discharge Machining (EDM).
We have applied the technique of electrical discharge machining to the cutting of TMC laminates. A primary advantage of EDM is that no physical forces are exerted onto the laminate. In addition, intricate shapes may be readily cut.

The mechanisms of material removal during EDM of metal matrix composite materials have been described by Gadalla (Reference 1) and Eubank and Bozkurt (Reference 2). Generally, the matrix is removed by melting and vaporization, while the ceramic reinforcement is removed either by melting or spalling due to thermal shock. Spalling results from the high internal stresses created in the fiber by the steep temperature gradients generated.

Characteristics of the EDM surface of a SCS-6 SiC/Ti-6Al-4V TMC laminate are shown in the SEM micrographs of Figure 5 and 6. As previously noted, curved surfaces and corners are readily continuously cut using EDM. Fibers intersected longitudinally by the curved cut are fractured at a certain cut depth, as indicated by the missing fiber segments shown in Figure 5(b). Fibers lying parallel to the cut surface in the plane of the cut are completely removed, as seen in Figure 5(c). Fibers oriented perpendicular to the plane of the cut show minimal damage below the cut surface, expecially when compared to fibers cut using the conventional techniques of shearing and diamond saw cutting.

Details of the cut surface shown in Figure 6 include the smooth melted and resolidified matrix surface, indicating that melting and vaporization are in fact the mechanisms of metal matrix removal. Because of the relatively thin melt layer and the large bulk of the workpiece, the melt region is rapidly solidified following cutting. The rapid quench rate results in the formation of a brittle glassy region which exhibits fine cracks formed by thermal stresses generated upon cooling. The fiber shows what appears to be a mixture of melting and fracture features. Some fiber regions appear to be smooth and rounded, indicating that melting has occurred, while the carbon core is definitely fractured in a brittle manner. Small spherical particles are also visible (Figure 6(b)). These particles

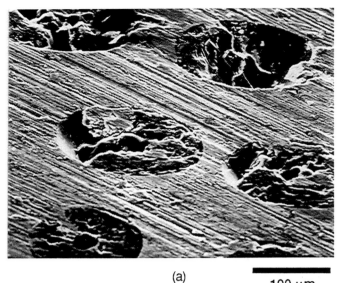

(a) 100 μm

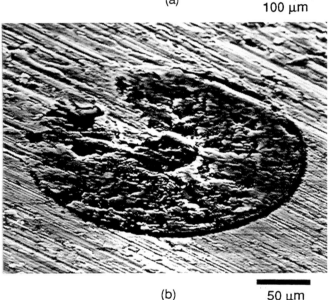

(b) 50 μm

Figure 4. Cut Surface Characteristics of Diamond Saw Cut SiC Fiber-Reinforced Beta Titanium Alloy Laminate, (a) General Surface Topography with Fiber Damage, (b) Matrix Cutting Debris.

are typically found on EDM surfaces, and are formed by melting of the EDM wire electrode and resolidification of small particles in the dielectric fluid.

The EDM surface shows improved surface quality compared to cut surfaces produced using conventional techniques. Extensive fiber damage beyond the cut surface is minimized, and the matrix surface is relatively smooth and uniform. The primary disadvantage of the EDM method is the heat affected zone formed by melting and resolidification of the matrix, which could possibly influence mechanical properties of the material.

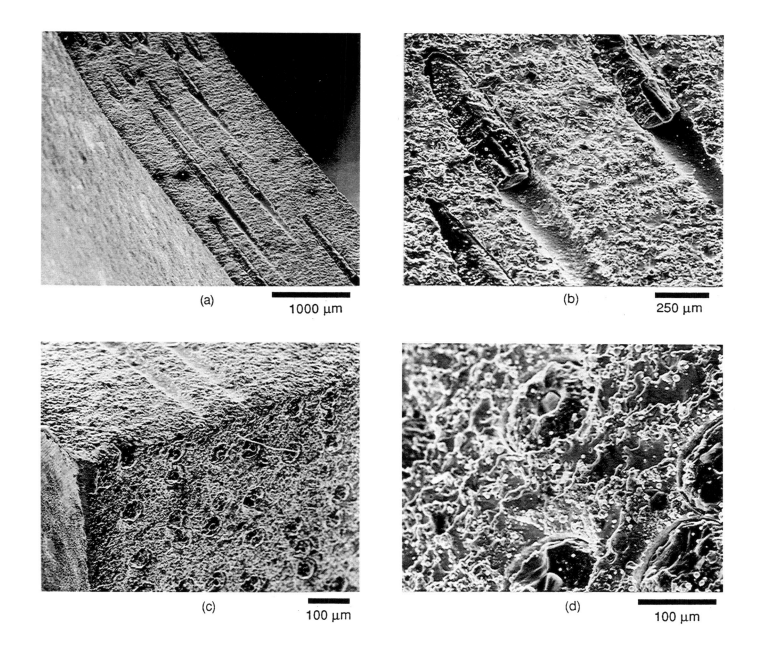

Figure 5. Cut Surface Characteristics of EDM Silicon Carbide Reinforced Ti-6Al-4V Laminate, (a) Curved Surface, (b) Transverse Fibers Intersected by Curved Cut, (c) Continuously Cut 90° Corner, (d) 0° Cut Fiber.

Abrasive Water Jet (AWJ) Machining. The final cut examined was produced by abrasive water jet (AWJ) machining. Like EDM, AWJ machining requires no physical force on the workpiece, and thus cuts can be produced with minimal damage to the laminate. AWJ cutting has the advantage, however, that no heat affected zone is formed adjacent to the cut surface.

Typically, the cut surface exhibits two distinct regions. The upper portion of the cut surface is typically smooth, and is formed by the process of cutting of the material by particles impacting at relatively shallow angles. With increasing depth of cut, striations appear on the cut surface which are formed by particles impacting at steeper angles. The cutting parameters can be controlled to produce the desired cut surface quality.

The cut surface of a beta TMC laminate reinforced with the SCS-6 SiC fiber is shown in Figure 7. Note that the entire surface shows striations, rather than a transition from a smooth to a striated region. The extent to which control of the cut can be maintained is evidenced by the thin shreds of matrix material remaining over a transverse fiber visible at the bottom of Figure 7(b). The extent of material damage on either side of the cut is minimal. Reinforcing fibers fail

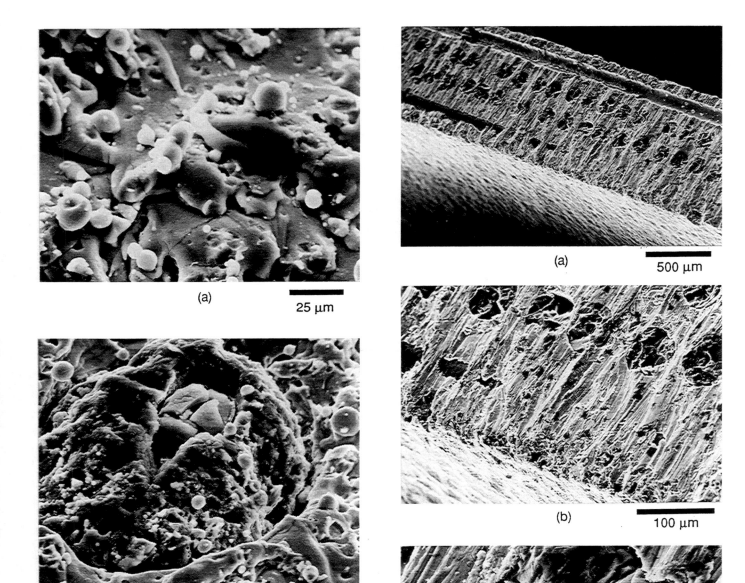

Figure 6. Details of EDM Cut TMC Surface, (a) Melted and Resolidified Matrix Alloy, (b) Combined Melting and Spalling Removal of Fiber.

by cleavage fracture, as seen in Figure 7(c).

Delamination is often observed in AWJ cutting of polymer matrix composites due to high stresses developed in the impingement zone. However, because the high temperatures and pressures used in the HIP consolidation process diffusion bond the matrix foils together into a single piece of metal, delamination is not observed at the outlet of the water jet. AWJ cutting produces cuts with minimal material damage. In addition, like EDM, complex shapes can be cut from the laminate. Because material removal is purely mechanical, no heat affected zone or melted region is formed adjacent to the cut.

Figure 7. Cut Surface Characteristics of AWJ 4-Ply Silicon Carbide Reinforced Beta Titanium Alloy Composite Laminate, (a) General Surface Topography, (b) Thin Matrix Shreds Covering a 90° Transverse Fiber, (c) Cleavage Fracture of SiC fiber and Striated Matrix Surface.

Summary and Conclusions

Thin gage TMC laminates can readily be cut by a variety of methods. Conventional processes such as shearing produce significant material damage and cut surface roughness, and require secondary finishing operations to produce quality cut surfaces. Processes such as electrical discharge machining and abrasive water jet machining, which exert no direct physical force on the laminate, produce cuts of higher quality with minimal material damage. In addition, complex shapes can be produced with these processes.

Acknowledgements

The assistance of G. A. Horst in performing the SEM analysis is greatly appreciated. This work was performed under the National Aerospace Plane Program, USAF/ASD Contract No. F33647-86-C-2126.

References

1. Gadalla, A. M., Thermal Spalling During Electro-Discharge Machining of Advanced Ceramics and Ceramic-Ceramic Composites, in Machining of Composite Materials, T. S. Srivatsan and D. M. Bowden, eds., ASM International, Materials Park, OH, 1992, 151-158.
2. Eubank, P. T., and Bozkurt, B., Recent Developments in Understanding the Fundamentals of Spark Erosion for Composite Materials, in Machining of Composite Materials, T. S. Srivatsan and D. M. Bowden, eds., ASM International, Materials Park, OH, 1992, 159-166.

Drilling and Tapping SiC Particle-Reinforced Aluminum

C. Lane
Duralcan USA
San Diego, California

Abstract

A study was made of the major factors affecting drill and tap performance in a typical metal matrix composite. Using 3 combinations of speeds and feeds, a series of 6.37-mm diameter holes were drilled through a 19-mm thick plate of *DURALCAN®* F3S.20S-T6 composite (A359/SiC/20p-T6). Every 50th hole was drilled in a gage block of the same material to measure tool forces and hole quality. Feed rate was determined to be the only significant variable. Using a feed rate of 0.25 mm/revolution., PCD-veined drills produced over 6000 diameters of holes in this composite with tolerances of 0.01 mm and flank wear of only 0.1 mm. A limited series of tapping tests were also conducted. Both thread-cutting and -forming carbide taps produced acceptable quality threads. However, further work is required to optimize their performance and economics.

METAL MATRIX COMPOSITES (MMCs) are becoming well accepted in industry as an alternative to more traditional materials. In particular, aluminum alloys reinforced with ceramic particles offer a very attractive combination of properties. However, these hard reinforcing particles are very abrasive to conventional steel or carbide cutting tools. Although polycrystalline diamond-tipped (PCD) cutting tools have proven successful in turning and milling these composites, drilling has proven more challenging. The geometry of a drill point is significantly more complex than an indexable insert used for turning. Thus, fabrication of drills using PCD blanks is limited by the size and design of the point geometry. This problem is even more significant for taps. At present, it is not practical to produce a PCD-edged tap using conventional brazed construction. In the course of this study, a new technology for integrally sintering a "vein" of PCD into a carbide tool body was evaluated for both drills and taps.

Tools and Workpiece Materials

Workpiece Material. To ensure that the results would be of interest to industry, rather than only to academia, a commercially available MMC was chosen for the workpiece. This type of ingot-metallurgy-based composite is one of the most widely used aluminium composites in the world. Per ANSI 35.5, this composite is generically referred to as A359/SiC/20p-T61. This describes an aluminum casting alloy with 9 wt% silicon and 0.6 wt% magnesium reinforced with 20 vol% silicon carbide particles, which is solution heat-treated, quenched, and artificially aged for maximum strength after casting.

The composite was remelted from 11-kg foundry pigs and sand-cast into plates 150 x 300 x 25 mm. Each plate was milled to remove the as-cast surface, resulting in a final thickness of 19 mm. The dendritic microstructure in Figure 1 is typical of this composite and process. The mean diameter of the SiC particles is 12.8 μm.

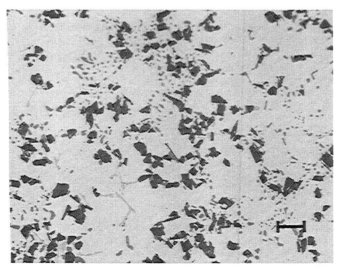

Figure 1: Microstructure of sand-cast A359/SiC/20p-T6.

Diamond Drills. An example of the as-received PCD-veined drill from Precorp is shown in Figure 2. This 6.37-mm diameter drill has a 4-facet, 118° point with web thinning and a 30° flute helix. Note how the PCD is contoured to the chisel edge, cutting lip, and corner of the margin. This is accomplished by cutting an angled slot in a carbide nib, filling it with diamond powder, and sintering the assembly at a temperature and pressure sufficient to fuse the diamond and carbide into an integral unit. The nib is then brazed to a carbide shank and the blank is ground like a conventional carbide drill – with the exception that diamond-plated wheels are required.

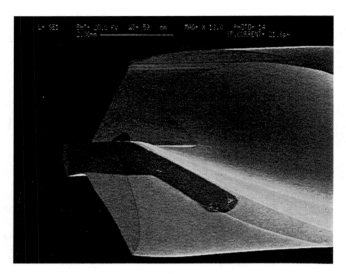

Figure 2: Precorp® PCD-veined drill.

Contrast this to the PCD-tipped drill in Figure 3 with the more common brazed-in point design. In this case, the point of a finished carbide drill is slotted. Then a small spade or chevron insert of PCD is carefully aligned and brazed in place. Temperature control is critical. The braze must melt and flow, but the PCD must not be allowed to degrade. PCD begins oxidizing at 650°C and graphitization begins at 750°C [1]. Most braze alloys used for joining PCD to carbide flow at 620-700°C [2]. Thus, maintaining consistent quality generally requires the precision of an induction brazing process. Producing drills in diameters ≤ 3 mm is expensive and impractical by this process. However, the Precorp process of sintering in a vein of PCD suffers from none of these limitations and can produce drills in diameters as small as 0.25 mm. Moreover, the point geometry is not limited by the 2-dimensional nature of a brazed-in chip of PCD.

Thread-Cutting Taps. Two different kinds of M8x1.25 taps were evaluated. The first kind was a series of prototype thread-cutting taps made by Precorp. One set was straight-fluted, solid carbide with a 6.8-mm entry diameter and an 8° entry chamfer. The four lands, 1.9-mm wide, were ground concentric with ≤5° positive rake. The core diameter of 6.8 mm was intended to strike a balance between tap strength and flute space. The second set was identical to the first, except for a 0.2-mm thick layer of diamond on the cutting face of the first 6-7 teeth of each land as shown in Figure 4.

Additional tests were performed using solid carbide taps with a straight, 6-fluted design. These taps were ground with 1.4-mm wide eccentric lands and a 7° positive rake.

Thread-Forming Taps. The second kind of tap tested was also M8x1.25. The first set was made from a standard M1 high speed steel (HSS) with very light lube grooves. The second type was titanium-nitride-coated D3 steel (TiN-HSS) with no lube grooves. The last set was C-2 tungsten carbide with large lube grooves.

Further tests were run using a slightly modified design of the HSS taps with a single large lube groove. These tools were supplied with the standard bright finish.

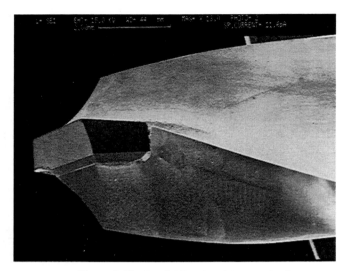

Figure 3: Typical PCD drill with brazed point.

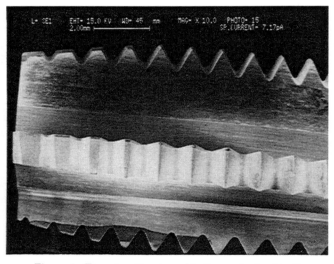

Figure 4 - Thread-cutting tap with diamond-edged teeth.

Test Procedures

Machining Center. The drilling tests were conducted on a Tongil TNC 80 vertical CNC machining center. The machine was driven with a variable-speed, AC motor capable of 80-8000 rpm and controlled with a FANUC Model 6M-B controller. The motor was capable of supplying a maximum of 18.3 kilowatts over a 30-minute duty cycle. The programmable feed rate along each axis was 0.254 to 4064 mm/min and the maximum traverse rate along each axis was 12000 mm/min. Positioning accuracy was ±0.033 mm/m, with a repeatability of ± 0.017 mm. Spindle runout in the taper was measured as 1.3-1.5 µm prior to testing[3]. The initial tapping tests used the same machine center. A Tapmatic 60X non-reversing tap holder with free axial float was used to control the tapping torque.

Drilling Procedures. Three drilling different conditions were chosen to assess the effects of speed and feed on tool life and hole quality as shown in Table I. All holes were drilled completely through the plate in one pass and a flood coolant of 5% water-soluble oil was used in all cases.

Table I. Test Conditions for Drilling.

Test Condition	Speed (m/min)	Revolutions per minute	Feed (mm/rev)
1	50	2500	0.10
2	50	2500	0.25
3	150	7500	0.25

Every fiftieth hole up to 1000 was drilled in a separate gage plate. (After 1000 holes, each hundredth hole up to 2000 was monitored.) The fifth hole for each drill was checked also to allow for "break-in," after the sharp, ground edges of the drill were removed. Torque and thrust were recorded with a Kistler type 9271A dynamometer. Hole diameter and roundness were checked at top and bottom by a Mitutoyo AE122 coordinate measuring machine. Interior surface roughness of each hole was measured twice and averaged by a Perthen Perthometer, Model M4P. Average and maximum flank wear on the drills were measured at 30X on a Nikon TM20 Measurescope with a CM-6S stage and a graticle with a resolution of 2.54-µm.

Tapping Procedures. The holes from the drilling study were reamed to 6.8-mm diameter for the thread-cutting taps and 7.4-mm diameter for the thread-forming taps. These hole sizes were selected to produce a 65-70% thread after tapping.

Tap performance for the initial phase of testing was monitored using the same equipment as for drilling. However, readings were taken on every hole. The thread profile was checked with a Mercury Style E screw plug gage. This gage had an ISO 6H class of fit, which corresponds to a "GO" pitch diameter of 7.20 mm and a "NO GO" pitch diameter of 7.35 mm. All tapping was done using a flood of 10% water-soluble oil. However, the speeds used varied significantly and are detailed in the Discussion section rather than here.

Subsequent testing of carbide cutting taps was performed on a Hillyer horizontal machining center (HMC 400) using a Tapmatic DSPL-12. This type of tapping head provides both axial and radial float as well as a safety clutch to minimize the chances of tap damage. A directed flood of water-soluble coolant (1:4) lubricated the workpiece. All threaded holes were checked by a screw plug gage with an ISO 6H class of fit. Tap wear was checked with an optical comparator by measuring the change in root-to-crest distance after every third hole, up to number 24, and for every tenth hole thereafter. Data were taken for the last chamfer tooth and first and second full teeth on each of the first, third, and fifth flutes.

The modified HSS form taps were tested on a Bridgeport vertical milling center fitted with a Tapmatic SPD-series tapping head. The work area was flooded with Bal Tap S, a cutting oil modified to provide maximum lubricity for tapping aluminum. Neither tool wear nor tool forces were monitored for these taps.

Results

PCD-Veined Drills. Three criteria were used for ending the drilling tests: a) hole diameter ≤6.27 mm, b) flank wear ≥0.25 mm, or c) ≥2000 holes drilled. As Figure 5 shows, drilling conditions 2

and 3 were halted at 2000 holes, while the lower feed rate of condition 1 resulted in sufficient wear to end that test at 700 holes. The hole diameter data in Figure 6 demonstrates the ±0.01-mm precision of which these drills are capable. Figure 7 further verifies the drill quality with average roughness (Ra) measurements of ≤1.0-µm inside the holes.

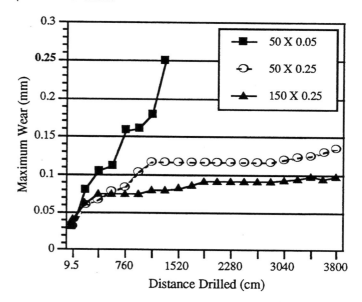

Figure 5 - Wear rate of PCD-veined drills (speed x feed).

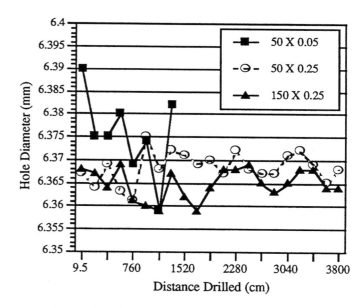

Figure 6 - Hole diameter vs. drill life (speed x feed).

Feed rate was much more significant than cutting speed for both torque and thrust forces on the drill. However as Figures 8 and 9 show, neither force was greatly affected by the amount of wear on the drill. Recall from Figure 5 that drill wear increased rapidly using the low feed rate, but note that the torque and thrust curves for this condition are nearly flat. However as Figure 10 shows, the flank wear in all cases is quite small and larger amounts of wear may show better correlation to tool forces.

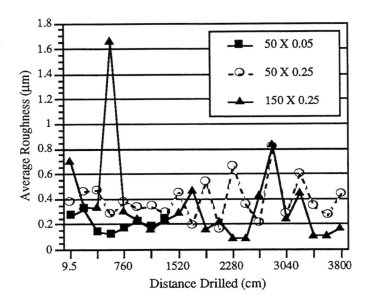

Figure 7 - Hole finish (Ra) vs. drill life (speed X feed).

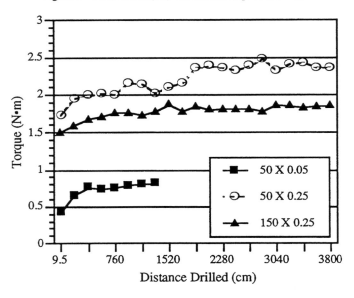

Figure 8 - Drill torque vs. drill life (speed X feed).

Thread-Cutting Taps. The 4-fluted carbide taps were tested at speeds of 2, 5, and 20 m/min. All taps broke during retraction after threading the first hole. The diamond-edged taps were run at 5, 25, and 40 m/min. The results are shown is Table II. The two 6-fluted carbide taps were run at 7.6 m/min and yielded 124 and 128 holes before breaking on retraction.

Table II. Results for PCD-Edged Thread Cutting Taps.

Tap #	Speed (m/min)	# of Holes	Failure Mode
1	5	3	Plug gage would not GO
2	5	7	
3	25	1	BROKE
4	40	3	Plug gage would not GO

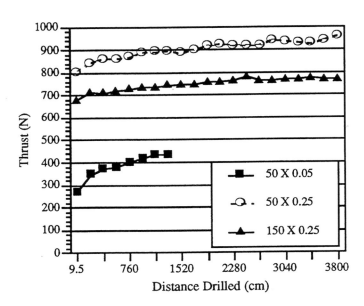

Figure 9 - Drill thrust vs. drill life (speed X feed).

Thread-Forming Taps. All taps in the initial test were run at 5 m/min. Although none of these taps broke, only the HSS taps produced more than 3 holes of acceptable thread quality. These two taps produced 25 and 30 holes respectively before the plug gage would not "GO".

Three modified HSS taps were run under different conditions. The first two taps were run at 4.5 m/min and broke on retraction from holes 24 and 38 respectively. The third tap was run at 1.2 m/min, however the hole thread depth was reduced to 13 mm and a backing plate was used to retain the flood coolant. This tap broke in hole 62 on retraction.

Discussion

Drill Wear. As observed in previous studies, feed rate is the most significant parameter when drilling cast aluminum composites [4,5]. The primary wear mechanism is abrasion by the hard SiC particles. Increasing the feed rate decreases the number of drill revolutions required to make a hole. This reduction in contact area between the cutting edge of the tool and the workpiece greatly reduces the wear rate.

Increasing the cutting speed did not appear to change the wear rate. However, it did reduce the break-in time for the drill and resulted in reaching a stable cutting condition more quickly than the lower speed. It should be noted that these speeds are quite low compared to the 400-700 m/min speeds used when turning these cast composites with PCD tools.

Tap Wear. Accurate measurements of wear for the taps used in this study were complicated by short tool lives and catastrophic failures. The only good wear measurements were made on the 6-fluted carbide taps. Each point on the curve in Figure 11 is the average of the measurements made on the last chamfer tooth of every other flute of the tested tap. As expected, wear on the first and second full teeth were significantly lower. However, as the chamfer teeth continued to wear, the cutting load was transferred back to full teeth. This would require increasing amounts of torque to drive the tap and ultimately cause tap failure. Although wear data were not available, the failure modes of the other taps in this study were quite instructive also.

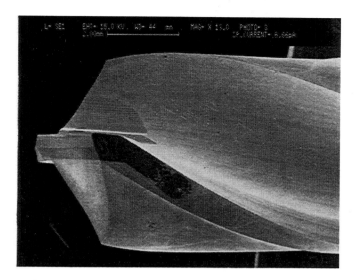

Figure 10 - Flank wear on drill (150 m/min x 0.25 mm/rev).

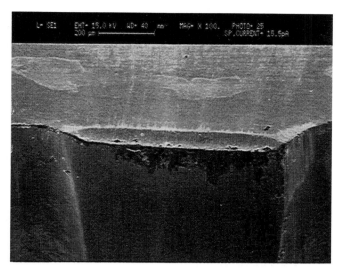

Figure 12 - Abrasive wear on the tooth of a carbide cutting tap.

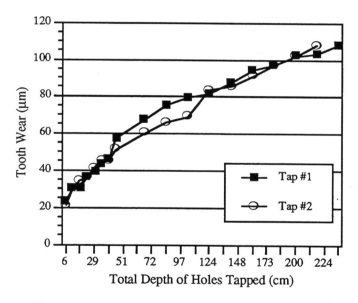

Figure 11 - Average tooth wear on the 6-fluted carbide taps.

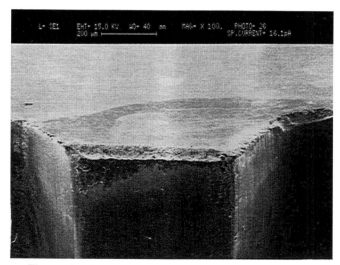

Figure 13 - Micro-chipping on the tooth of a PCD-edged tap.

Thread-Cutting Taps. Two distinct forms of wear were observed in these taps. The carbide taps exhibited the uniform wear lands typical of abrasive wear (Figure 12). However, the diamond-edged taps were more prone to micro-chipping (Figure 13). More significant, however, is the wear land on the trailing edge of the tooth in both taps. This indicates that the withdrawal rate of these taps exceeded the pitch of their thread. It is not known whether this was the result of a CNC programming error or of backlash in the lead screw. Since the tapping head used in this test was non-reversing model, there was also the possibility of backlash when the spindle of the machine tool reversed.

Thread-Forming Taps. Since they are ground eccentric, rather than concentric, form taps accumulate wear on the periphery of their lobes, where they contact the wall of the hole (similar to the rotor in a Wankel engine). In Figure 14, this wear increases as the diameter of the thread form increases, then tapers off for the non-working threads. As in the thread-cutting taps, the primary wear area moves back the tap to the next larger thread as wear progresses. Note that unlike the cutting taps, wear on the forming taps also extends into the root area of the thread form.

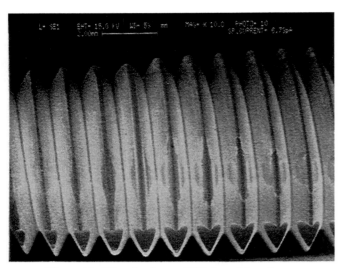

Figure 14 - Wear lands on a HSS thread-forming tap.

Tool Forces. Wear on cutting tools is impractical to monitor in-process. Although "Pass-Fail" dimensional tests are widely used to check parts, this still does not yield timely information about the condition of the tool. One common means of monitoring tool wear indirectly is by measuring the forces on the cutting tool. Since the rupture force of a drill or tap can usually be predicted quite accurately, the operator can program a set-point in the machine to change tools before the tolerances are exceeded – or more importantly, before the tools break.

Both the drilling and tapping tests conducted in this study were rather severe. Holes that are 3 drill diameters deep or greater generally require special drill designs or feeding in multiple steps. Tapping holes that are more than 1.5 diameters deep usually entails switching to a coarser thread or reducing the percentage of thread. The number of fractured taps in this study reflects a failure to compensate for these factors adequately.

Drills. Feed rate was also the more significant parameter in determining force on the drill. Thrust is the reaction force against the drill's advance into the workpiece. Thus, it should increase directly with feed rate. Likewise, torque is a reaction to the chip load of the drill and also should increase with feed rate.

The following standard equations exist for predicting torque and thrust of sharp twist drills [6]:

$$\tau = Kf^{0.8}d^{1.8}A \qquad (1)$$

$$T = 2Kf^{0.8}d^{0.8}B + Kd^2E \qquad (2)$$

where:
τ = torque (in-lbf)
T = thrust (lb)
K = work-material constant
f = drill feed (in/rev)
d = drill diameter (in)
A, B, E = design constants

From tables in Ref. 6, K equals 7000 for most aluminium alloys. Tabulated values of A, B, and E are a function of the ratio of chisel length to drill diameter. Measuring the diamond-veined drill yields a ratio of 0.18 and values of A, B, and E of 1.085, 1.355, and 0.030 respectively.

Entering these values in equations 1 and 2 and converting the answers to SI units predict the torque and thrust values in Table III.

Table III. Drill thrust and torque vs. feed rate.

feed (mm/rev)	Torque (N·m)	Thrust (N)
0.05	0.49	252
0.25	1.79	760

Comparing the predicted values with the measured data at the high speed and feed condition reveals excellent agreement. This indicates that the work-material constant (K) for this composite is virtually the same as for conventional aluminium alloys. However, data for the lower cutting speeds is somewhat higher than predicted. Apparently as speed decreases, the shearing efficiency of the cutting edge also decreases. This results in slightly increased tool forces over the predicted values.

Thread-Cutting Taps. The 4-fluted, solid carbide taps all failed in the first hole. A diamond-plated slitting saw was used to axially cross-section one of these broken taps. As Figure 15 shows, the percent thread for this tap is ~85%. Since tapping torque increases much faster than thread strength as a function of percent thread, taps with thread percentages greater than 75 are generally not used (Figure 16). (This design oversight may be attributed to the fact that Precorp is a drill, rather than a tap manufacturer.) All other features being equal, tap life would probably improve significantly if the thread percentage were reduced to 65%.

Owing to their premature failure, no torque data were recorded for these solid carbide taps. However, torque for the diamond-edged taps varied between 4.5-6.5 N·m at 5 m/min. The only other torque datum for these taps was 9.5 N·m, recorded at 40 m/min. This level of torque should not break a micrograin carbide tap with a transverse rupture strength of 3.1 GPa. However, it should be noted that the torque data were recorded during the cutting portion of the cycle and that the taps failed during the withdrawal portion of the cycle. Failure of these solid carbide taps was probably the result of seizure in the hole, rather than a gradual increase of cutting forces.

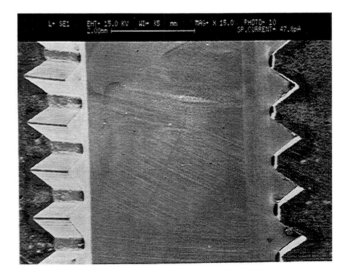

Figure 15 - Axial cross-section of 4-fluted solid-carbide tap.

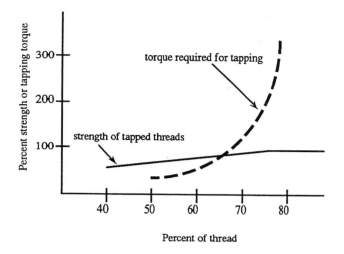

Figure 16 - Effect of % thread on tapping torque and thread strength.

Thread-Forming Taps. Only the first set of HSS taps threaded sufficient holes to generate any meaningful torque data. As Figure 17 shows, the torque increase was rapid and linear, however the slope decreased ~50% after the first dozen holes. Although the wear rate of these taps was not measured, it is likely that the increase in tapping torque was directly related to the increase in friction between the tap and the workpiece as the size of the wear lands on the teeth increased.

Although no tool force data was recorded for the second set of HSS form taps, the operator noted that the clutch of the tapping head was slipping intermittently during reversal and retraction. Applying and removing a load at very high rates can fail a material even at quite small loads. (Consider 3-point bending versus an unnotched Charpy test.)

Furthermore these taps were actually M7.5x1.4. Through a miscommunication, the operator chose a tap to fit the existing hole size, rather than reaming the hole to accept the desired M8x1.25 tap. This nonstandard tap size may have contributed to the problem, since among other things, it resulted in a 70% thread rather than the 65% thread used in the initial taps.

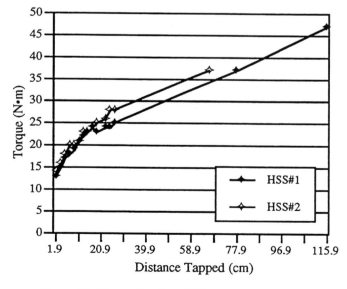

Figure 17 - Torque data from HSS thread-forming taps.

Hole Quality. Often the determining factor in drill life is not flank wear on the cutting edge, but instead the quality of the hole produced. Engineers require that holes be round, straight, and of a certain diameter – all within certain tolerances. Although perpendicularity was not measured in this test, diameter and roundness were carefully monitored. Variations in hole diameter and roundness were <15 μm in all cases. Measuring dimensional variations at this scale is most likely an exercise in determining where the reinforcing particles lie with respect to the drilled surface.

With the exception of one outlying datum, the average surface roughness of all holes fell well below 1.0 μm. A drill capable of this performance can eliminate a reaming operation, which is usually required prior to tapping. This results in cost savings for both tooling and time and decreases the payback period of the PCD-veined drill.

Thread Quality. Because of the fundamentally different mechanism by which the threads are produced, cut threads and formed threads are normally easy to visually distinguish. However, as Figures 18 and 19 show, this is not always the case. "Seaming" is a typical feature of formed threads and is a result of material flowing up the flanks of the thread form more readily than up the center. Seams in threads are generally not detrimental, unless placed in a corrosive service environment.

The presence of seams in the cut threads is more unusual. It implies that the tap is not cutting cleanly and is instead pushing some of the workpiece material aside. Further tests are planned to evaluate the degree of seaming as a function of tap design and wear.

Figure 18 - Profile of threads formed by a HSS tap.

Economics. It is clear from the data that this type of PCD-veined drill is very efficient at making holes in particle-reinforced aluminium. However, PCD drills and other complex shank tools are notoriously expensive to purchase. This causes fabricators to avoid these tools and rely instead on conventional carbide tools without adequately considering the true cost of operation.

Drills. The PCD-veined drill tested here costs $307 in quantities of 10-25. If stopped at a wear level of ≤0.10 mm, it can be resharpened 3 times at $50 each. In this study, that yields 4 sets of 2000 holes each 19-mm deep. The tool cost per hole would be less than $0.06, or less than $0.03/cm drilled.

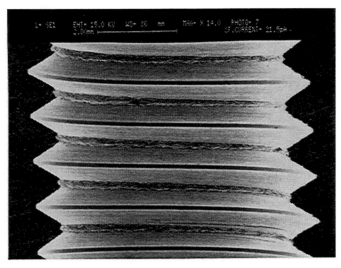

Figure 19 - Profile of threads cut by a carbide tap.

A comparable solid carbide drill would cost $41 initially and $14 to resharpen. However, it would only drill 100 holes per resharpening in this material [7]. This gives a cost per hole of $0.21, or $0.11/cm drilled. This does not consider that the interior surface roughness of the hole is in excess of 3 μm or that exit burring becomes noticeable as the carbide drill wears.

Clearly, the life-cycle cost of tooling favors the PCD-veined drill. Including the cost savings derived from higher operating speeds (reduced cycle times) and from the elimination of reaming would further increase the economic advantage over carbide drills.

Taps. Sufficient data only existed for a cursory examination of tapping economics. In the case of the HSS form taps, an average of 32 holes (19-mm deep) were produced by each $11 tap. Thus, the average tap cost per hole was $0.18/cm.

The solid carbide, 6-fluted taps produced an average of 126 holes that were each 19-mm deep. In quantities of 12-24, this tap costs $86. The cost of $0.36/cm tapped more than double that of the HSS form taps. However, the higher operating speed of thread-cutting taps could offset this in the final analysis. Given the variations in experimental procedure and tap design, it is likely that both of these tapping cost could be reduced significantly in an actual production scenario.

Conclusions

Drilling this type of composite is very straightforward. As is the case with other MMC machining operations, proper tool selection and usage alleviate most problems. Tapping, on the other hand, is still not well understood. The process is much more sensitive to the set-up and operation of the machine tool. There is also room for much improvement in tap design.

Feed rate was the most significant parameter affecting drill life and tool forces. Increasing the feed rate increased tool forces significantly, but improved drill life dramatically. Feed rates must be significantly higher than 0.05 mm/rev in order to achieve acceptable tool life. Speed had little effect on the parameters measured. Neither feed rate nor drilling speed affected hole quality, which was sufficiently good to eliminate the need for reaming. These drills are significantly more economical to operate than carbide drills.

Both thread-cutting and thread-forming taps can be used with this composite. However, several factors complicated the testing. Better tool life would result from reducing thread percentage and hole depths to more generally accepted levels.

Although the specific factors were not identified, design of the cutting taps was found to be critical. At this time, it is uncertain what combination of land area, rake angle, and relief are responsible for the difference in performance between the 4-fluted and 6-fluted taps. Technology for a diamond-edged tap was demonstrated and further design improvements should yield a commercial product.

Forming taps offer a economical alternative to cutting taps small numbers of holes. It is expected that the use of solid carbide in forming taps, rather than HSS, could enhance their performance significantly. Better lubricants could also extend tap life or increase the operating speed.

Acknowledgments

This work was performed at the Institute of Advanced Manufacturing Sciences, Cleveland Twist Drill, and Balax Inc. John Bunting of Precorp merits special recognition for his extensive effort in developing the diamond-veined tools and discussing their results.

References

1] Gigl, P. D., "New Synthesis Techniques, Properties and Applications for Industrial Diamond," in Proceedings of IDA Ultrahard Materials Seminar, Toronto, Ontario, Sept. 1989.

2] Metals Handbook, 9th Edition – Vol.16 Machining, ASM International, 1989, p 108.

3) M. Finn and G. Hughes, "Precision Hole Making in *DURALCAN* Composites," (Report No. APQ-270, Institute of Advanced Manufacturing Sciences, 1993).

4) M. Finn and G. Hughes, "Machinability of Metal Matrix Composites," (Report No. APQ-142, Institute of Advanced Manufacturing Sciences, 1991).

5) W. Zdeblick and G. Hughes, "Evaluation of 10%, 15%, and 20% SiC/A356 Cast Aluminum MMC," (Report No. MP-2852-51368, Institute of Advanced Manufacturing Sciences, 1990).

6) Tool and Manufacturing Engineers Handbook, 3rd Edition – Volume 1, Chapter 9, Drilling, Reaming and Related Processes, Society of Manufacturing Engineers, 1988, pp 78-80.

7) M. Lesher, "State of the Art Assessment for Machining Non-Homogeneous Materials," (Report No. 05-3751, Southwest Research Institute, 1991), pp 14-26.

MACHINING OF ZIRCONIUM DIBORIDE AND ITS COMPOSITES

Ahmed M. Gadalla and Yu-Min Cheng
Department of Chemical Engineering
Texas A&M University
College Station, TX 77843-3122

Abstract

A two dimensional unsteady state heat conduction model was used to simulate the cutting process in pure ZrB_2. Modeling results and experimental observations indicate that a molten pool is formed in contact with the plasma and the heat propagates causing spalling at a deeper depth. Accordingly spalling is the determining mechanism in accessing material removal rate (MRR). Zirconium diboride composites were fabricated using both wire-cutting and die-sinking electrical discharge machines (EDM). Melting mechanism controls MRR in ZrB_2-Si, ZrB_2-Mo and ZrB_2-Cu and MRR increases with increasing current, pulse duration and pulse frequency. Die-sinking machine causes the surfaces to be covered with large areas of solidified liquid phases and produced higher roughness.

ELECTRICAL DISCHARGE MACHINING (EDM-ing) is a technique in which material is removed by electro-thermal energy. In EDM, three principal components exist : (i) workpiece, (ii) cutting tool and (iii) dielectric fluid. The workpiece and tool are initially insulated by the dielectric flowing between them. Once the dielectric breaks down, a closed circuit is formed and the discharge energy will erode the material by either a melting (accompanied sometimes by evaporating) or a spalling mechanism.[1] The dielectric restricts the growth of discharge channel, during applying the pulse, to create an extremely high heat flux. During the pause periods, the discharge channel collapses and the dielectric liquid flushes the developed liquid phase and/or loose aggregates and cools the surface.

Since there is no direct contact between the workpiece and the tool, no mechanical stresses are exerted on the workpiece and the high temperature relieves the surface from the residual stresses, thus decreasing its hardness. Accordingly, EDM-ing is an ideal process for machining hard and brittle ceramics.[2] In our laboratory several materials were successfully cut and Table 1 shows some of the materials investigated using a wire-cutting machine. It is suggested that a maximum electrical resistivity of 100 Ω-cm is required for successful EDM-ing.

Although ZrB_2 has a very high melting point and maintains high strength up to very high temperatures, its application has been limited due to its brittleness and poor thermal shock resistance. Moreover, its covalent character makes it difficult to sinter to high densities and its high strength and hardness make it difficult to machine to intricate shapes. Fortunately, these problems can be minimized by metal addition which serves as a sintering aid, increases tensile strength, ductility, toughness and also increases the electrical conductivity required for EDM-ing.

The stability of zirconium diboride in contact with molten metals has led to its use as crucibles for the vacuum evaporation of aluminum, copper,.... etc. Other recommended applications for ZrB_2 include high temperature fire-proof materials, nose caps, rocket nozzle inserts and so on. Alloys of zirconium diboride with molybdenum are superior in mechanical strength, oxidation resistance and heat resistance to pure ZrB_2 and can resist attack by molten steel and iron. Gas impermeable jackets for thermocouples are made of ZrB_2 impregnated by Mo metal [3]. The Zr-B-Si system has been the subject of considerable investigations due to the refractory

Table 1 Some materials successfully EDM-ed by wire-cutting machine in TAMU.

materials	composition (mass %)*	density (g/cm^3)	electrical resistivity (Ω–cm)
TiB$_2$		4.52	1.8e-7
B$_4$C		2.5	0.5
Al$_2$O$_3$-TiC	70/30	4.23	3.5e-3
Si-SiC	5/95	3.09	1.43e-4
Sialon-TiN	80/20	4.0	7.0e-4
Si$_3$N$_4$-TiN	75/25	3.75	1.5e-3
SiC-TiB$_2$	80/20	3.3	1.0
BN-TiB$_2$	70-80/30-20	2.52-2.84	1.2e-3
WC-Co	94-76/6-24	15.41-12.58	2.0e-5

* First value corresponds to first phase listed.

Table 2 Properties of ZrB$_2$ and its composites.

	ZrB$_2$	ZrB$_2$-Mo	ZrB$_2$-Si	ZrB$_2$-Cu
composition* (mass %)	100	95/5	90/10	
theoretical density (g/cm^3)	6.085	6.21	5.24	
bulk density (g/cm^3)	5.67	5.07	4.69	6.51
relative density (%)	93.28	81.46	90.76	
phases existing in specimens	ZrB$_2$	ZrB$_2$, ZrC, MoB	ZrB$_2$, ZrSi$_2$, B$_4$C	ZrB$_2$, Cu, CuO
new phases existing in debris**		Mo$_2$B, ZrO, ZrO$_2$	SiC	Carbon
R$_{max}$ (μm) wire-cutting#	9.65	7.58	14.82	
R$_{max}$ (μm) die-sinking+	37.93	20.7	43.1	

* First value corresponds to first phase listed.
\# operating conditions: I=0.5 A, f=10 kHz, t=1.5 μs
\+ operating conditions: I=18.3 A, t=75 μs, p=130 μs
**In addition, a glassy phase exists. When wire-cutting machine was used Cu and Zn also exists.

properties and the potential of using its compounds as high temperature oxidation protectors [4]. Hashimoto and Yasuhiko reported that Cu-based alloys can be hardened with dispersed ZrB$_2$ and the resulting composites show high electrical conductivity, thermal conductivity and resistance to heat and wear[5]. It is also reported by Buichi and Shinsaku that the electrodeposited Cu-ZrB$_2$ composites can be applied for electrical contacts in switches and similar applications[6].

Experimental Techniques

Characterization of Materials Investigated. Pure ZrB$_2$ and the composites ZrB$_2$-Si, ZrB$_2$-Mo and ZrB$_2$-Cu were machined by both wire-cutting and die-sinking electrical discharge machines. Some properties of these materials were listed in Table 2. Microscopic examination showed that the average grain size of pure ZrB$_2$ is about 5 μm. The theoretical (and accordingly the relative) densities were calculated by assuming the volume of each mixture is equal to the volume of the constituents. The stated bulk densities were measured by mercury displacement.

While ZrB$_2$, ZrB$_2$-Si and ZrB$_2$-Cu were supplied by Hi-Z Technology Inc., ZrB$_2$-Mo was prepared by the authors using cold isostatic pressing followed by sintering. The original ZrB$_2$ and Mo powders were purchased from CERAC, incorporated. The purity of ZrB$_2$ was stated by the supplier to be 99.5% with 4.27 μm average grain size. Mo powder has a purity of 99.9 % and grain size of 2.28 μm. 5 mass % of Mo powder was mixed with ZrB$_2$ powder in alcohol for 20 hours. The resulting slurry was filtered, sieved and isostatically pressed at room temperature to prepare the green bodies which were sintered in an argon atmosphere, containing less than 2 ppm O$_2$, at 2050 ^{o}C under 15 psi for 15 minutes.

X-ray diffraction patterns of the investigated specimens were obtained by a Kratos XSAM 800 machine to identify the phases existing in the material.

Machining Procedures. An AGIECUT 612 wire-cut machine with a CNC-100 controller was used to study the effect of different operating parameters. The dielectric fluid in this machine was a mixture of deionized and tap water. Their ratio was adjusted to obtain an electrical conductivity of 15 μS/cm. A brass wire with a composition of 63 % copper and 37 % zinc and 150 μm in diameter was

Table 3 Parameters' settings for current, pulse duration and frequency (wire-cutting machine).

parameters studied	current (ampere)	pulse-duration (μs)	frequency (10kHz)
current	0.50, 0.75, 1.00, 1.25	1.5	1.00
frequency	0.75	1.5	0.60, 1.00, 1.25, 1.50
pulse duration	0.50	1.0, 1.5, 2.7, 3.5	1.00

used as the cutting tool. Several parameters can be set by the operator, including average working current (I), pulse duration (t), pulse frequency (f), electrical conductivity of dielectric fluid and workpiece feed rate (vf). In this study, the current, pulse frequency and pulse duration were changed. Unless otherwise stated, the workpiece feed rate was kept constant at 10 mm/minute. The parameter settings for studying the effect of current, pulse duration and pulse frequency are listed in Table 3.

In addition to the wire-cutting machine, an AGIETRON 1U die-sinking machine was used to study the effect of current. Currents of 5.6, 10.8 and 18.3 amperes were used to cut into the workpiece to a depth of 3 mm. Pulse duration "t" was kept at 75 μs while the pause-time "p" was kept at 130 μs . A POCO EDM-C-1 premium grade ultrafine graphite electrode was used as the cutting tool and the dielectric fluid was BP cutting oil.

Material Removal Rate and Wear Ratio. The volume of material removed during EDM-ing was simply determined by following the change in weight during machining and dividing the mass removed per unit time by bulk density of material. During machining, not only material will be removed from workpiece, but also some material is lost from the cutting tool. The wear ratio is expressed as the volume of workpiece removed relative to that removed from the tool during machining. A wear ratio lower than 1 indicates that the loss in the tool is more than that in the workpiece.

Surface Roughness Measurement. After machining the surface roughness was determined by examining the transverse edge of the cut under the microscope. The maximum roughness (R_{max}) was measured between the highest peak and the deepest valley.

Surface Characterization & Debris Analysis. A JEOL JSM-6400 scanning electron microscope was used to study the morphology of the cut and uncut surfaces and to determine the cutting mechanism. The debris collected from different positions around the sample during EDM-ing was analyzed to determine the mechanism of material removal. A JSM-6400 scanning electron microscope was used to examine the morphology of debris. X-ray diffraction pattern of debris obtained by using a Kratos XSAM800 machine was studied to detect any phase change during EDM-ing.

Modeling the Machining Process During Wire-Cutting

To help understand the cutting process and mechanism of material removal, two dimensional (cylindrical coordinates) unsteady state heat conduction model is employed to simulate the machining process. The following assumptions are made to simplify the calculation and reduce the computation time.

(1) There is only one spark per pulse.
(2) The plasma forms a disc heat source that grows with time according to the equation a = $a_0t^{0.75}$.[7,8] Where a_0 is a constant and t is the time after breakdown.
(3) Heat transfer mechanism through the workpiece is by conduction.
(4) Average thermophysical properties for workpiece material apply over the temperature range from room temperature to that for temperature of the superheated liquid at the surface.
(5) Vaporization of electrode materials is negligible because of high plasma pressure.
(6) A constant fraction of total power is transferred to the workpiece. There are controversies about the fraction of power transferred to the electrodes. Snoeys and Van Dijck[9] suggested that only 2-10 % of spark energy is released into the electrode surface. Other authors assumed that most of the electric energy is transferred into heat which is delivered to workpiece and tool[10,11]. Actually, the value of the fraction transferred depends on the dielectric fluid, workpiece and tool employed. In this study, the fractions of 8, 12, 16 and 20 % were used to simulate material removal rate for currents of 0.5 and 1.25 ampere. After comparing with the experimental results, fractions of energy of 20.38 and 17.2 % were found to match the results obtained for 0.5 and 1.25 amperes respectively. An average fraction of 18.79 % was thus used in the following calculations.
(7) Heat of fusion can be taken into account by using a modified thermal diffusivity. The thermal diffusivity d is replaced by $d' = \frac{\kappa}{\rho c'}$.

Where $c' = c + \frac{m}{Tm}$ (10,12,13), κ is thermal conductivity, ρ is density of workpiece, m is latent heat of fusion, c is specific heat and Tm is the melting point in Kelvin. Since the latent heat of fusion for ZrB_2 is not available, an approximate value of $0.025 \frac{kJ}{mole^oK}$ was used for $\frac{m}{Tm}$. (This is an approximate value for the entropy change for inorganic compounds)

(8) Except for the portion where the heat source is acting, the dielectric fluid is effective in cooling the rest of the surfaces and keeping them at room temperature.

(9) The material is isotropic, i.e., the properties are the same in all directions. Also the heating source is small relative to grain size and does not hit a grain boundary. (i.e. the material is homogeneous and continuous with isotropic properties).

Based on the above assumptions, the temperature distribution is governed by the equation:

$$\frac{1}{d'} \frac{\partial T}{\partial t} = \frac{\partial^2 T}{\partial r^2} + \frac{1}{r} \frac{\partial T}{\partial r} + \frac{\partial^2 T}{\partial z^2}$$

Initial condition:

$$T(r,z,0) = Tr = 298.0 \, ^oK$$

Boundary conditions[8]:

The heat flux, $q(t) = -\kappa \dfrac{\partial T(r,0,t)}{\partial z}$ for $0<r<a(t)$

and $q(t) = 0.0$ for $r>a(t)$

Where κ = thermal conductivity &

$$q(t) = \frac{fVI}{\pi a_0^2 (t^{0.75})^2} \qquad (8)$$

$$T(\propto,z,t) = T(r,\propto,t) = Tr$$

$$\frac{\partial T(0,z,t)}{\partial r} = 0.0$$

Where, t is the time after breakdown in μs, V is voltage, I is the discharge current in ampere and f is the fraction of total power which is transferred to the workpiece.

Methodology. Alternative Direction Implicit (A.D.I.) finite difference method was used to calculate the temperature distribution in the workpiece after a certain pulse duration. The workpiece was divided into several nodes in r and z direction respectively. The temperature of every node at any time during one pulse (from t=0 to t=any time required) can be calculated as explained below.

The following normalizations are used in order to obtain non-dimensional set of variables and equations .

$$\tau = \frac{d't}{SrSz} \qquad \underline{r} = \frac{r}{Sr} \qquad \underline{z} = \frac{z}{Sz} \qquad \theta = \frac{T-Tr}{Tm-Tr}$$

Here Sr is radius of workpiece and Sz is thickness of workpiece.

The governing equation, initial and boundary conditions in dimensionless forms are given below:

$$\frac{\partial \theta}{\partial \tau} = \frac{Sz}{Sr} \frac{\partial^2 \theta}{\partial \underline{r}^2} + \frac{Sz}{Sr} \frac{1}{\underline{r}} \frac{\partial \theta}{\partial \underline{r}} + \frac{Sr}{Sz} \frac{\partial^2 \theta}{\partial \underline{z}^2}$$

Initial condition:

$$\theta(\underline{r},\underline{z},0)=0.0$$

boundary conditions:

$$\theta(\underline{r},1,\tau) = 0.0$$
$$\theta(1,\underline{z},\tau) = 0.0$$
$$\frac{\partial \theta(0,\underline{z},\tau)}{\partial \underline{r}} = 0.0$$

$$\kappa \frac{Tm-Tr}{Sz} \frac{\partial \theta(\underline{r},0,\tau)}{\partial \underline{z}} = -q(\tau) \quad \text{for } \underline{r} \le a_0 (\frac{\tau SrSz}{d'})^{0.75}/Sr$$

$$= 0.0 \quad \text{for } \underline{r} > a_0 (\frac{\tau SrSz}{d'})^{0.75}/Sr$$

$$q(\tau) = \frac{fVI}{\pi a_0^2 [(\frac{\tau SrSz}{d'})^{0.75}]^2}$$

Once the temperature at each point is obtained, an IMSL subroutine QDVAL is called to get isotherms for specific temperatures. The isotherm corresponding to the melting temperature bounds the pool of molten liquid and determines the maximum amount of liquid which can be removed assuming a 100 % flushing efficiency.

The thermal stresses created inside the material depend on the temperature and for isotropic materials, it is governed by the equation:

20

$$\sigma = \frac{E\alpha\Delta T}{1-2\gamma} \quad (1)$$ in each of the principal directions. Where γ is poisson's ratio, E is modulus of elasticity, α is the coefficient of thermal expansion and ΔT is the temperature change from room temperature to the temperature under consideration. The force F_i at any isotherm T_i can be calculated from that obtained at a lower isotherm using the equation:

$$F_i = F_{i-1} + \sigma(A_i - A_{i-1}).$$

Stresses created at this isotherm $= \frac{F_i}{A_i}$.

The plasma pressure was found to be negligible relative to pressure created due to thermal stresses and was thus ignored.

The advantage of the above procedure is to calculate the temperature distribution without assuming average values for their properties if their temperature dependence is known.

Results and Discussions

Table 4 Input data for simulation

Properties	Value
melting point (^{o}K)	3300 [14]
density (g/cm^3)	5.67
thermal conductivity (W/m^{o}K)	46.9365 [15]
thermal diffusivity ($\mu m^2/\mu s$)	10.8658 [15,16]
compressive strength (GPa)	1.56 @ 20°C, 0.711 @ 800 ^{o}C 0.3 @ 1200°C [14]
thermal expansion coeff. ($10^{-6}/^o$K)	8.88 [17]
poisson's ratio	0.144 [14]
Young's modulus (GPa)	320 [18,19]

Simulation Results for Pure ZrB$_2$. The properties of pure ZrB$_2$, used in this study, are listed in Table 4. Fig. 1 (a) shows the temperature distribution in ZrB$_2$ exposed to a discharge channel for 1.5 μs using a current of 0.75 ampere and a frequency of 10 kHz. It also indicates that a pool of molten ZrB$_2$ will form to a depth of 1.6 μm. Fig.

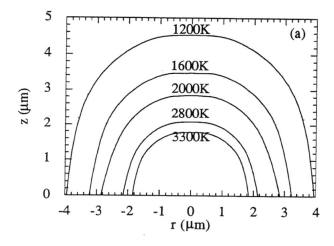

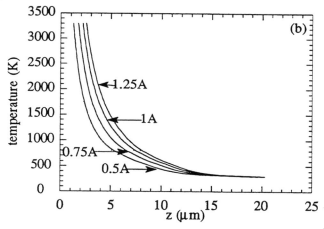

Fig.1 Temperature distribution : (a) in a section perpendicular to the surface and passing through the centerline of plasma, I=0.75 A, t=1.5 μs, f=10 kHz, (b) along z-axis using different currents, t=1.5 μs, f=10kHz.

1(b) shows the temperature distribution along the z-axis inside ZrB$_2$ after 1.5 μs, using different currents. The corresponding variation in the depth and diameter of the melt-cavity is shown in Fig. 2(a). The variation of the cavities' dimensions with duration periods and frequencies are expressed in Fig. 2(b)&(c).

To obtain the depth of spalling under various conditions, the temperature distribution was determined along the z-axis as shown in Fig. 3, curve (a). At each point the created compressive stress was calculated giving curve (b) shown in Fig. 3. The intersection of the curves showing the change in ultimate compressive strength vs temperature (curve c) with curve (b) determines the spalling depth and the corresponding spalling temperature. The isotherm at which breaking will occur is called the idealized spalling isotherm. The

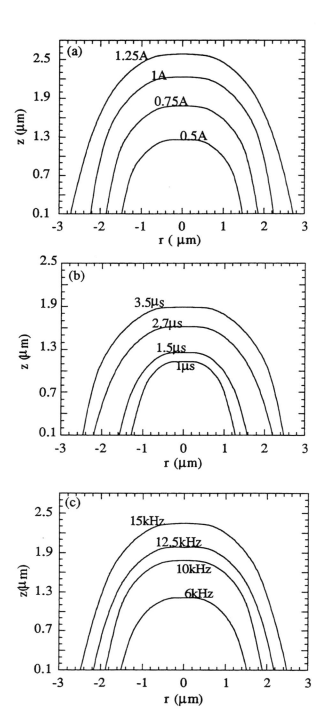

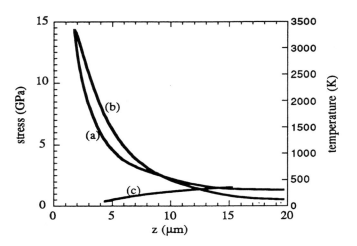

Fig. 3 The method for determining the spalling depth : curve (a) temperature distribution, I=0.75 A, t=1.5 μs, f=10 kHz, curve (b) created thermal compressive stress, and curve (c) variation of the ultimate compressive strength with temperature.

Fig. 2 Variation of radius and depth of molten pool with : (a) currents, t=1.5 μs, f=10kHz, (b) pulse durations, I=0.5 A, f=10 kHz, and (c) pulse frequencies, I=0.75 A, t=1.5 μs.

determined spalling depth at different currents, pulse durations and frequencies are shown in Fig. 4.

As previously stated, the amount of material removed per discharge is taken as the volume bound by the melting isotherm in case of material removal by melting, assuming that the flushing efficiency is 100 %. For the material removed by spalling, we follow assumption 9, i.e., the material is completely isotropic (no grain boundaries and no crystallographic planes or directions where the atomic density is maximum) and take the volume bound by the idealized spalling isotherm. This assumption, however, is not realistic due to the presence of well crystalline ZrB_2. Fig. 5(a)&(b) show the realistic amount of material removed per discharge by spalling. If the plasma is smaller than the size of one grain, the fracture in this grain will occur at the plane of maximum atomic density (basal plane in this case) in the direction of maximum atomic density. Fig. 5(a) indicates an extreme case where the broken part cannot be removed due to the surrounding grains which restrict its removal. In case (b), on the other hand, more materials may be removed than that expected by the idealized spalling isotherm. For polycrystalline ZrB_2 with small grains the predicted depth of spalling may be bigger than the grain size and more than one grain can be removed per discharge as shown in Fig. 5(c). Several flat surfaces will develop and close to the grain boundaries, when the motion is restricted, bending may occur. Fig. 5 indicates that it is impossible to calculate the actual material removal rate by spalling mechanism, therefore, the material removed by spalling is taken as volume bound by the idealized spalling isotherm. However, selecting the proper value for the fraction of power transferred to the electrode (0.188), will give reasonable values as shown later.

22

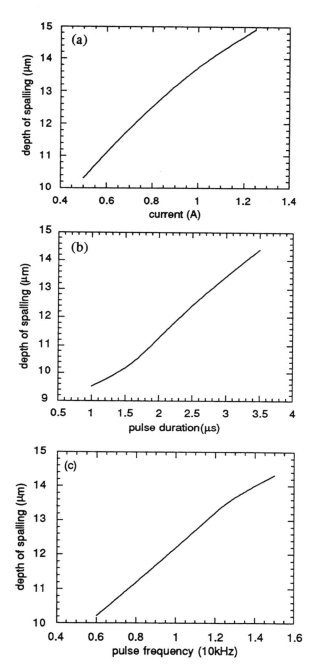

Fig. 4 Variation of spalling depth along z-axis; (a) using different currents, t=1.5 μs, f=10 kHz , (b) using different pulse durations, I=0.5 A, f=10kHz, (c) using different frequencies, I=0.75 A, t=1.5 μs.

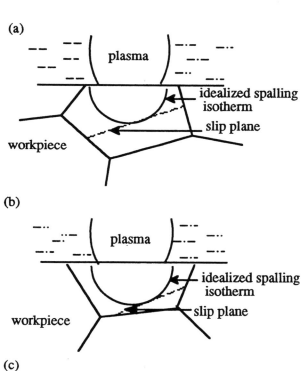

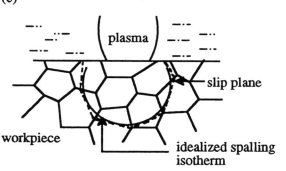

Fig. 5 Spalling in polycrystalline material as compared to idealized spalling in homogeneous isotropic materal:
(a) surrounding crystals restrict the removal,
(b) surrounding crystals facilitate removal,
(c) spalling depth is larger than the graiin size.

By comparing Fig. 2 and Fig.4, it is obvious that both melting and spalling will occur but since the volume removed by spalling is much larger than that by melting, it can be concluded that spalling is the governing mechanism. Accordingly the spalling isotherm is used to determine the volume removed per discharge , which was used in constructing Fig. 6. The experimental results obtained at the operating conditions (as will be explained later) were also plotted in Fig. 6. It is obvious that selecting the fraction of power transferred to the workpiece to be 0.188 gives good results. The material removal rate increases with increasing current and pulse frequency. Increasing pulse durations up to 3.5 μs causes also the material removal rate to increase. It is expected, however, that with longer pulse duration the expansion of plasma channel causes the power input to be distributed over larger areas, thus decreasing the heat flux.[20] Fig. 7 (a) indicates that the pool of liquid material will change its shape and after reaching a depth of penetration about 2 μm, the

23

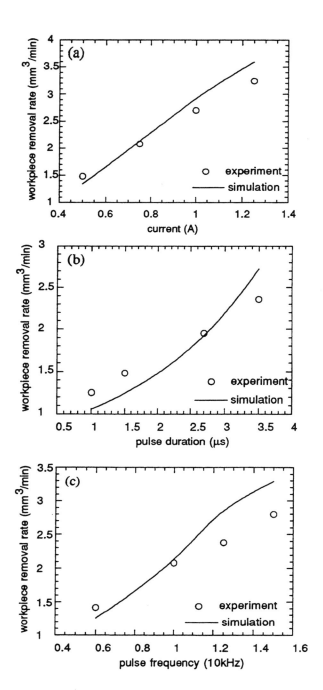

Fig. 6 Comparison of simulation results with experimental results using different: (a) currents, t=1.5 μs, f=10 kHz, (b) pulse durations, I=0.5 A, f=10 kHz, and (c) pulse frequencies, I=0.75 A, t=1.5 μs.

diameter of the pool increases but the depth decreases implying solidification. This phenomena is particularly clear for the materials with high thermal conductivity since they have a fast response for heat. However, trials to adjust the duration of pulse in the wire-cutting machine above 3.5 μs caused wire

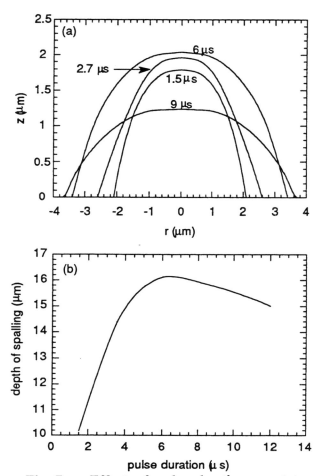

Fig. 7 Effect of pulse duration on: (a) dimension of the melt front, and (b) depth of spalling, using I=0.5 A, f=10kHz.

breakage. Fig. 7(b) shows that after reaching a depth of 16.15 μm at a pulse duration of 6μs, spalling depth decreased thus causing less material removal.

Experimental Results. Experimental results for pure ZrB_2, were plotted in Fig. 6 to show that these results are in harmony with those predicted by modeling. The results were also used in Fig. 8, 9, 10 and 11 to compare them with those obtained for composites containing ZrB_2.

X-ray diffraction indicates that the mixtures investigated cannot be represented as binary mixtures (Table 2). In the case of ZrB_2-Si and ZrB_2-Mo the metal was not detected indicating that these mixtures are not cermets and that reactions with ZrB_2 occur producing $ZrSi_2$ and B_4C in the mixture containing ZrB_2-Si and MoB and ZrC in the mixture containing ZrB_2-Mo. The carbon was present as impurity in the second case.

Wire-cutting. The material removal rates obtained experimentally from the workpieces and the corresponding wear ratios are shown in Figures 8, 9 & 10. The material removal rate increases, for each

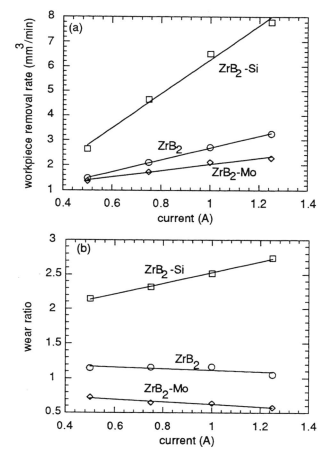

Fig. 8 (a) Material removal rate from the workpiece, and (b) wear ratio at different currents, using t=1.5 μs, f=10kHz.

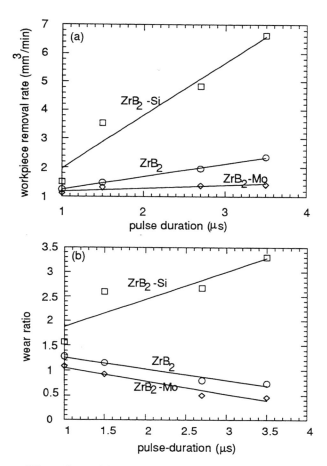

Fig. 9 (a)Material removal rate from workpiece, and (b) wear ratio at different pulse durations using I=0.5 A, f=10 kHz.

material, with increasing current, pulse frequency and pulse duration. This is due to higher power input. Wire breakage occurred at pulse duration higher than 3.5 μs, and accordingly the optimum pulse duration was not observed. Using the above mentioned operating conditions, ZrB_2-Cu could not be machined in spite of presence of conducting metallic copper. It seems that the workpiece is covered with a thin layer of insulating oxide which caused the difficulty of machining. The presence of CuO was confirmed by X-ray diffraction. It should be noted, however, that with much lower feed rates and low currents, this composite can be machined. Using a feed rate of 0.5 mm/min and currents of 0.25 & 0.5 amperes at a frequency of 10 kHz and pulse duration of 1.5 μs, ZrB_2-Cu was eroded slowly with MRR increasing with current. With a current of 1 ampere, the wire broke several times.

Machining with the die-sinker. The results obtained using the die-sinking machine are summarized in Fig. 11 which indicates that, like

wire-cutting machine, a higher current yields higher material removal rate due to higher power input. However, with a die-sinker, it was possible to machine ZrB_2-Cu but it requires long time to achieve limited wear with excessive tool wear. It is, thus, recommended to use this composite as a cutting tool in die-sinking machine.

Machining mechanism and debris analysis. Fig. 12 shows the morphologies of EDM-ed surfaces of ZrB_2 using both die-sinking and wire-cutting machines. While the cleavage observed indicates spalling, the solidified liquid phase indicates melting. Scanning electron microscopy analysis was performed on the debris collected during machining. Two kinds of debris were collected and are shown in Fig. 13. The liquid phase removed by melting mechanism tends to solidify to spherical particles with minimum surface area. On the other hand, polycrystalline particles with some flat surfaces (Fig. 13(b)) indicates spalling to a depth greater than the grain size of the specimen. These observations are in harmony with the model and indicate that a molten

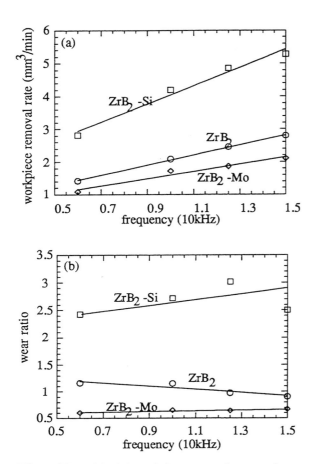

Fig. 10 (a) Material removal rate from workpiece, (b) wear ratio at different pulse frequencies using I=0.75 A, t=1.5 μs.

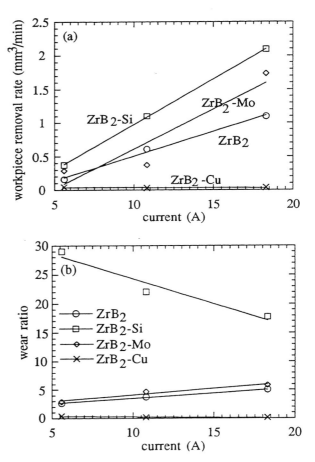

Fig. 11 (a) Material removal rate from workpiece (b) wear ratio at different currents using die-sinking machine (t=75 μs, p=130 μs).

pool is formed adjacent to the plasma and the heat propagated caused spalling at a lower depth as shown in Fig. 5(c). The operating conditions for obtaining the particle in Fig. 13 (b); I=0.75 A, f=6 kHz and t=1.5 μs, corresponds to a spalling depth of about 10 μm (Fig. 4c). At this depth, the spalling isotherm has a diameter of about 20 μm on the surface. The particle collected in Fig. 13 (b) has close dimensions to those predicted.

Fig. 14 shows the EDM-ed surfaces of ZrB_2-Si cut by wire-cutting and die-sinking machines. These mixtures consist initially of ZrB_2, $ZrSi_2$ and B_4C and the debris consists of SiC and glassy phase, in addition to the original three crystalline phases. It seems that melting is the only mechanism. The multicomponent system produces a liquid phase that loosens the grains. During the pause time, these grains are dislodged and collected in the debris as irregular particles while the liquid quenches to glass.

Fig. 15 shows the EDM-ed surfaces of ZrB_2-Mo using the two machines. It seems also that melting is responsible for material removal. In

addition to ZrB_2, tetragonal MoB and ZrC, Mo_2B, orthorhombic MoB (β phase), tetragonal ZrO_2 and ZrO were identified to exist in the debris. Since β-MoB, tetragonal ZrO_2 and ZrO are not stable at room temperature, it can be concluded that the rapid cooling rate preserved these high temperature phases to room temperature. Rudy and Windisch[21] reported that under equilibrium conditions : (a) tetragonal MoB decomposes into Mo_2B and β-MoB at about 2180 °C, (b) Mo_2B melts peritectically to β-MoB and a liquid phase at 2280 °C, and (c) β-MoB melts congruently at 2600 °C.

The morphology of the cut surface of ZrB_2-Cu is shown in Fig. 16 which suggests that cutting occurred by a melting mechanism since the whole surface is covered by resolidified melt. Due to the high wear of the tool, carbon was also obtained in the debris.

It should be noted that the debris collected using the wire cutting machine always contained Cu and Zn which are due to the erosion of the brass wire. In

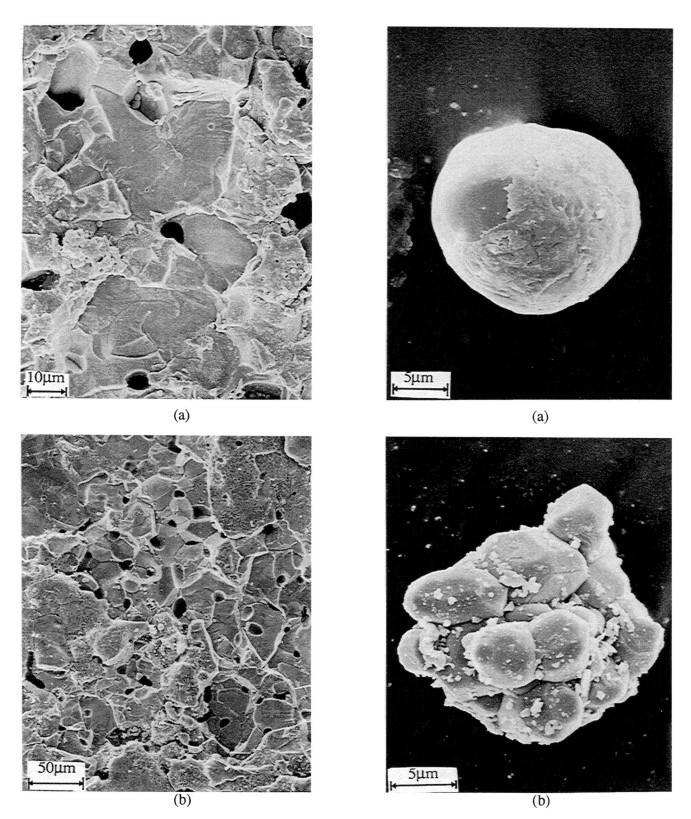

Fig. 12 SEM photomicrograph for ZrB$_2$ surface prepared by : (a) wire-cutting (I=1 A, t=1.5 μs, f=10 kHz), and (b) die-sinking (I=18.3 A, t=75 μs, p=130 μs).

Fig. 13 SEM photomicrograph for ZrB$_2$ debris collected; (a) a spherical particle (b) a polycrystalline particle.

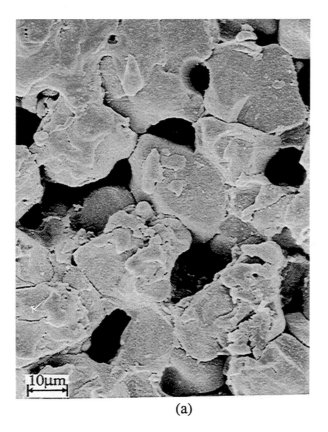

(a)

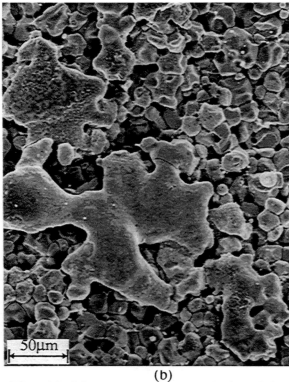

(b)

Fig. 14 SEM photomicrograph for ZrB$_2$-Si surface prepared by : (a) wire-cutting (I=1 A, t=1.5 μs, f=10 kHz), (b) die-sinking (I=18.3 A, t=75 μs, p=130 μs).

(a)

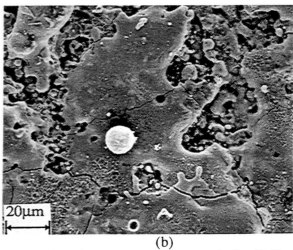

(b)

Fig. 15 SEM photomicrograph for ZrB$_2$-Mo surface prepared by : (a) wire-cutting (I=1 A, t=1.5 μs, f=10 kHz), (b) die-sinking (I=18.3 A, t=75 μs, p=130 μs).

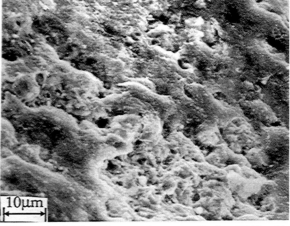

Fig. 16 SEM photomicrograph for ZrB$_2$-Cu surface prepared by : die-sinking (I=18.3 A, t=75 μs, p=130 μs).

addition, a small amount of non-crystalline phase existed in debris.

Part of the results obtained for the measured roughness are indicated in Table 2. It is noted that, the roughness obtained by die-sinking is much higher than that obtained by wire-cutting and the debris obtained by die-sinking contains much bigger flat particles. It seems that with this technique a lower flushing efficiency is achieved causing part of the debris to sinter to platelets and the surface to be covered with large areas of solidified liquid.

Conclusion

The material removal rate during electrical discharge machining increase with increasing current and pulse frequency. For long pulse durations, the material removal rate also increases up to a certain value above which it decreases due to the expansion of plasma channel and the decrease in heat flux. With wire cutting this maximum value was not established since the wire breaks.

For ZrB_2 both spalling and melting occur with spalling as the determining mechanism for material removal. The debris analysis confirms the model results and polycrystalline particles with cleavage surfaces were collected. For ZrB_2-Si, ZrB_2-Cu and ZrB_2-Mo, only melting was observed as the controlling mechanism. In each case, the and form irregular crystalline particles in the debris.

The die-sinking machining produces rougher surfaces than the wire-cutting machine with the liquid phase spreading over larger areas.

Acknowledgments

The authors would like to express their appreciation for the Texas Higher Education Coordinating Board for funding this research and the NSF for their contribution in buying the die-sinking machine. Thanks are also due to Hi-Z Technology Inc. for providing ZrB_2 .

References

1   Gadalla, A. M., Bozkurt, B. and Faulk, N. M., Journal of American ceramic Society, **74**(4), 801-6 (1991).
2   Petrofes, N. F., Gadalla, A. M., American Ceramic Society Bulletin, **67**, 1048-52 (1988)
3   Kislyi, P. S. and Kuzenkova, M. A., Poroshkovaya Met., Akad. Nauk Ukr SSR, **5**(1), 32-6 (1965).
4   Goldschmidt, H. J., "Interstitial alloys", 288-92, Plenum press, New York, N. Y. (1971).
5   Hashimoto and Yasuhiko, Japan patent 89 65,236.
6   Buichi, I., Shinsaku, M., Tohoku Kogyo Daigaku Kiyo, **1**(8), 25-32 (1988).
7   Robinson, J. W., Journal of applied physics, **44** , 72-75 (1973).
8   Patel, M. R., Barrufet M. A. and Eubank, P. T., Journal of applied physics, **66**(9), 4104-11 (1989).
9   Snoeys R. and van Dijck, F., Annals of the CIRP, **21**(1), 39-40 (1972).
10 Heuvelman C. J., Annals of the CIRP, **17**,195-9 (1969).
11. Erden, A. and Kaftanoglu, B., Int. J. Mach. Tool Des. Res., **1**(21), 351-8 (1981).
12. Jilani, S. T. and Pandey, P. C., Precision Engineering, **4**(4), 215-21 (1982).
13 Van Dijck, F. S. and Dutre, W. L., Appl. Physics, **7**(4), 889-910 (1974).
14 Samsonov, G. V., "Higher Temperature Materials", Plenum Press, New York, N. Y. (1964).
15 Fridlender, B. A., Neshpor, V. S., Ordan'yan, S. S. and Unrod, V. I, Teplofizika Vysokikh Temperatur, **17**(6), 1210-1215 (1979).
16 Lynch, J. F., Ruderer, C. G. and Duckworth, W. H., "Engineering Properties of Selected Ceramic Material", The American Ceramic Society, Inc, Columbus, Ohio (1966).
17 Lonnberg, B., Journal of Less Common Metals, **141**, 145-56 (1988).
18 Wiley, D. E., Manning, W. R. and Hunter, JR., O., Journal of Less Common Metals, **8** 149-57 (1969).
19 Lang, S. M., Nat. Bur. Std (U.S.) monograph, 6 march (1960).
20 van Osenbruggen, C., Philips Tech. Rev., **30**, 195-208 (1969).
21 Rudy, E and Windisch, St., "Ternary Phase Equilibria in Transition Metal-Boron-Carbon-Silicon Systems. Part I, Related Systems, Vol.III Systems Mo-B and W-B", Report no. AFML-TR-65-2, Part I, Vol III (1965).

Proceedings of the ASM 1993 Materials Congress, Pittsburgh, Pennsylvania, October 17-21, 1993

Advanced Tooling and Technology for Drilling Metal-Matrix Composite Materials

J. M. Burkes, M. R. Lesher
Southwest Research Institute
San Antonio, Texas

ABSTRACT

As part of a National Center for Manufacturing Sciences program that focuses on improving holemaking techniques for nonhomogeneous materials, Southwest Research Institute (SwRI) has conducted research involved in improving conventional drilling techniques for metal matrix composite materials. A testing program is presented in this paper which focuses on the evaluation of a variety of new tools and coatings prepared by commercial tooling suppliers. The results of this testing are summarized in tabular format. Additionally, research was conducted in the use of infrared thermography as a method for evaluating new tool designs and tool/work combinations by revealing the thermal environment at the tool/work material interface. Previous research had shown that the thermal environment plays a major role in the life of the drill tool and the quality of the holes produced with that tool. Accordingly, the ability to measure the temperature distribution along the cutting edges of a tool represents a valuable aid to those engaged in the development of tooling and process parameters for the host of composite materials being considered for production applications. The information presented includes a description of the instrumentation and the specialized test configurations in use. Research testing results are examined to ascertain the resolution and significance of the technique for evaluating complex drill geometries. The overall goal of this research is to produce better tooling geometries for the work material of interest through testing and improved evaluation techniques.

Program Overview and Goals

Drill Tool Design and Testing Goals. The primary goal of this program is to improve conventional drilling processes for non-homogeneous materials. Although early drill testing in the program included laminated graphite and titanium work materials, the program goals were focused upon aluminum-silicon alloy materials and Metal Matrix Composite (MMC) aluminum materials throughout most of the program testing. The drill test data presented in this paper pertains to drilling a hypereutectic silicon-aluminum alloy (similar to A390) and aluminum MMC materials. The diameter of all holes drilled during the testing program was

.250 inch (6.35mm). The principal testing result which was used to benchmark progress during this work was a measurement of the resulting hole quality. The hole quality goals for this work were established as follows:

- Hole surface quality: 32 μinches Ra, max.
- Hole perpendicularity: within 2° max.
- Hole roundness: Round
- Hole dimensional tolerance: +.003, -.000 inches.

Additional constraints in achieving the above goals were as follows:

- Drill geometry had to be "self-centering", drill bushings/guides were not to be used in achieving the above goals.

- Drilling speeds were to be within normal capabilities of most common machine shop speeds. Normally, test speeds were under 8000 rpm.

- No special coolants were used in this work; generally, water with a rust inhibitor was used in a flood coolant mode. The last set of drill tools tested, however, did include through-the-tool coolant holes.

- All holes prepared during this testing were through holes, to reveal break-through/burr formation performance. Generally holes were slightly less than 1" deep.

- One continuous feed drilling operation was used for each hole; no "peck drilling", change of tooling, or withdrawal of the tool was allowed before completion of the hole.

Infrared Imaging Research Goals. During this program, SwRI completed an investigation on the use of infrared (IR) thermography as a method for evaluating new tool designs and tool/work combinations. The specific objectives of this effort were as follows:

1. To establish the protocol by which tool cutting edge temperature profiles can be measured with an infrared imaging system.

2. To investigate the effects that tool geometry, operating conditions, and work material have on the tool's thermal profile.

3. To develop a methodology to using this technique to quickly evaluate tool designs and to suggest refinements in cutting edge specification (geometry, material, coatings, etc.) and/or operating conditions. Insights such as these could provide a quick and precise specification of operating conditions in the absence of a database with the potential advantages of quicker start-ups, fewer quality problems, and reduced production costs.[1]

Program Methodology & Testing Procedures

The majority of tool testing was performed at the Institute of Advanced Manufacturing Sciences using their Tongil, instrumented machining center. Spindle speeds utilized for this testing were limited to a maximum of 7640 rpm. Runout of this machining center spindle was checked and certified to be within 50 μinches.

Later testing was performed in a factory environment at Allison Gas Turbine Division of General Motors on a Milwaukee-Matic, 5 Axis horizontal machining center. Spindle runout on this machine was certified to within 25 μinches; total runout of tool in holder in machine was held to within .0005" for this testing. This machine was limited to a spindle speed of 3,591 rpm (235 SFPM at .250" diameter). Therefore, testing with diamond coated and several other tools were performed at these reduced speeds.

Tooling Development and Testing. One of the primary aspects of this research was the development of customized and unique drill bit geometries for the work materials of interest, and the subsequent testing of tools with these geometries. The testing sessions typically included a standard carbide commercially available bit for a baseline comparison to evaluate the performance improvements of the new tooling designs. The work materials considered for the drill tooling development during this program were Aluminum alloy/MMC (Duralcan alloy F3S.15S) and a hypereutectic silicon-aluminum alloy similar to Al 390.

Commercially Available Drill Bit Evaluation. Table 1 lists the commercially available drill bit geometries which were considered during this program. The commercial tooling was selected on the basis of both manufacturers' information and documented research information attained through database searches performed during the program. Out of a large variety of commercial geometry styles

initially tested, the performance of the types listed in this table were found to be most worthy of consideration in drilling the abrasive aluminum materials. As can be seen in this table, a solid carbide, 4-facet geometry bit was used as the baseline cutting tool for performance comparison to the other tools. Superabrasive tooling, e.g. tools utilizing polycrystalline diamond (PCD) inserts, proved to be the optimum commercially available technology for drilling these materials. Therefore, the test results shown for commercially available tooling are limited to PCD styles only.

Drill Bit Geometry Development and Testing. The tooling geometries, which were specially designed for drilling in abrasive aluminum materials, are shown in Table 2. Note that two unique bit geometries were considered under this testing program; the Multifacet Drill (MFD) bit and the diametral lip drill bit geometries. Also, two tools were developed based on modified geometries of a more conventional nature, hereafter referred to as project designs 1 and 2.

The MFD geometry bit was considered under this program due to this geometry's potential for making better holes compared to standard, chisel edge designs. The MFD geometry is designed to improve drilling performance by improving the following areas:

a) Reduction of cutting forces
b) Strengthening the center of the bit
c) Increasing the heat transfer from the work material
d) Improving the tool's centering capability
e) Facilitating chip ejection.[2]

The MFD geometry's use of curved cutting lips helps to facilitate centering, thus improving hole quality. Also, the curved, uniquely designed edges help to produce curved, segmented chips, which break more easily, thus further reducing drilling forces, and potentially improving drilling life. In the past three decades, some 25 different styles of MFD bits have been developed for specific classes of materials.[3] Note that for this program, two iterations of an MFD bit were developed and tested for abrasive aluminum alloy materials. The first iteration MFD tool tested had a small step included to reduce abrasion at high wear areas on the outer edges of the cutting lips. This design technique is similar to certain commercial drill bits such as the Black & Decker "bullet" style drill bits. Initial evaluation of these drill bits prior to delivery for testing, indicated an 18 to 27% improvement in drilling forces with these drills (compared to an "off the shelf", standard 4-facet grind carbide bit) when drilling in Al/SiCp MMC material. The second iteration of the MFD drill bits were designed with a major

TABLE 1. COMMERCIAL DRILL BIT GEOMETRIES TESTED

BIT NO.	TOOL TYPE	MATERIALS TESTED	BIT GEOMETRY	COMMENTS
1	SOLID CARBIDE	390 AL.& MMC AL.	4 FACET, 118 DEG. POINT ANGLE	BASELINE TOOL
2	PCD DIAMOND BRAZED INSERT	MMC AL.	4 FACET, INC. WEB THIN	BRAZED INSERT ON SOLID CARBIDE
3	PCD DIAMOND VEINED INSERT	MMC AL.	4 FACET, OPTIMIZED FOR AL. ALLOYS	GEOMETRY OPTIMIZED BY MANUFACTURER
4	PCD DIAMOND INSERT	390 AL.& MMC AL.	'G'TYPE, STRAIGHT FLUTE, 4 MARGIN	BRAZED INSERT ON SOLID CARBIDE

TABLE 2. CUSTOM DRILL BIT GEOMETRIES TESTED

BIT NO.	TOOL TYPE	MATERIALS TESTED	BIT GEOMETRY	COMMENTS
1	SOLID CARBIDE MFD #1	MMC AL.	1ST ITERATION MFD	CUSTOM GEOMETRY DEVELOPED FOR PROGRAM
2	SOLID CARBIDE MFD #2	MMC AL.	2ND ITERATION MFD	CUSTOM GEOMETRY DEVELOPED FOR PROGRAM
3	SOLID CARBIDE DIAMETRAL LIP	390 AL.	DIAMETERAL LIP: OPTIMIZED FOR ALUM.	CUSTOMIZED GEOMETRY FOR PROGRAM
4	SOLID CARBIDE PROJ. DESIGN #1	MMC AL.	4 FACET WEB THINNED, WITH EDGE RADIUS	CUSTOM DESIGN, WITH COOLANT HOLES
5	SOLID CARBIDE PROJ. DESIGN #2	MMC AL.	SPLIT POINT, WITH EDGE RADIUS	CUSTOM DESIGN, WITH COOLANT HOLES
6	PCD VEINED PROJ. DESIGN #1	MMC AL.	4 FACET WEB THINNED, WITH EDGE RADIUS	CUSTOM DESIGN, WITH COOLANT HOLES
7	PCD VEINED PROJ. DESIGN #2	MMC AL.	SPLIT POINT, WITH EDGE RADIUS	CUSTOM DESIGN, WITH COOLANT HOLES

consideration of improving the life of the tool compared to standard drill point bits. The geometry of the second iteration was a more "traditional" type of MFD design. Cutting surfaces are asymmetrical to improve chip production and to help balance the workload on the cutting edges. Initial evaluations of these bits prior to delivery to SwRI showed a 24 to 31% improvement in drilling forces over standard, 4-facet bits.

Another type of unique geometry was considered under this test program, the diametral lip geometry. The diametral lip geometry is based upon a new flute contour designed to yield a symmetric drill configuration with straight-diametral lips which can then be extended to provide a single cutting edge and so eliminate the chisel edge. Also, the configuration provides a more uniform rake angle along the cutting edges of the new drill geometry.[4] Tools with this geometry can provide improved drilling performance compared to tools with a standard chisel edge geometry due to the elimination of the chisel edge, and the more uniform rake angle along the cutting edges. Additionally, this drill

point is easier to grind than the MFD geometry, while providing many of the more complex MFD geometry's performance benefits, such as reduced drilling forces, and improved tool centering capabilities. For this program a diametral lip geometry bit was designed for aluminum alloy materials. 15X micro-photographs of the drill point geometry are shown in Figure 1. Note that the geometry has no chisel edge, and could be routinely resharpened, requiring only 2 grinding parameters; a definite advantage over MFD designs. Due to schedule limitations, the performance of these tools was tested drilling aluminum 390 alloy material only.

Two types of drill geometries were designed by experts who have practical experience in drilling aluminum alloy materials in both industrial and research laboratory settings. Project design #1 was a modified 4-facet point geometry, and project design #2 was a modified split point (crankshaft style) geometry. The 4-facet design incorporated web thinning to .028 inch web thickness. A .030 inch corner radius was also incorporated in this design to

FIGURE 1. DIAMETRAL LIP DRILL BIT GEOMETRY

improve breakthrough performance. This design had a 38° helix angle. The split point design had a larger corner radius of .125 inch, and a helix angle of 30°. Both designs had 118° point angles, which is generally recommended for drilling MMC aluminum materials.[5] Also, both designs incorporated through-the-tool coolant to facilitate chip removal and to improve coolant delivery to the cutting areas of the tools. Additionally, the two designs were ground into diamond veined drill bits to the extent that this technology would allow these designs to be reproduced in the veined blanks. The project designed bits were tested in MMC aluminum material on a K&T Milwaukee-Matic horizontal machining center.

Testing of Tooling Coatings. Table 3 lists the tooling coatings which were considered for drilling the aluminum materials. The coatings were selected on the basis of literature reviews performed in this program and on guidance of various experts in the field of machine tooling. Note that three types of coatings were considered; abrasive diamond grit plated to high speed steel tooling, boron carbide (B_4C) vacuum deposition coating on carbide tooling, and thin film diamond applied to carbide using a chemical vapor deposition process. Diamond and B_4C were the only plating materials considered capable of withstanding the abrasive nature of silicon carbide particles in the MMC work material. The abrasive diamond plating involved a plating process where the diamond particles were co-deposited to the HSS material within a metallic alloy matrix. The process is commonly used to coat diamond dental drill bits and grinding wheels. Tools used for this testing were plated with coatings containing four diamond grain sizes ranging from approximately .5 mm to 5-12 microns. Standard, HSS, split point drill bits were coated with the abrasive diamond material for this testing. The boron carbide plating was deposited on carbide tools using a physical vapor deposition process. The process is low temperature, (250°C) and as such the material can be deposited on hardened steel tooling as well as carbide tooling. The coating thickness of the B_4C is typically 70 μinch and is claimed to have a hardness of Rockwell C 93. Carbide tools of the standard 4-facet type, and MFD tooling was coated with the B_4C material for this testing. Other than diamond coatings, the B_4C material was considered the only alternative material capable of

withstanding the SiC filled work material. Also, B_4C is a relatively inexpensive coating process compared to thin film diamond CVD processes, or alternative tooling using PCD insert technology.

An interesting aspect of this work was the testing of the performance of CVD thin film diamond coating applied to carbide drill tools. This testing was done to demonstrate the capability of a commercially available CVD diamond coating to adhear to carbide drill tooling while cutting the MMC material. Tools coated were the project designs 1 and 2, and they incorporated through-the-tool coolant holes. Figure 2 shows SEM images of one of the diamond coated tools. Note that the coating was uniformly applied over the cutting edges and of good quality. A Raman spectrum analysis of the coating indicated that the diamond was adherent to the carbide substrate. Some diamond-like carbon was seen to be built up in the areas of the coolant holes, but the film was of uniform quality otherwise on the cutting surfaces of the tools. The diamond coating was applied over a 1 inch length of the flutes back from the drill tip to insure coating coverage to the depth of the holes drilled in this testing. The diamond coated tools were tested at identical machining conditions to uncoated versions of the project designed tools and were also compared to PCD insert tools under identical conditions.

Infrared Imaging Research. The intent of this work was to develop an adjunct to aid in the development of new drill bit geometries and gain a better understanding of the thermal processes at the cutting edge of drill tooling.

Experimental Design. Infrared thermography represents a recent technology whereby electromagnetic energy emitted by an object is used to create a real-time thermal image. Commercial systems are comprised of a scanner (or camera) and the controller/recording system. Operationally, these devices function much like a video camcorder. By virtue of their ability to scan and record at frame rates up to 25 Hz, thermography systems are well suited to the investigation of "thermally dynamic" events, provided the scanner has a clear view of the active surface(s). With knowledge of surface emissivity, each image in a recorded sequence can be subjected to a broad range of analytical operations to include

TABLE 3. TOOL COATINGS TESTED

TRIAL NO.	COATING TYPE	COATING PROCESS	MATERIALS DRILLED	COMMENTS
1	ABRASIVE DIAMOND COATED	COURSE, ELECTRO-PLATED DIAMOND	AL. MMC, (SiC REINFORCED)	LARGE DIAMOND GRAINS PLATED ON HSS CHISEL POINT BIT.
2	ABRASIVE DIAMOND COATED	FINE GRAIN, ELECTRO-PLATED DIAMOND	390 AL.	325/400 MICRON DIAMOND, ON HSS SPLIT POINT BIT.
3	ABRASIVE DIAMOND COATED	FINE GRAIN, ELECTRO-PLATED DIAMOND	390 AL.	18/22 MICRON DIAMOND, ON HSS SPLIT POINT BIT.
4	ABRASIVE DIAMOND COATED	FINE GRAIN, ELECTRO-PLATED DIAMOND	390 AL.	5/12 MICRON DIAMOND, ON HSS SPLIT POINT BIT.
5	BORON CARBIDE, (B4C)	BORON CARBIDE, VACUUM DEPOSITION LO-TEMP PROCESS	AL. MMC, (SiC REINFORCED)	70 MICRO" THICK, ROCKWELL C-95, ON SOLID CARBIDE BIT
6	THIN FILM DIAMOND COATING	CVD DIAMOND THIN FILM COATING	AL. MMC, (SiC REINFORCED)	100 MICRO" THICK (APPROX.) ON SOLID CARBIDE BIT

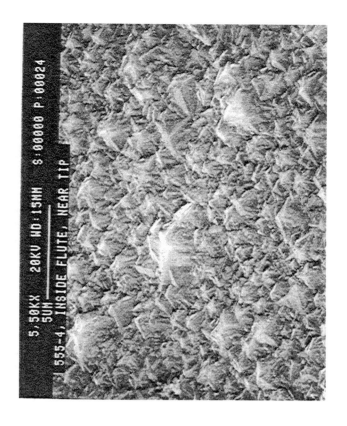

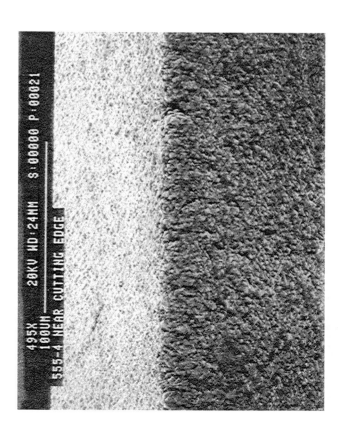

FIGURE 2. SEM PHOTOGRAPHS OF CVD DIAMOND COATED TOOL

the measurement of the temperature at a given spot, definition of isotherms or the generation of a profile(s) between user-defined points.

Testing Methodology. Two test configurations were set up to evaluate the IR concept so that the tool edges, which are normally obscured from view, become visible to the imaging system. One arrangement utilized a vertical milling machine as the test bed and the other made use of a lathe. For the mill, maximum exposure of the tool edge was achieved by reducing the specimen diameter to slightly less than the diameter of the drill tool (less than .250" in this case). The test arrangement for the mill imaging setup is illustrated in Figure 3. For the lathe, exposure was achieved by viewing the tool (through the chuck spindle) as it penetrates through the work material specimen. The lathe imaging setup is illustrated in Figure 4. In both set-ups, the drill tool was held stationary while the work rotates. By doing so, the imaging system could be used to obtain detailed thermal images of the cutting edge of the tool under test.

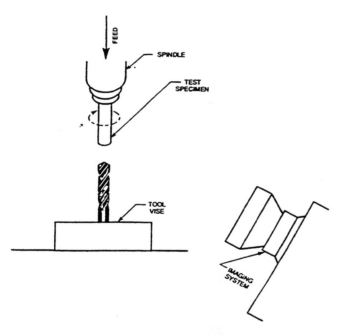

FIGURE 3. MILL CONFIGURATION

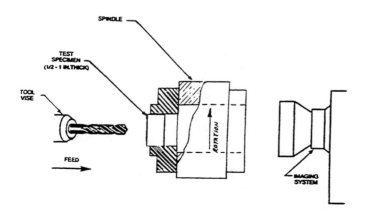

FIGURE 4. LATHE CONFIGURATION

The following parameters were investigated during this testing:

1. Bit Type (Conventional vs. MFD)

2. Bit Condition (New vs. Worn)

3. Work Material (Aluminum MMC vs. Titanium)

4. Operating Conditions (Constant Depth of Cut, Variable Removal Rates)

The images were recorded with an AGEMA infrared imaging system. After the images were selected for analysis, further processing was done with a Sun SPARC system and image processing software. Software routines applied offsets and scale factors to the image data and supported the acquisition of thermal profiles that approximated the tool tip geometry as it appeared in the two-dimensional space. For the mill tests, the profile shape was dependent on the tool geometry, i.e.: triangular for the conventional, and flat for the MFD. For the lathe tests, the profile was taken along a straight line that extended across the image and essentially parallel to the cutting edges.

Data Analysis. For each of the tests that were performed with the infrared system, a 20-second interval was recorded in the controller's random access memory. The sequences typically contained 500 individual images. The event could then be played back, frame by frame, so that the images of greatest interest could be extracted and analyzed.

The general location of the tool/work interface was established through characteristic bench marks that were visible within the image, and through the use of multiple profiles taken through the zone of interest. In other words, the zone was divided into increments, with a profile taken for each increment to create a "scan". The effects of the various test parameters were then characterized using this profile data in conjunction with the visual content of the image.

Results and Discussion

Results of the Drill Testing. The results of the drill tool testing shown in this report include the data from several testing sessions performed on a Tongil vertical machining center and a Milwaukee Matic horizontal machining center in an industrial setting. Machining speeds were limited to those typically associated with slower speed machining, or in the case of the Milwaukee Matic, the fastest speed available on that machine (235 SFPM). The fastest machining speed used was 500 SFPM (7640 RPM), which was near the upper limit of the vertical machine's spindle. Very little chip packing was noticed at the higher speeds, and less built up edge (BUE) was noted at these speeds, indicating that still higher drilling speeds could be exploited to reap increased economic benefits. Aggressive feed rates of .010 to .012 IPR were used to maximize productivity and minimize abrasive wearing of the SiC particles against the cutting tool edges.

Results of the Commercial Drill Bit Testing. The test results of the commercially available drill tools are shown in Table 4. Note that none of the commercially available drill bits shown here utilize through-the-tool coolant. The first trial shown was run with

TABLE 4. COMMERCIAL BIT GEOMETRY TEST RESULTS

TRIAL NO.	DRILL BIT TYPE	WORK MATERIAL	MACHINING CONDITIONS		HOLE QUALITY RESULTS	DRILLING PERFORANCE		COMMENTS
			SPEED: (RPM/SFPM)	FEED: (IPR)		TORQUE: (FT. LB.)	THRUST: (LB.)	
1	SOLID CARBIDE, 4 FACET	AL. MMC	3820/250	.010	9.8 Ra, microIN. AVG. -.0027" AVG. HOLE DIA.	1.7 1st HOLE, 3.4 50th HOLE	358 1st HOLE, 658 50th HOLE	.032" AVG. TOOL WEAR AFTER 50 HOLES
2	SOLID CARBIDE, 4 FACET	390 AL.	3820/250	.012	144.6 Ra, microIN. AVG. +.0006" AVG. HOLE DIA.	1.02	201	MODERATE BURR FORMATION EXCESS B.U.E.
3	PCD BRAZED INSERT, 4 FACET	AL. MMC	3820/250	.012	18.5 Ra, AVG. -.0006" AVG. HOLE DIA.	N.A.	N.A.	TOOL FRACTURED AFTER 36 HOLES.
4	PCD VEINED INSERT, 4 FACET	AL. MMC	3820/250	.012	34 Ra, AVG. -.0001" AVG. HOLE DIA.	N.A.	N.A.	TEST STOPPED AFTER 1000 HOLES, .002" TOOL WEAR
5	'G' STYLE, DIAMOND INSERT	390 AL.	3820/250	.012	14.1 Ra, AVG. -.0002" AVG. HOLE DIA.	1.05 (.75 @ 500 SFPM)	223 (187 @ 500 SFPM)	22.8 Ra @ 500 SFPM
6	'G' STYLE, DIAMOND INSERT	AL. MMC	3591/235	.012	9.2 Ra, AVG. -.0003" AVG. HOLE DIA.	1.42, 1st HOLE, 1.38, 30th HOLE	267, 1st HOLE, 285, 30th HOLE	MINIMAL WEAR, INSIGNIFICANT BURR FORMATION

a standard, commercially available 4-facet bit. As shown in the drilling performance column, the torque and thrust values nearly doubled after drilling 50 holes. This was approximately the life of this tool in the MMC material, as the tool was worn to the extent that 1/32" of the cutting edges were worn away. The hole quality was quite good, with 9.8 μin surface roughness noted on average. Average hole diameter was significantly undersized however, by .0027" (possibly due to the excess wear which occurred with this tool). Undersized holes were a common occurrence in drilling the MMC aluminum material throughout this testing. The performance of the same type of tool was also tested in drilling alloy 390 aluminum at similar rates. Hole diameter was only slightly undersized in this material, but surface roughness was considerably worse than with the same tool in MMC material. This is thought to be due to excess BUE which occurred with the 390 material, which may have been more readily abraded away by the SiC particles of the MMC material. Average drilling forces were less in the 390 material.

The test results of a brazed PCD insert, 4-facet geometry drill bit is shown in Trial 3. This drill bit successfully completed 35 holes in the MMC material, but fractured during the 36th, leaving the drill tip embedded in the hole. The holes which were completed were of excellent quality, with 18.5 Ra average surface roughness. It is not known whether the tool failed due to the braze joint experiencing excess heat, or if an excess force condition was encountered by the PCD insert. Several manufacturers of brazed PCD insert tools were tested during this program, which could not productively drill the MMC material. It is believed that brazing technology is generally not up to the task of drilling the MMC material due to excess temperature and force conditions

encountered. The test results of a 4-facet PCD veined insert tool is shown in Trial 4. This tool demonstrated the highest productivity capability of all the tools tested during this program. With the veined insert technology, a PCD insert is sintered into the carbide shank material, producing a tool with superior strength. As shown in the data, over 1000 holes were drilled before testing was stopped with less than .002" of general tool wear on the cutting edges.

Finally, of the commercial tooling tested, the 'G' style drill bit was the only PCD brazed insert tool to demonstrate a productive capability in drilling the MMC material. These tools were tested in both the 390 aluminum alloy, and the MMC material. The 'G' style drill bits have a 4-facet point, with straight flutes and 4 margins. Two PCD inserts are provided at the edges of the drilling point; the center portion of the tip being carbide. The "reamer style" of this tool is thought to provide the superior quality of the holes produced. This tool generally provided the best surface roughness values of all tools tested in both materials. However, at this time the tool has not been tested beyond 50 holes. It has yet to be demonstrated whether this drill can provide the quantity of holes available from the PCD veined style tool.

Results of the Custom Drill Bit Testing. The test results of the tools which were specially developed for this program are shown in Table 5. Trials 1 and 2 of this table show the results of the two iterations of MFD drill bits which were developed for abrasive aluminum materials. Due to the complex nature of the geometries of these tools, they were uncoated, solid carbide, without diamond inserts. The tools were expected to produce substantially better life than standard 4-facet designs. Although they did provide lower

TABLE 5. CUSTOM BIT GEOMETRY TEST RESULTS

TRIAL NO.	DRILL BIT TYPE	WORK MATERIAL	MACHINING CONDITIONS		HOLE QUALITY RESULTS	DRILLING PERFORANCE		COMMENTS
			SPEED: (RPM/SFPM)	FEED: (IPR)		TORQUE: (FT. LB.)	THRUST: (LB.)	
1	SOLID CARBIDE, MFD #1	AL. MMC	3820/250	.012	17.3 Ra, microIN. AVG. -.0003" AVG. HOLE DIA.	1.3 AVG. 1ST HOLE, 2.94 AVG. LAST HOLE (60 TO 160 HOLES)	133 1ST HOLE, 266 60TH HOLE	.041" AVG. TOOL WEAR
2	SOLID CARBIDE, MFD #2	AL. MMC	3820/250	.012	12.2 Ra, AVG. -.0004" AVG. HOLE DIA.	1.97 AVG. 1ST HOLE, 2.82 AVG. LAST HOLE (60 & 80 HOLES)	163 AVG. 1ST HOLE, 300 AVG. LAST HOLE (60 & 80 HOLES)	.048" AVG. TOOL WEAR
3	SOLID CARBIDE DIAMETRAL LIP	390 AL.	3820/250	.012	56.2 Ra, AVG. +.0002" AVG. HOLE DIA.	1.17 (.85 @ 500 SFPM)	297 (247 @ 500 SFPM)	B.U.E. AT BIT CENTER
4	SOLID CARBIDE PROJ. DESIGN #1	AL. MMC	3591/235	.012	21.0 AVG, 36 MAX. CORNERS ROUNDED	-	-	NEAR LIFE LIMIT AFTER 30 HOLES.
5	SOLID CARBIDE PROJ. DESIGN #2	AL. MMC	3591/235	.012	24.7 AVG, 42 MAX. CORNERS ROUNDED	1.8 1st HOLE, 2.4 30TH HOLE.	228, 1st HOLE, 290, 30th HOLE.	NEAR LIFE LIMIT AFTER 30 HOLES.
6	PCD VEINED PROJ. DESIGN #1	AL. MMC	3591/235	.012	37.2 AVG, 86 MAX. .001" AVG. WEAR	1.20 1st HOLE, 1.37 30th HOLE.	127, 1st HOLE, 233, 30th HOLE.	1 TOOL FAILED.
7	PCD VEINED PROJ. DESIGN #2	AL. MMC	3591/235	.012	97.6 AVG, 162 MAX. .001" WEAR, 1 TOOL.	1.20, 1st HOLE, 1.19, 30th HOLE.	107, 1st HOLE, 121, 30th HOLE.	POSSIB. ANOMALOUS MAX., 2 TOOLS FAILED.

machining forces on average, this did not translate into significantly improved drill life. After 60 to 160 holes, the cutting surfaces were completely worn out. Also, they did not significantly improve hole quality.

The diametral lip bit was tested only using the 390 alloy material due to scheduling constraints. This design, although less complex than the MFD, provided similar improvements in drilling forces over conventional drill geometries. Surface roughness results were worse, possibly due to excess BUE at the central portion of the point in this material. Testing these bits at higher speeds tended to reduce the BUE and MMC material may further reduce the BUE occurrence. Also diametral lip tools of greater than .25 inch diameter may produce less BUE due to the reduced area of the cutting edges taken up by the flank surfaces.

The two project designs were produced in solid carbide with PCD veined insert technology as shown in Trials 4 through 7. Both of the solid carbide versions of these tools were near the end of the tools' useful life after drilling 30 holes in the MMC material. Drilling forces were near average for the carbide tools tested. The breakthrough performance of both these tools were similar, varying from tool to tool, and ranging from virtually burr free breakthrough, to moderate production of burrs. Surface roughness produced with these tools was on average within project limitations, but also varied widely between tools. The PCD insert tools appeared to produce lower drilling forces than those recorded for solid carbide, project design #2 (Trial 5). However, surface roughness of the PCD tools was on average worse than the solid carbide designs. Analysis has not revealed at this time if the surface roughness variations recorded here were due to the numerous anomalies within the work material (such as voids or inclusions). Several of the PCD tools failed before 30 holes could

be produced in the MMC material. It is believed that the coolant holes in these PCD veined tools decreased the tools capability to withstand the drilling forces in the MMC material. Also, 6% cobalt carbide material was used in these tools, which, though harder, exhibits less toughness than carbides with greater cobalt content.

Results of the Tool Coating Testing. Summaries of the results of the testing that was performed with the coated tooling are listed in Tables 6, 7, and 8. Table 6 gives results of the tooling with abrasive diamond coating on HSS tooling. Note that all of these tools produced moderate to heavy exit burrs in drilling the aluminum material. None of these tools were used to drill more than 12 holes, as the poor hole quality produced by them did not justify further testing. Note that smaller diamond particle size correlated with improved hole quality results. Also, increasing the drilling speed from 250 to 500 SFPM improved hole roughness quality. The smallest grit size tool (5/12 micron) did produce average hole quality as low as 71 μinch Ra at a tooling speed of 500 SFPM. Severe BUE and associated clogging of the abrasive grains on the tools with the aluminum work material caused serious drilling problems in all cases.

Table 7 shows the results of the Boron Carbide coated tooling compared to identical tools which were uncoated carbide. The point geometries of these drills were the baseline, commercial, 4-facet tool, and the second iteration MFD geometry developed for the program. Three tools were tested in each trial; aluminum MMC was the work material. Drilling performance forces listed represent averages for the three tools tested in each trial. Statistically, no significant improvement in hole quality or drilling forces was seen as a result of the B$_4$C coating. Average tool wear on the cutting surfaces of both coated and uncoated bits was .028"

 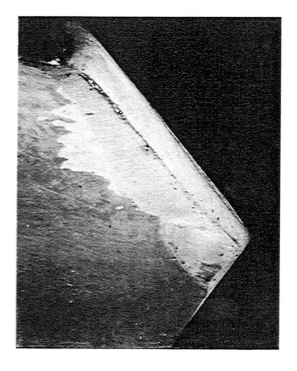

FIGURE 5. BORON CARBIDE COATED TOOL AFTER TESTING

TABLE 6. TOOL COATING TEST RESULTS

TRIAL NO.	TOOL COATING TYPE	WORK MATERIAL	TOOL TYPE	MACHINING CONDITIONS SPEED: (RPM/SFPM)	FEED: (IPR)	HOLE QUALITY RESULTS (Ra micro In.)	DRILLING PERFORANCE TORQUE: (FT-LB)	THRUST: (LB)	COMMENTS
1	ABRASIVE DIAMOND PLATED (> 5 mm)	AL. MMC (15% SIC)	STANDARD CHISEL POINT (HSS BIT)	3055/200 & 7640/500	.002 - .004	42 - 140			VERY HEAVY EXIT BURRS (.12"), FRACTURED AFTER 12 HOLES.
2	ABRASIVE DIAMOND PLATED (325/400 micron)	390 AL.	STANDARD SPLIT POINT (HSS BIT)	3820/250 & 7640/500	.012	114 & 71 AVG.	1.34 @ 250 SFPM 1.74 @ 500	214 @ 250 SFPM 426 @ 500	MODERATE BURR FORMATION, IMPROVED HOLE ROUGHNESS @ 500 SFPM.
3	ABRASIVE DIAMOND PLATED (18/22 micron)	390 AL.	STANDARD SPLIT POINT (HSS BIT)	3820/250 & 7640/500	.012	138 & 97 AVG.	1.13 @ 250 SFPM 2.22 @ 500	193 @ 250 SFPM 664 @ 500	MODERATE BURR FORMATION, IMPROVED HOLE ROUGHNESS @ 500 SFPM.
4	ABRASIVE DIAMOND PLATED (5/12 micron)	390 AL.	STANDARD SPLIT POINT (HSS BIT)	3820/250 & 7640/500	.012	301 & 144 AVG.	1.62 @ 250 SFPM 1.34 @ 500	354 @ 250 SFPM 275 @ 500	MODERATE BURR FORMATION, IMPROVED HOLE ROUGHNESS @ 500 SFPM.

TABLE 7. TOOL COATING TEST RESULTS

TRIAL NO.	TOOL COATING TYPE	WORK MATERIAL	TOOL TYPE	MACHINING CONDITIONS SPEED: (RPM/SFPM)	FEED: (IPR)	HOLE QUALITY RESULTS (Ra micro In.)	DRILLING PERFORANCE TORQUE: (FT-LB)	THRUST: (LB)	COMMENTS
5	BORON CARBIDE (B4C)	AL. MMC (15% SIC)	4 FACET BASELINE (SOLID CARBIDE)	3820/250	.010	10.5 AVG, 28 MAX.	2.3 1ST HOLE, 2.9 30TH HOLE	288 1ST HOLE, 591 30TH HOLE	AVG. TOOL WEAR = .028" NO SIGNIFICANT IMPROVEMENT IN TOOL LIFE OR FORCES
	NONE	AL. MMC (15% SIC)	4 FACET BASELINE (SOLID CARBIDE)	3820/250	.010	9.8 AVG, 19 MAX.	1.7 1ST HOLE, 3.4 50TH HOLE	368 1ST HOLE, 658 50TH HOLE	AVG. TOOL WEAR = .032"
6	BORON CARBIDE (B4C)	AL. MMC (15% SIC)	2ND ITERATION MFD (SOLID CARBIDE)	3820/250	.010	9.3 AVG, 11 MAX.	2.2 1ST HOLE, 2.9 30TH HOLE	232 1ST HOLE, 475 30TH HOLE	AVG. TOOL WEAR = .035" NO SIGNIFICANT IMPROVEMENT IN TOOL LIFE OR FORCES
	NONE	AL. MMC (15% SIC)	2ND ITERATION MFD (SOLID CARBIDE)	3820/250	.010	7 AVG, 12 MAX.	2.3 1ST HOLE, 3.0 30TH HOLE	225 1ST HOLE, 500 30TH HOLE	AVG. TOOL WEAR = .032"

TABLE 8. TOOL COATING TEST RESULTS

TRIAL NO.	TOOL COATING TYPE	WORK MATERIAL	TOOL TYPE	MACHINING CONDITIONS SPEED: (RPM/SFPM)	FEED: (IPR)	HOLE QUALITY RESULTS (Ra micro In.)	DRILLING PERFORANCE TORQUE: (FT-LB)	THRUST: (LB)	COMMENTS
7	THIN FILM DIAMOND, CVD, COATING *	AL. MMC (15% SIC)	4 FACET, WEB THINNED * (SOLID CARBIDE)	3591/235	.012	24.2 AVG, 53 MAX.	1.26, 1ST HOLE, 1.33, 30TH HOLE.	171, 1ST HOLE, 176, 30TH HOLE.	NO SIGNIFICANT DIFFERENCE IN HOLE QUALITY FOR COATED TOOLS.
	NONE	AL. MMC (15% SIC)	4 FACET, WEB THINNED * (SOLID CARBIDE)	3591/235	.012	21.0 AVG, 36 MAX.	·	·	
8	THIN FILM DIAMOND, CVD, COATING **	AL. MMC (15% SIC)	SPLIT POINT, EDGE RADIUS ** (SOLID CARBIDE)	3591/235	.012	42.3 AVG, 120 MAX.	1.36, 1ST HOLE, 1.39, 30TH HOLE.	183, 1ST HOLE, 184, 30TH HOLE.	POSSIBLE ANOMOLOUS MAX. ROUGHNESS READING.
	NONE	AL. MMC (15% SIC)	SPLIT POINT, EDGE RADIUS ** (SOLID CARBIDE)	3591/235	.012	24.7 AVG, 42 MAX.	1.8, 1ST HOLE, 2.4, 30th HOLE.	228, 1st HOLE, 290, 30th HOLE.	

* PROJECT DESIGN #1.
** PROJECT DESIGN #2.

to .035" after 30 holes. Figure 5 illustrates the typical condition of one of the B$_4$C coated tools after testing. Note that the coating appears to have completely failed due to abrasion by the SiC particles in the matrix material.

The results of the thin film diamond coated drill bits are listed in Table 8. The two project designed geometries were used in this series of testing. Coated tools are compared to uncoated tool performance in drilling the aluminum MMC work material. The diamond coating did not improve the hole quality performance significantly. However, from the force measurements listed for project design #2 (Trial 8) the drilling torque forces were reduced from 24% to 42% on the first and 30th holes drilled with the coated tools. Thrust forces were reduced from 20% to 36% with coated tools. Force measurements for the uncoated project design #1 tools were not available. Visual inspection of the coated tools after testing revealed some chipping of the coating and apparent removal from the flute areas.

Results of the SwRI Infrared Image Testing. At the completion of the testing, image analysis was performed to reveal thermal information from images of the drill bit cutting edges. Figure 6 is typical of the images obtained from each set-up. Of the two configurations, the lathe images provided the greater consistency in the clarity of the drill cutting edges. The following trends and conclusions are supported by the analysis of the resulting video images from this testing.

- In regard to test set-up (i.e., lathe vs. mill), there does not appear to be a large difference between the temperatures observed. The lathe test tends to register higher temperatures.

- The MFD bit typically runs cooler than the conventional tool for the same conditions of speed and feed. The thermal images obtained from the conventional and MFD bits illustrate this and an example is shown in Figure 7. Thermal profiles which were subsequently generated from these images are shown in Figures 8 and 9 for both MMC and titanium alloy materials.

- As the edges of a drill tool wear, the temperature profile tends to reflect less variation across the edge, but undergoes a general elevation in magnitude.

- The drill bit edge temperatures appear to increase in proportion to an increase in proportion to an increase in removal rate.

- Drilling titanium produces higher temperatures as compared to drilling aluminum/MMC, despite the fact that the removal rate of titanium was five times less than in the Al/MMC.

- The range in temperature(s) observed is comparable to that documented in other experimental efforts.[6]

More extensive research must be performed beyond this initial work to further refine these observations and to fully develop the design methodology enhancements detailed herein. Plans for implementing future research in this area would primarily include test methodology refinements to facilitate data analysis and to improve the consistency and accuracy of the results. Additional testing should be performed to divulge all aspects of these

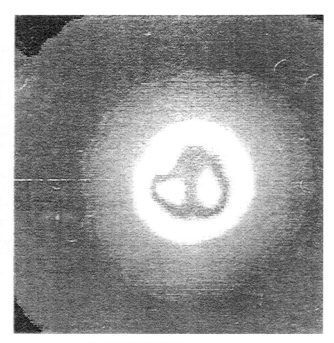

*MILL TEST
*CONVENTIONAL BIT

*LATHE TEST
*CONVENTIONAL BIT
*EDGES VERTICAL

FIGURE 6. MILL VS LATHE THERMAL IMAGE COMPARISON

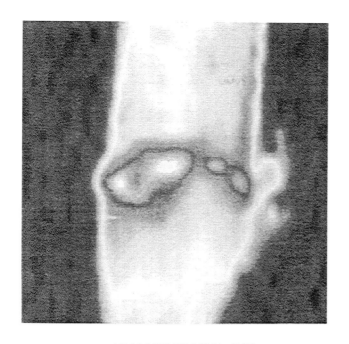

*CONVENTIONAL BIT

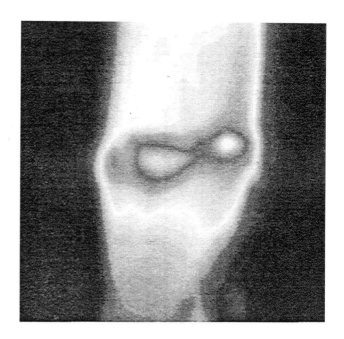

*MFD

FIGURE 7. CONVENTIONAL VS MFD BIT THERMAL IMAGES

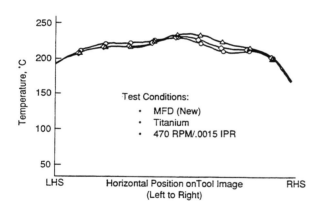

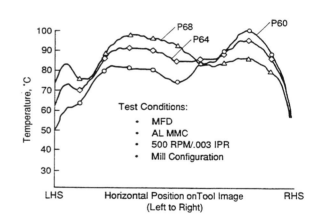

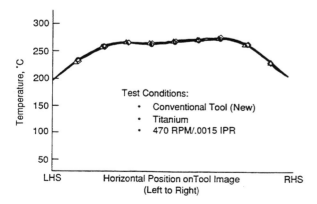

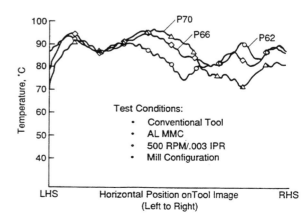

FIGURE 8. THERMAL PROFILES FOR CONVENTIONAL
AND MFD TOOLS CUTTING TITANIUM

FIGURE 9. THERMAL PROFILES FOR CONVENTIONAL
AND MFD TOOLS CUTTING AL. MMC

parameter variations. An infrared evaluation can be performed on the second or third generation MFD drill bits, since only one iteration MFD drill point was available at the time of the initial research, or other styles of drill bit geometries could be evaluated. Insights can be gained regarding the effect on the thermal profile that variations to specific geometries produce. Finally, an abbreviated series of tests can be performed using a conventional drill bit (with modified geometry) to reveal additional insights into the effects of minor geometry changes on the thermal profile of more conventional cutting tool edge(s).

Summary and Conclusions

Conclusions of the Drill Testing. The only commercial tool which provided reasonable holemaking capabilities in the MMC material used diamond veined insert technology. The productivity capability of this tool was demonstrated during testing when the tool produced over 1000 holes, with minimal tool wear. The hole quality produced by this tool was marginally acceptable based on the surface roughness test criteria for this program. Minor modifications to the flute geometry could improve hole quality. Other types of brazed PCD insert tools (which were not sintered directly into the carbide tool material) fractured catastrophically due to brazing joint failure or excess forces on the PCD insert.

The 'G' drill geometry gave best hole quality results, apparently due to it's straight fluted, reamer-like design with 4 margin areas. It was not proven if the tool could achieve acceptable life in drilling MMC aluminum material to justify it's high cost. It is unknown at this time if the brazed insert technology can withstand long term drilling in the MMC material. The carbide point design of the tip may wear prematurely, leading to early failure of the tool due to excessive wear at that area. Further life testing of this tool should reveal if productive quantities of quality holes can be achieved in the MMC material.

Testing of the capabilities of the various tooling coatings indicated that the abrasive diamond plated tools were not acceptable for drilling in MMC or aluminum alloy materials. The nature of the aluminum materials caused clogging of the cutting surfaces and subsequent early tool failure with unacceptable hole quality. The abrasive particle coated tools may be useful for holemaking in brittle, composite materials if the hole roughness produced was acceptable, especially the smaller diamond particle coating sizes (5-12 micron). Testing also indicated that, although the boron carbide coating material is second only to diamond in hardness, it could not withstand the abrasive action of the SiC particles; the material was abraded away within 30 holes.

The two custom designs tested during the program did not improve the hole quality or longevity of the tools in the MMC materials. The diametral lip drill design gave similar lower thrust and torque values to more complex MFD design, but did not improve hole quality or drill point life. Further modifications to the diametral lip geometry and the incorporation of a PCD insert technology could improve hole quality and extend tooling life of this geometry to acceptable limits.

Finally, testing indicated that the use of thin film CVD diamond coating of carbide tooling may have the potential to benefit the holemaking process in MMC and similar materials. Although visual inspection of the tools indicated significant chipping of the diamond coating after 30 holes were produced, lower drilling forces were measured with the diamond coated tools. Further refinements to the coating process are required so that the life of the coating can be extended beyond this quantity of holes. Use of this coating may eventually be the basis for producing acceptable quality holes at lower costs than PCD insert tooling can provide.

Conclusions of the IR Imaging Work. This research represented a preliminary evaluation of infrared thermography systems as a design aid in the development of new tools for cutting advanced materials such as aluminum MMC. The results indicate that useful information for tool geometry design is obtainable through its use. Furthermore, the benefits can extend beyond research topics and could be applied to production issues. Additional work is required, however, to completely explore the capabilities. The scope of these additional investigations should include refining the methodology, increasing the variability within test parameters considered (i.e. greater range in tip geometry), and eventually considering other machining processes such as turning, milling and broaching.

References

1. Burkes, J., Lesher M., Lowe M., "*The Use of Infrared Thermography for Drill Tool Evaluation*", ASM Materials Week Symposium, Chicago, Il. November, 1992.

2. Wu, S. M., Shen, J. M. and Chen, L. H., "*Multifacet Drills (MFD's)*", 14th National SAMPE Technical Conference, Volume 14, October, 1982, pp 456–463.

3. Madison, James and Schaible, James, "*Multiple Improvements*" Cutting Tool Engineering, February, 1991.

4. Thornley, R. H. and El-Wahab, A. B. and Maiden, J. D., "*A New Approach to Eliminate Twist Drill Chisel Edge, Parts 1 & 2*", International Journal of Production Research, 1987.

5. "*Machining Guidelines for Duralcan Composites*", Duralcan USA Inc., August, 1991.

6. DeVries, M. F., Saxena, U. K. and Wu, S. M., "*Temperature Distributions in Drilling*", Journal of Engineering for Industry, Transactions of ASME, Series B, Vol. 90, No. 2, May, 1968, pp 231-238.

Electrical Discharge Machining of Particulate Metal-Matrix Composites

S. K. Poon, T. C. Lee
Hong Kong Polytechnic
Hong Kong

Abstract

Particulate metal matrix composites (MMC) exhibit higher specific strength and modulus than monolithic aluminum alloys. However, this type of composite cannot be easily processed by conventional machining techniques without using expensive cutting tools.

An investigation has been made into the feasibility of using Electrical Discharge Machining (EDM) technique as a means of machining particulate MMC with different levels of silicon carbide content. EDM die-sinking of MMC was performed at a selected range of discharge currents, pulse durations, pulse-off time and gap voltages with different combinations of tool materials and polarity. It was found that, in EDM die-sinking processes, copper electrodes perform better than graphite in terms of tool wear and surface finish, and tools with positive polarity give higher material removal rate and lower tool wear. The results of investigation indicated that it is entirely feasible to machine particulate metal matrix composites by EDM processes although the higher the amount of silicon content in the MMC workpiece the higher will be the tool wear.

Introduction

With the introduction of boron reinforced 6061 aluminum in 1960's, metal matrix composites (MMC) have been used extensively, and research in the area of MMC has increased rapidly. MMC possess high specific modulus, high specific strength (strength-to-weight ratio), good corrosion resistance, and good impact and thermal shock resistance. Typically, in the case of particulate MMC, the material can offer the strength and density of AA7075 aluminum with the stiffness of titanium. This can translate into weight saving of 15-45% while the bulk wear rate (against steel) is reduced by about 30 times. (Kjar, Michelich, Sritharan and Heathcock [1], 1989).

Particulate MMCs are produced by powder metallurgy process which reinforces aluminum alloys with very fine silicon carbide (SiC) particles of an average size of 2-3 μm. The material is available in a number of grades with various reinforcement levels and alloy matrices.

The manufacturing technique is one of the most important factors in the successful use of MMC. Primary fabrication processes developed include rolling and forming while secondary fabrication operations include joining and machining. In machining MMC using conventional cutting methods, there occurs extreme tool wear due to the presence of fine, hard SiC particles. The difficulties increase with increasing volume fraction of SiC.

Electrical discharge machining (EDM) has been shown to be a versatile method for machining difficult-to-work materials ranging from heat-treated steels. tungsten carbides and various ceramics, specially when irregular shape is required. Recently, this technique has been applied to metal-ceramics and ceramic-ceramics (Petrofes [2], 1988). It is believed that EDM processes, including EDM die-sinking and Wire EDM, will open up an opportunity for the machining of MMC. Apart from the generation of complicated geometries, the negligible forces produced by the EDM process enable MMC to be machined without distortion and hence produces burr free surfaces with high accuracy.

The following sections attempts to outline the experiments involving the machining of particulate MMC by EDM under a variety of machining conditions. A brief introduction of the EDM die-sinking process is also given.

EDM Die-sinking Process

The application of the EDM process requires a system, which is constructed as shown schematically in Fig. 1. The tool electrode and the workpiece are mounted in the machining space of the machine tool in a suitable starting position relative to each other in a working medium. The medium, generally known as dielectric fluid, is stored in a working fluid tank and circulated through a filter to the working area where the workpiece is located.

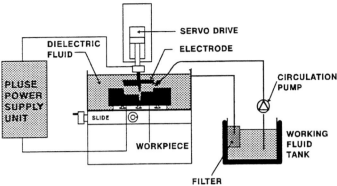

Fig. 1 - General scheme of EDM die-sinking process

A servo-control circuit, for which an average operating voltage is used as one of the controlling variables, maintains the proper operating gap for the discharges between the workpiece and the tool. With this control device the machining process is made automatic.

The mechanism of metal removal in EDM involves complex thermal erosion effects from electric sparks generated by a direct current power supply in form of high frequency pulses. The sparks are generated between two closely spaced electrodes under the influence of dielectric fluid. Since the discharge can take place in any spatial direction, whenever the tool and the workpiece face each other at a suitably close distance, the optional superimposition of additional movements is possible [3].

EDM is a complex physical thermal process and there is no comprehensive theory yet to explain simultaneously all the effects of machining and material parameters on machining performance. Empirical evidence suggests the following occurs [4]. In EDM the material removing effect of electrical spark discharges is utilized. The applied gap voltage creates an ionized channel between the nearest points of the workpiece and the tool electrode in the initial stage. In the next stage the actual discharge takes place with a heavy flow of current and the resistance of the ionized channel gradually decreases. The high intensity of current continues to further ionize the channel and a powerful magnetic field will be generated. This magnetic field compresses the ionized channel and results in localized heating. Even with sparks of very short duration, the temperature of the electrodes can be raised locally to more than the normal boiling point of the workpiece due to transformation of the kinetic energy of electrons into heat. Thus the high energy density erodes a part of material from both the tool and workpiece by locally melting and vaporizing.

Both electrodes, the tool and the workpiece, are stressed and subject to wear with different rates during the removing action of electrical discharges. Which one will have a less amount of wear cannot always be predicted physically, and the

choice of polarity is therefore as a rule based on empirical experiments.

Materials

Two grades of commercial particulate metal matrix composite (MMC) of the same product family but with different levels of silicon carbide (SiC) content were used as the workpiece materials for this study. These composites were formed by extrusion, 75 mm wide and 19 mm thick, with the following properties:

Material designation	MMC-17	MMC-25
Matrix alloy	AA2124	AA2124
SiC Vol. %	17%	25%
Modulus (GPa)	100	115
UTS (MPa)	610	700
0.2% PS (MPa)	500	500

Commercial aluminum of the same base alloy was also used for comparison.

The chemical composition of the as-received base alloy of the above particulate MMC is given in Table I.

Table I.   Chemical composition of base alloy (2124)

Material	Element (wt %)								
Alloy	Cu	Mg	Mn	Fe	Zn	Si	Cr	Ti	Al
2124	4.2	1.3	0.4	0.3	0.25	0.2	0.1	0.2	Balance

For the tool electrodes, copper, tungsten copper and graphite with a cross-section of 10 x 10 mm were used. The physical properties are given in Table II.

Table II   Physical properties of tool electrodes

Tool material	Density (g/cm^3)	Melting pt. (C	Resistivity (Ωcm x 10^{-2})
Copper (Cu 99.9%)	8.904	1083	0.009-0.07
Graphite	1.811	3350	0.04-0.1
Tungsten Copper (W70%)	15.228	3500	

Measures of EDM Performance

For EDM machining the performance measures which have been considered by others include metal removal rate (MRR), relative wear rate (RWR), tool wear rate (TWR), surface finish (SF) and overcut.

The investigation of Berkan [5] (1983) showed that the wear of a electrode depends significantly on both the shape and the flushing conditions involved. These factors affect the spatial distribution of discharges. Nevertheless, Berkan concluded that it is difficult to formulate precisely the principles of the physical phenomena that occur with the spark gap without methods which would allow one to measure directly the spatial distribution concerned.

Effects of discharge energy and pulse trains on EDM processes have also been the major subject of research. In the development of EDM, continuous efforts have been put into enhancing the control of the pulse characteristics for achieving optimum machining results. Earlier investigation work indicated that the discharge energy is determined by both the intensity of the spark and the time it flows, and it is a function of the control parameters such as discharge current, gap voltage, pulse duration, pulse off time and the characteristics of the electrodes (Lazarenko [6] 1964, Ricci *et al.* [7] 1987, Cogun [8] 1990, and Scott *et al.* [4] 1991). These parameters have proved to be the most significant factors which affect the material removal rate, tool wear and surface finish of the workpiece produced.

The performance measures here will therefore include material removal rate (MRR), relative wear rate (RWR), and surface finish (SF), taking into account the effects of discharge current (I_p), pulse duration (T_{on}), polarity and electrode material.

Material removal rate
MRR   =   (V_w)/t   (mm^3/min)

Relative wear rate
RWR   =   (V_e)/(V_w)   (%)

Surface Finish
SF   =   Surface roughness, Ra   (μm)

where V_w =   volume of workpiece material removed
        V_e =   volume of tool electrode material removed
        t   =   time

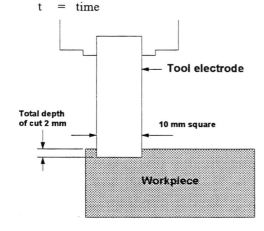

Fig. 2 - Size of tool electrode

Experimental Work

Experimental work was conducted on a AGIETRON U1 EDM Die-sinking machine fitted with an Agiepuls 30 M1 integrated pulse generator and Agiematic CNC-T integrated control system. The effectiveness of the EDM process with particulate MMC was evaluated in terms of the material removal rate (MRR), the relative wear rate (RWR), the dimensional accuracy and the surface finish (SF) quality of the workpiece produced.

The voltage (V) between the two electrodes was 120 volts across the gap and the discharge currents (I_p) ranged from 4 to 37 A. The pulse duration (T_{on}) ranged from 180 μ-sec to 1000 μ-sec, and the pulse-off time was set at 560 μ-sec. Shell 4919 dielectric fluid was used. The total depth of cut for each test was 2 mm (see Fig. 2).

During the experiment, the fluid pressure was kept to a minimum with a constant flow of dielectric fluid across the working area.

A Tektronix 2201 Digital Storage Oscilloscope was used to record the voltage-current-time characteristics of current discharge. The weight of material removed was measured with a Denver AC-1200D Electronic Balance (1200 gm x 0.01 gm - 120 gm x 0.001 gm).

The surface roughness of the machined composite was evaluated with a Hommel T1000 Surface Tester, and the topography of the as-bought and the as-machined surface was examined with an Olympus BH2-UMA microscope and built-in color video camera. Figure 3 shows the micrographs of the as-bought surface of MMC-17 and MMC-25 particulate MMC. No coating was applied to the EDM surface prior to microscopic examination.

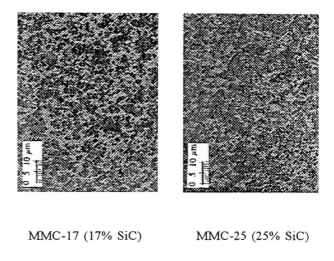

MMC-17 (17% SiC)   MMC-25 (25% SiC)

Fig. 3 - Micrographs of the as-bought surface of MMC-17 (left) and MMC-25 (right), showing the size and distribution of SiC particles before EDM.

Results

Effect of current. The effect of discharge current on the material removal rate is shown in Fig. 4. Under the condition of 180 μ-sec pulse duration, 560 μ-sec pulse-off time and 120 volts gap voltage, the value of material removal rate increased with the intensity of discharge current. The same phenomenon was noted in the testing of all specimens including Aluminum, MMC-17 and MMC-25.

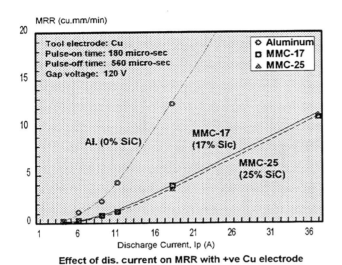

Effect of dis. current on MRR with +ve Cu electrode

Fig. 4

The material removal rate of Aluminum (with no SiC content) was much higher than the removal rate of particulate MMC, and, between MMC-17 and MMC-25, the one with lower SiC content had a better performance in terms of material removal rate. Therefore, it suffices to say that the material removal rate has a certain degree of correlation with the amount of SiC

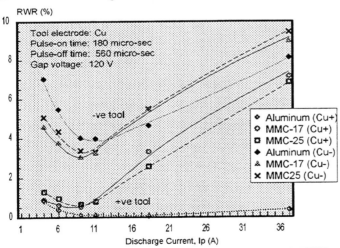

Effect of dis. current (Ip) and polarity on relative wear ratio (RWR)

Fig. 5

content in the workpiece. The material removal rate decreases while the level of SiC content increases.

The effect of discharge current on the relative wear rate is shown in Fig. 5. For the given area eroded, the wear rate decreased slightly up to about 10 A and then increased. The optimum relative wear rate for MMC-25 took place at a discharge current intensity of 10.3 A. The relative wear ratio was influenced by the level of SiC. It can be seen that the more SiC in the workpiece the higher will be the relative wear ratio and tool wear.

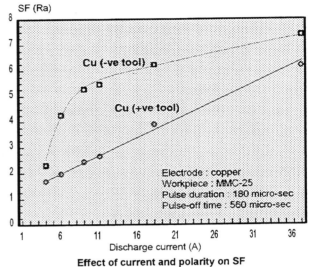

Effect of current and polarity on SF

Fig. 6

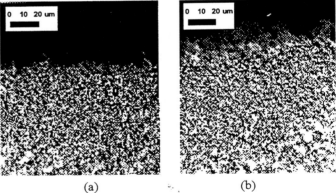

Fig. 7 - Micrographs showing EDM heat affected surface of MMC-25 with different discharge current: (a) 4 A, and (b) 14.8 A

The effect of current on surface finish is shown in Fig. 6. The surface roughness resulted from electrical discharge machining increased with the discharge current and ranged from 1.69 μm at 4 A to 7.39 μm at 37 A. Of special note, a copper tool with positive polarity produced a better finish than a negative tool, but using a negative tool would be an advantage at a low current range below 4 A for obtaining a fine surface finish.

Microscopic studies of the cross-sections of the machined surface (Fig. 7) revealed that the surface finish left by EDM on aluminum based MMC does not consist of two distinct thermally affected layers as what normally happens in the case of machining steel with EDM. No significant change in the surface structure was noted in the heat affected zone except minute craters due to spark erosion were found. These tiny craters are something normal with all EDM work.

Fig. 8a - 8c show the surface texture of the heat affected surfaces. Each micrograph illustrates SiC grains in a aluminum matrix. The surface was formed by current discharge and spark erosion, and under the discharge pressure, and high amount of heat generated, the SiC particles and base metal melted and vaporized. A partial `remelt' took place and some SiC particles were bound by a aluminum matrix.

The surface `damage' of MMC-25 resulting from different discharge currents is shown in the same micrographs (Fig. 8a-8c). At low current of 4 A, the material removal rate was low (0.1867 mm^3/min) and the SiC particles were not disturbed (Fig. 8a). At a current intensity of 10.8 A, some particles were dislodged from their original positions (Fig. 8b). Severe melting of the composite surface was found at a high current intensity of 37 A, and the molten layer flowed into irregular patterns without distinction between the SiC particles and the base metal. A built-up material adhered to the workpiece surface could be seen (Fig. 8c).

It was illustrated by the micrographs that the lower the discharge current the finer will be surface texture.

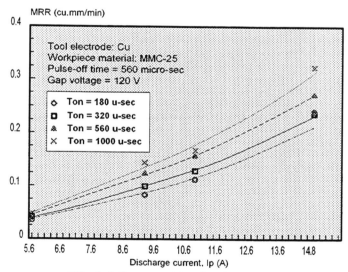

Effect of dis. current & pulse duration on MRR

Fig. 9

Effect of pulse duration on material removal rate and relative wear rate. Fig. 9 indicates that both pulse duration and discharge current affect the material removal rate. The material removal rate increased steadily with the level of pulse duration (T_{on}) and the discharge current (I_p). The higher the value of T_{on} or I_p the larger will be the material removal rate (MRR).

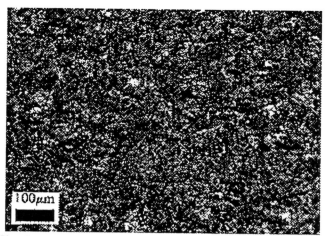

Fig. 8a - Micrograph showing the EDM surface of MMC-25 with a discharge current of 4 A.

Fig. 8b - Micrograph showing the EDM surface of MMC-25 with a discharge current of 10.8 A.

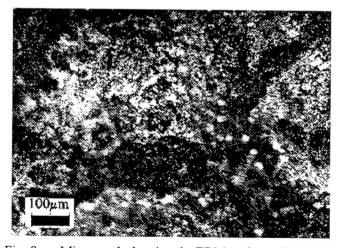

Fig. 8c - Micrograph showing the EDM surface of MMC-25 with a discharge current of 37 A.

Fig. 10 shows the effects of the discharge current and pulse duration on the relative wear rate. Attempts were made to "zoom" into the region where the optimum conditions took place. At low current intensity below 10 A, the relative wear rates were relatively low compared with those beyond 10 A. In the testing range from 4 A to about 10 A, with either setting of 180, 320, 560 or 1000 μ-sec pulse duration, the relative wear ratio (RWR) decreased slightly with discharge current (I_p) up to about 10 A, and then started to increase at a more rapid rate. The optimum condition took place at about 10 A, and with this current setting the relative wear rate became minimum at either setting of pulse-on time.

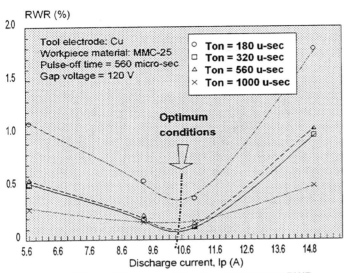

Effect of dis. current & pulse duration on RWR

Fig. 10

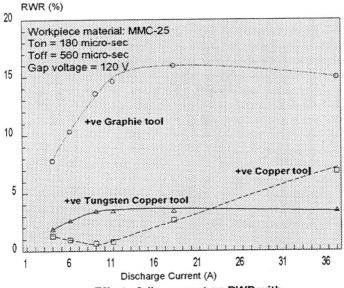

Effect of dis. current on RWR with +ve tool electrodes of Cu, CW & Gr.

Fig. 11

Effect of tool material on relative wear rate. It is shown in Fig. 11 that copper and tungsten copper (CuW) are both suitable for use as tool electrode in electrical discharge machining of particulate MMC. In particular with CuW, the relative wear rate was maintained at a level below 3.5% for the whole range of current settings under investigation (ie up to 37 A). This is a desirable property for both roughing and finishing work. However, in the range of current settings between 4 to 22 A, copper electrodes would be a better choice from a technical or economical point of view.

As far as the graphite electrode is concerned, the tool wore out much more rapidly. The relative wear rate induced by using a positive graphite tool went up to 15% with current intensity beyond 12 A. With a high wear rate, graphite could not be used effectively for EDM applications on particulate MMC.

Effect of tool material on material removal rate and surface finish. The copper tool and the tungsten copper tool were comparable in material removal rate that can be attained under the same machining conditions (Fig. 12) and in surface finish of the machined part (Fig. 13). In overall terms, these two materials (Cu and CuW) performed better than graphite tools in terms of material removal rate and surface finishing although at a high current intensity (above 26 A) graphite could produce a better surface than copper and tungsten copper.

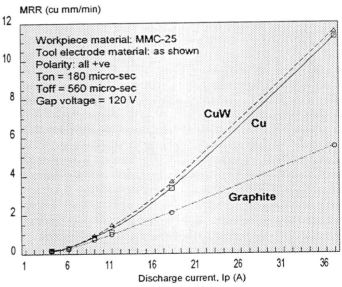

Effect of tool material on material removal rate

Fig. 12

Effect of polarity. Positive tool electrodes were found to have a higher material rate (Fig. 14), lower relative wear rate (Fig.15) and better surface finish of the workpiece produced (Fig. 6). This results were independent of the tool material investigated. The optimum material removal rate in that could be achieved in rough or medium machining with a positive copper tool was about 50% of that with a negative tool. The

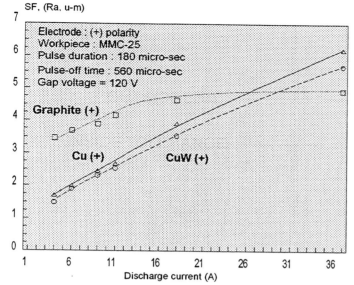

Effect of tool material on surface finish

Fig. 13

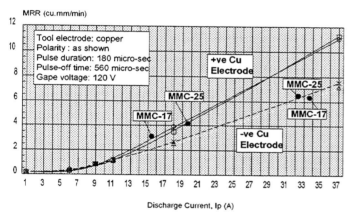

Effect of dis. current (Ip) and polarity on metal removal rate (MRR)

Fig. 14

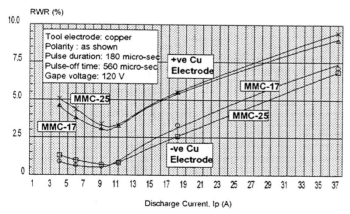

Effect of dis. current (Ip) and polarity on relative wear rate (RWR)

Fig. 15

relative wear rate at optimum condition was also found to be about four times less than that of a negative tool. From these observations, it is evident that positive tools perform better than negative tools in terms of material removal rate, dimensional accuracy and surface finish of the workpiece produced.

Discussion

From the experiments, it was observed that the physical phenomenon that occurs in EDM of particulate MMC with SiC content is generally similar to that which occurs in the base material, aluminum. Certain difference arise depending on the material of the electrode used and the level of SiC content in the MMC workpiece. The base material (aluminum) is highly conductive, but silicon carbide particles inside the alloy is not. It was observed that the more SiC content in MMC the higher will be the tool wear rate and, on the contrary, lower material removal rate. The presence of SiC in MMC has imposed considerable problems in conventional machining. It was however proved in this investigation that it is entirely feasible to machine particulate MMC by EDM processes. The advantage of such processes with MMC is the capability of producing irregular shaped cavities and holes with a fine surface finish (up to about 2 μm Ra surface roughness) and a good dimensional accuracy (with a relative wear rate below 1%). EDM processes also help overcome many of the machining problems caused by the high wear resistance property due to the SiC content in the composites.

As far as electrode material is concerned, among the three chosen materials, tungsten copper (CuW) appears to be more stable than the others in terms of relative wear ratio. RWR can be maintained at a low level (ie. below 3.5% in the machining of MMC-25 with 25% of SiC content by volume fraction) throughout the testing range from 4 to 37 ampere discharge current intensity. The performance of copper electrode is comparable with CuW, especially at a current range below 22 A. Graphite is the worst, and therefore *not* suitable for electrical discharge machining of particulate MMC. This finding coincides with what was observed by Lee and Lau [9] in their study of the characteristics of EDM in machining conductive ceramics. In EDM of particulate MMC with ceramic particles, the phenomenon is quite similar to the case of using graphite as a tool for machining ceramics. The two materials, graphite and ceramic, are quite similar in some of their properties such as melting temperature, thermal conductivity as well as resistivity. These similarities make them more difficult to be differentiated as being tool or workpiece. So, in the choice of electrode materials, either copper or tungsten copper is suitable (see Fig. 11). Both of them have their own merits. Copper is more suitable for precision machining whilst tungsten copper serves better than the others in roughing work.

The effect of polarity on material removal rate, relative wear rate and surface finish is worth mentioning. Higher

MRR, lower RWR and better SF are associated with positive tool polarity under a variety of machining conditions. This is found in line with the general trend observed in the machining of other common metals [10]. The tool wear rate of positive copper tool is about 4 times less than that of a negative tool at the optimum setting.

In general the higher the material removal rate and the lower the wear rate the better. Unfortunately, the goals of high material removal rate and low tool wear rate are, to some extent, conflicting with one another. The same applies to surface finish and material removal rate. No particular combination of control parameters can be expected to result simultaneously in the best MRR, the lowest RWR and the best SF. Very often these goals have to be taken separately at different stages of work.

The EDM process generally consists of several stages, a rough cut phase, a rough cut with finishing stage, and finally a finishing stage. During the rough cut phase material removal rate is of primary importance and a high current intensity has to be set. On the other hand, when approaching the finishing stage, a fine tool and optimum control settings are required for attaining the best surface finish and precision machining result. By knowing the effects of the various machining parameters, these goals can be achieved with ease. For roughing work, the higher the discharge current the more efficient will be the process in terms of material removal rate. For precision machining, the optimum condition of relative wear rate and surface finish takes place at a discharge current of 10.3 amp, pulse duration 320 μ-sec, pulse-off time 560 μ-sec and a gap voltage of 120 volts. This applies to the machining of MMC-25 with 25% of Sic (by volume fraction) using the equipment mentioned above. The findings confirm that there exists an optimum condition for precision machining of particulate MMC although the condition may vary with the composition of the material, the accuracy of the machine, and other external factors.

Conclusion

In this study, the feasibility of using EDM to machine particulate MMC was investigated. Since EDM is a complex thermal machining process and there is no comprehensive theory yet to explain simultaneously all the effects of EDM control parameters and material influence on machining performance, selection of optimum machining conditions for new materials still relies on well planned experiments. From a technical point of view, it can be concluded that:

1. It is entirely feasible to machine particulate metal matrix composites by electrical discharge machining processes. The advantage of using EDM on MMC is the capability of producing irregular shaped cavities with good surface finish and dimensional accuracy.

2. Positive polarity should be used for machining particulate MMC in order to achieve a low tool wear ratio for better dimensional accuracy and stability in electrical discharge machining of MMC.

3. Copper and tungsten copper (CuW) electrodes are proved to be better than graphite tools in terms of material removal rate, tool wear and surface finish. Tungsten copper is more stable than the others but copper at low current intensity is more suitable for precision work.

4. The material removal rate and the relative wear rate vary with the amount of SiC content in the workpiece. The material removal rate decreases while the level of SiC content increases. On the contrary, the relative wear rate goes up with the increase amount of SiC content in the workpiece.

5. Optimum material removal rate and relative wear rate are two conflicting goals which cannot be achieved simultaneously with a particular combination of control settings. The same applies to material removal rate and surface finish. To achieve the best machining results, the goals have to be taken separately in different phases of work with different emphasis.

References

[1] Kjar, A.R., J.L. Michelich, T. Sritharan, and C.J. Heathcock, Particulate Reinforced Aluminum-based Composites, *Light-weight Alloys for Aerospace Applications*, The Minerals, Metals & Materials Society (1989).

[2] Petrofes, N.F. and M. Gadalla, *Ceramics Bull.* **67**, 1048 (1988).

[3] Stoeckhert, K. and K. Alex, *Mold Making Handbook for the Plastics Engineer*, p. 327, Hanser, New York (1983).

[4] Scott, D., S. Boyina and K.P. Rajurkar, Analysis and Optimisation of Parameter Combinations in Wire Electrical Discharge Machining, *Int. J. Prod. Res.*, **29**, 2189-2207 (1991).

[5] Berkan, J., Shape Wear of Tool Electrodes and its Influence on Technology in Electrical Discharge Machining, *Proc. 7th Int. Symp. on Electro Machining (ISEM 7)*, Birmingham, U. K., 211-217 (1983).

[6] Lazarenko, B.R., *Electrospark Machining of Metals*, Consultants Bureau, New York, p.3 (1964).

[7] Ricci, W.S., W.R. Blumenthal and H.A. Skeele, Electrical Discharge Machinability of Ceramics, *Proceedings of Eastern Manufacturing of Technology Conference*, Springfield, Massachusetts, November, session 6, (1989).

[8] Cogun, C., A Technique and its Application for Evaluation of Material Removal Contributions of Pulses in EDM, *Int. J. Mach. Tools Manufact.* **30**, 19-31, (1990).

[9] Lee, T.C. and W.S. Lau, Some Characteristics of Electrical Discharge Machining of Conductive Ceramics, *Matl. & Manufact. Processes*, 6(4), 635-648 (1991).

[10] Buckow, I.A. and M. Cole, *Metall. Rev.* **14**, 135 (1969).

A REVIEW OF MACHINING STUDIES FOR CASTABLE AND PREFORM INFILTRATED REINFORCED ALUMINUM METAL MATRIX COMPOSITES

Russell G. Smith, Cameron May
Lanxide Corporation
Newark, DE

Harold A. Fell
Martin Marietta Energy Systems, Inc.
Oak Ridge, TN

Abstract

Reinforced metals, also known as metal matrix composites (MMCs), offer significant advantages in high specific stiffness, strength, wear resistance, weight reduction, high thermal conductivity, long term dimensional stability, high vibration damping, and low coefficient of thermal expansion.

These materials are candidates for use in such areas as automotive, electronics, and precision equipment. Although LANXIDE™ MMC technology is capable of producing certain composites to net shape, other components may require some machining.

Machining evaluations are being conducted for two principle types of reinforced aluminum metal matrix composites as part of a Cooperative Research and Development Agreement (CRADA) between Lanxide Corporation and Martin Marietta Energy Systems, Inc. Studies are being conducted on castable MMCs comprised of 30-35 volume per cent silicon carbide particulates and on aluminum MMCs with 40-50 volume percent SiC particulates.

The objective of this program is to develop advanced technology and manufacturing practices for machining and inspecting aluminum MMCs. A major portion of the program is to determine economical machining parameters for a wide range of filler loadings, chemistries and, morphologies.

ALUMINUM BASED METAL MATRIX COMPOSITES (MMC) are being evaluated widely for automotive applications because of their attractive high temperature mechanical properties, high stiffness, light weight and high wear resistance. These applications are in such areas as brake rotors and calipers, cylinder liners, drive shafts, connecting rods, rocker arms, and transmission components.

The use of these aluminum MMC materials offer precision equipment manufacturers new ways to meet customers' demands for greater accuracy, repeatability, speed, and payload.

Another important application area for these composites is in packaging, substrates and support structures for electronic components. For these applications a high loading of SiC particles is incorporated in an aluminum alloy matrix to obtain the desired combination of properties. These properties are a low coefficient of thermal expansion matched to that of the electronic device, high thermal conductivity for heat dissipation, high stiffness to minimize distortion, and low density for minimum weight.

Since different applications require different reinforcement materials, loadings, reinforcement size, and morphology as well as different matrix chemistries, the development of the machining parameters for this range of materials is important.

This is being done as part of a CRADA between Lanxide Corporation and Martin Marietta Energy Systems, Inc. where Martin Marietta is developing the machining parameters on the materials supplied by Lanxide. The initial work is being done by turning. Other machining operations such as milling, drilling, tapping, and grinding will be studied.

Metal Matrix Composite Technology

Lanxide Corporation has invented and patented technology that permits the economical fabrication of a broad range of aluminum matrix composites. A variety of ceramic reinforcements, such as particles or fibers of silicon carbide or aluminum oxide, can be combined with aluminum metal using a molten metal infiltration process. This PRIMEX™ pressureless metal infiltration process forms composites featuring 30 to 75 or more volume percent reinforcement, uniform microstructures, and net or near-net shapes (References 1 to 5). A wide variety of reinforcement shapes, such as fibers, platelets, particulates (with sizes down to < 1 μm) can be used.

The basic process is shown in Figure 1. In the first step, the reinforcement is formed into the desired shape using traditional ceramic-forming methods; this "preform" contains 30 to 50 volume percent interconnected porosity. In the next step, the preform is placed in contact with an aluminum alloy in an environment that causes the ceramic reinforcement to be wet by the molten matrix alloy, resulting in the spontaneous infiltration of the preform to form the composite. The infiltration is conducted in a nitrogen atmosphere at ambient pressure and at a temperature above the melting point of aluminum.

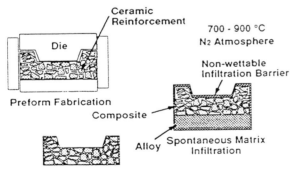

Figure 1. Schematic of PRIMEX™ pressureless metal infiltration process

The resulting components are completely infiltrated with matrix alloy and feature uniform distributions of particles, as shown in Figure 2. Parts having complex geometrys can be made to net or near-net shape (requiring finishing of only the critical dimensions).

Recently, Lanxide has adapted this technology to traditional aluminum casting methods. The PRIMEX CAST™ casting process can produce aluminum components reinforced with 1 to 40 volume percent silicon carbide particles (Reference 6). Parts have been made using investment shell, die, squeeze, and sand casting methods in production foundries, Figure 3, demonstrating the feasibility of economical production of cast MMCs using existing manufacturing capacity. A schematic of the process is shown in Figure 4. The key first step uses PRIMEX™ pressureless metal infiltration with an excess of aluminum. The reinforcement is made highly wettable by the molten aluminum - a crucial requirement for achieving the best mechanical properties. The second step involves uniformly dispersing the reinforcement in preparation for casting. Sizes and dimensional accuracy's of MMC castings fall within typical ranges for the various casting processes. The silicon carbide particles are uniformly distributed in the aluminum matrix as shown in the microstructure in Figure 5.

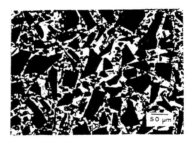

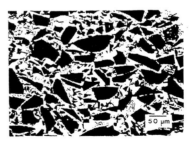

Figure 2. Microstructure of reinforced aluminum made by the PRIMEX™ pressureless metal infiltration process: 70 volume percent silicon carbide (top); 55 volume percent silicon carbide (bottom).

Figure 3. Components make of PRIMEX CAST™ 91-X-1060 MMC.

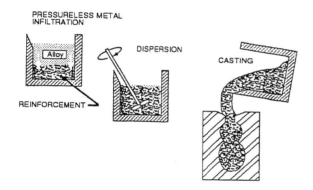

Figure 4. Schematic of the PRIMEX CAST™ casting process.

The inherent flexibility of these two processes enables component properties to be tailored to the application by manipulating the reinforcement volume fraction and type, the matrix alloy composition, and the microstructural features.

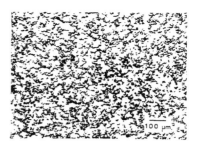

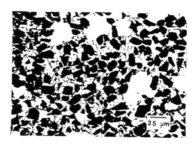

Figure 5. Microstructure of reinforced aluminum made by the PRIMEX CAST™ process: 30 volume percent silicon carbide.

Experimental Procedure

The initial study is focused on developing optimum machining parameters for turning. The variables listed in Table I were selected for the study.

Table I. Variables in Machining Study

Variable	Values
Volume % reinforcement	30 %, 45%
Particle size of reinforcement (μm)	66,45,17
Heat treatment	yes (T6), no
Particle morphology	regular, round
Coolant	yes, no
Cutting tool	PCD, CVD
Reinforcement chemistry	SiC, Al_2O_3

The simple combinations of loading percentage, grit size, heat treat condition, particle morphology, coolant, tool material, and vendor provided a full factorial experiment consisting of 192 different tests without replications. Further experimental planning allowed the turning experiments to begin with only seven carefully chosen MMC logs. These are listed in Table II. All logs contained SiC particulates as the reinforcement and no coolant was used for the machining experiments.

Table II. Experimental Logs for Turning Study

Log #	Reinforcement loading (Vol. %)	Reinforcement Material	Reinforcement Particle Size (μm)	Heat Treatment	Particle Morphology
1	45	SiC	17	NO	Regular
2	30	SiC	17	NO	Regular
3	45	SiC	66	NO	Regular
4	30	SiC	66	NO	Regular
5	30	SiC	17	YES	Regular
6	30	SiC	31	NO	Regular
7	30	SiC	17	NO	Round

Assuming that there is no interaction between the material variables, this initial selection of material allows comparisons to be made between high and low loading, coarse, medium and fine grain size, heat treated versus not heat treated, and round and regular particle morphology.

Traditional tool wear tests involve determining flank wear as a function of time. Since the cost of the tool and metal removal rates are known, this can be translated to the cost per volume of material removed neglecting the cost of labor and machine downtime for tool replacement and the mitigating effect of tool resharpening and reuse.

A numerically controlled turret lathe is being utilized for the cutting tests. Adequate power is applied to maintain spindle speed during cutting. The ability to vary the spindle speed in small increments to compensate for the constantly changing diameter, and hooding and ventilation to control dust or coolant are features of this machine.

As each MMC log was received at the Y-12 plant, hardness measurements were made on the log. Results of the tests on the logs are shown in Figure 6. From this graph, it can be concluded that hardness increases with the amount of reinforcement, is higher for smaller particle size, and can be drastically altered by heat treating.

Initial screening tests were performed to bracket cutting parameters, to eliminate unsuitable tools, and to discover tools and

parameters which should be investigated. Logs of 60% loaded material were available and were utilized for these tests. A range of cutting speeds was investigated that provided adequate material removal rates while protecting the machine, tool, and personnel. The cutting rates chosen are 229, 152, and 107 surface meters per minute (SMM) based on performance of the most promising tool. It is anticipated that higher cutting speeds may be possible with different tool configurations and with different loadings, and these will be investigated.

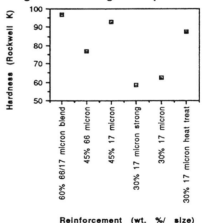

Figure 6. Average Composite Hardness

The feed rate utilized in the screening tests was 0.508mm per revolution . Depth of cut was 0.254mm . Two passes, each 152mm long are made along the diameter of the log with measurement of the log for taper between and after the cutting passes. On the highly loaded logs used for the screening tests, this provided adequate cutting time for measurable tool wear. This was not the case for some logs having lower loading.

The most promising tool used in the screening tests is a 75% polycrystalline diamond bonded by silicon carbide, manufactured in Australia. The form of the tool is a flat cylinder approximately 10mm diameter by 3mm thick which can be used as a cutting tool without being bonded to a substrate. During screening tests, this tool's performance was such that it was chosen as the tool to be utilized in the testing phase Because of possible commercial unavailability of this tool and other drawbacks, other tools will be tested and included in the list of recommended tools.

An advantage of this tool is that a large portion of the cutting test may be performed using a single tool by indexing the cutting edge, thereby removing differences between tools as a variable. A second tool from the same manufacturer was utilized during cutting and results of cutting using the two tools compared. Disadvantages of the tool are the difficulty in obtaining a positive rake configuration or a small nose radius to allow comparison with other available tools. Figure 7 shows the performance of two diamond tools at three cutting speeds on the 60% loaded material.

lower amount of reinforcement, tool wear is not pronounced as it was on the 60% loaded logs used for screening tests. This has caused the measurement of flank wear to become critical and even beyond the capability of the instrument used.

Figure 8 shows the results of turning using the Australian diamond tool on one of test logs(45% SiC reinforced) in the planned experiment and the 60% reinforced material. Note that emphasis has been placed on cutting speeds in the 107 to 229 surface meters per minute (SMM) cutting range, and that the two tests made above this range led to results which were not acceptable. Flank wear data for this test is not considered reliable.

Figure 8. Work Piece Taper vs Cutting Speed

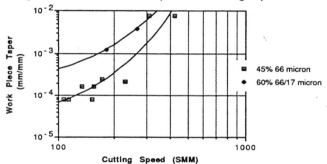

Conclusion

Machining parameters for turning aluminum metal matrix composites having SiC particulate reinforcement loadings between 60 wt %. and 30 wt. % and particle sizes between 66 and 17 microns were investigated. Several types of tungsten carbide, polycrystalline diamond, and CVD diamond cutting tools were investigated. Preliminary results indicate that machining parameters must be optimized for each type of metal matrix composite of interest.

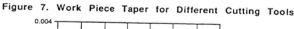

Figure 7. Work Piece Taper for Different Cutting Tools

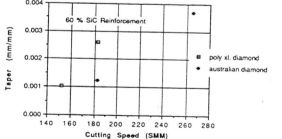

Cutting test were performed on the logs listed in Table II. Analysis of the data from the cutting tests have shown several testing deficiencies. Since the logs are loaded to a

References

1. Aghajanian, M. K., Burke, J. T., White, D. R. , and Nagelberg, A. S. SAMPE Quarterly, 20, [4] 43-46 (1989).

2. Aghajanian, M. K. , Rocazella, M. A., Burke, J. T., and Keck, S. D., J. Mater. Sci., 26 [2] 447-54 (1991).

3. Materials Engineering, 106 [4] 18 (1989).

4. Materials and Processing Report, 4 [3] 2-3 (1989).

5. DoD Metal Matrix Composite Information Analysis Center Current Highlights, 9 [3] 1-3 (1989).

6. Incast, 14, Volume IV, Number 5 (1991).

CUTTING, TRIMMING, AND DRILLING OF TITANIUM MATRIX COMPOSITES FOR STRUCTURAL APPLICATIONS

S. M. Sullivan
McDonnell Douglas Aerospace
P. O. Box 516
St. Louis, MO 63166 USA

Abstract

Processing techniques required to produce useful titanium matrix composite (TMC) structural components have been developed. Following consolidation, simple shapes are cut, trimmed, drilled, and bonded for assembly into more complex built-up structures. These structures have ranged in size from small 4-ply laminates to airframe structures measuring 8 feet in length utilizing 28-ply laminates. In this paper, techniques for cutting, trimming, and drilling of TMC laminates will be reviewed.

DURING THE EARLY DEVELOPMENT OF TITANIUM MATRIX COMPOSITES, reinforcing fiber mat and matrix alloy foils required for layup were cut by hand using patterns to guide the cutting process. These plies are then stacked, consolidated by hot isostatic pressing to full density, and assembled into larger structures, as shown in Figure 1. As larger structures were built, this hand cutting method was carried over into production. However, it was recognized that improved cutting methods were needed to increase production rates and lower cost. Conventional hand cutting is labor intensive, particularly if a large number of plies are required, and the increased template handling and cutting increases the chance for error. In addition, fiber is wasted because the quality of the hand-cut edge is not adequate for use as the edge of the next piece.

After looking at different automated cutting systems, we found that the numerically-controlled cutting system used for organic composite materials works well, with only minor changes in set-up required. This cutting method utilizes a mechanical chisel cutter system, sometimes called a Gerber cutter. Cutter wear is more than normal, due to the abrasiveness of the silicon carbide fibers, but the cost in tool wear is acceptable when compared to the time and effort required to hand cut the materials. Once the fiber and foil plies are laid out on the cutting bed and aligned, the numerically-controlled cutting is fast and efficient. A cutting operation is shown in Figure 2, which contrasts the hand cutting process with the automated process. The computer-aided system also helps nest the individual plies within the larger sheet for maximum material utilization. Over 1600 individual ply pieces have been successfully cut with this automated system.

While titanium matrix foil has been cut using the same system, most small pieces are still cut with hand shears. Once the fiber and foil plies are cut and stacked, they are placed over or pressed into a hard steel tool, which defines the shape of the final part. Then, a preformed steel bladder is placed over the layup, and pressed into the tool. as shown in Figure 3. The bladder is then welded to the tool landing, providing an airtight seal, and the layup pack is evacuated, heated to drive off entrapped moisture and gases, and then consolidated by hot isostatic pressing (HIP). Following consolidation, the bladder is machined off, and the consolidated part is removed from the tool. The parts, such as the C-channels shown in Figure 4, are then cleaned, inspected, and cut and trimmed to the desired final shape.

Cutting and Trimming of Laminates. Several methods of cutting and trimming TMC laminates have been evaluated. The material is highly abrasive, and tool costs can be high. Improper cutting not only damages tools, but also can cause damage to the part itself. Abrasive waterjet cutting (AWJ), illustrated in Figure 5, has been found to be an effective method of cutting TMC laminates with minimal damage.

Consolidated C-channel parts are being cut into crenelated angles by AWJ cutting, as shown in

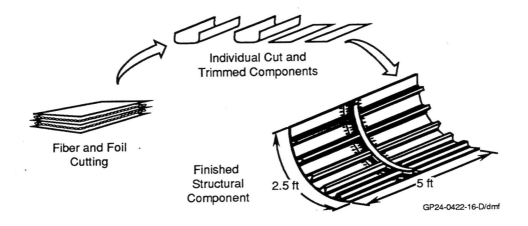

Fiber and Foil Cutting

Individual Cut and Trimmed Components

Finished Structural Component

2.5 ft

5 ft

GP24-0422-16-D/dmf

Figure 1. Specialized Cutting Techniques are Required for All Phases of TMC Fabrication.

Conventional Hand Cutting

Improved Numerically Controlled Cutting

GP24-0422-13

Figure 2. SCS-6 Silicon Carbide Fiber Adapts Well to Modern Ply Cutting Techniques.

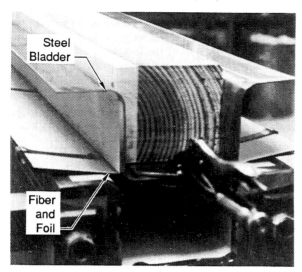

GP24-0422-17

Figure 3. Cut Fiber and Foil are Pressed into a Consolidation Tool to Form a C-Channel.

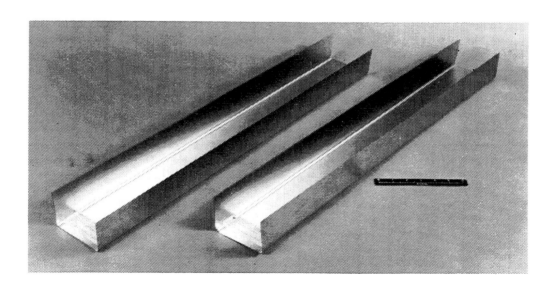

Figure 4. Consolidated TMC C-Channels are Ready for Further Processing.

59

Figure 6. These angles are then overlapped and diffusion bonded together to form a curved I-beam. The waterjet cutter has multi-axis capability and can make uninterrupted straight and curved cuts. Multiple parts with identical geometries can be produced at cutting rates of up to 30 inches per minute, making this cutting technique attractive as a production process. A typical waterjet cut edge is shown in the photomicrograph of Figure 7. The cutting process produces little damage to the material itself.

The diamond cutting wheel, shown in Figure 8, also produces excellent cuts in TMC laminates. However, this method is limited to straight cuts. The diamond cutting wheel is mounted on a horizontal mill and cutting is done with controlled speeds and feed rates. Because this method is basically a grinding operation, cutting rates are typically slow. Short flanges of a curved I-beam are shown being trimmed with the diamond wheel in Figure 8. The typical cut edge quality is illustrated in the photomicrograph shown in Figure 9.

Wire electrical discharge machining (EDM) is a flexible method of cutting TMCs. The photograph of Figure 10 shows a typical EDM setup. The unit is self-contained, with a power system and coolant. The completed spar, shown being cut in Figure 10, is 14 inches in length and 5 inches in height, with scalloped corners to allow the spar to splice into the side of an I-beam. This cut, which may have been difficult or impossible to make with some techniques, was easily made with the EDM process.

Like waterjet cutting, EDM is programmable and can make uninterrupted straight or curved cuts. EDM is considered a non-contact cutting method that removes material through melting and vaporization by high frequency electrical sparks. The quality of a typical EDM cut edge is illustrated in the photomicrograph of Figure 12.

One large TMC structure built that required a great deal of cutting and trimming is the Stabilator Torque Box, which represents the torque box section of a moveable aircraft wing. This structure was fabricated from simple preconsolidated shapes such as C-channels that were diffusion bonded together to form more complex components. The C-channels were diffusion bonded back to back to form the I-beam configuration. These C-channels and I-beams required extensive trimming. The edges of the I-beams were waterjet cut, and the

GP24-0422-19

Figure 5. Abrasive Waterjet Cutting is a Flexible Method for Cutting and Trimming TMC.

Cutting Crenelated Pattern In
TMC C-Channel

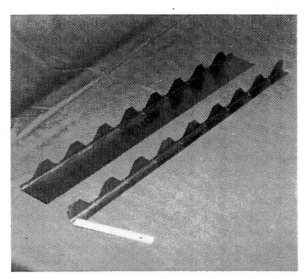

Two Finished Components For
TMC I-Beam

GP24-0422-20

Figure 6. Multi-axis Capability of Waterjet Cutter Allows Uninterrupted Cuts.

ends were cut to finish size with the diamond wheel. The spar components were trimmed using the wire EDM process. The corners were scalloped to allow the spars to splice into the side of the I-beams. The TMC substructure of the stabilator torque box is shown in the photograph of Figure 13.

Hole Generation. Several methods have been used to cut holes in TMC laminates. For thin laminates, requiring few holes, conventional high speed steel or cobalt twist drills can be used successfully with power feed equipment. One method investigated is punching, which is used extensively on thin aluminum and titanium sheet metal. Punching works well on thin laminates, and at fastener locations near an edge. Using conventional dies, punching is fast and clean, with no coolant required. Unfortunately, tool wear is erratic.

Punching is not used extensively because of the large number of fastener holes required in aircraft structures. In addition, typical load bearing sections become too thick for punching. The thickest TMC laminate that has been successfully punched, shown in Figure 14, is a 24-ply SCS-6 SiC/Ti-15V-3Cr-3Sn-3Al laminate. The left photograph in Figure 14 shows the typical hole finish after punching. Fiber damage and metal smearing is apparent. However, most of the disturbed material can be removed in a subsequent reaming operation, as shown in the photograph on the right.

In TMC components of this thickness, punch deflection becomes a concern, and tool wear becomes unpredictable. Some punched holes can be cleaned by reaming, as shown in Figure 14. However, some holes require several reaming operations, and in some cases, reaming actually reduces the diameter of the reamer, rather than increasing the diameter of the hole.

Neither conventional twist drills nor punching will consistently produce high quality holes in TMC laminates. The use of diamond core drills has greatly improved hole drilling quality in thick TMC components. Diamond core drills are tubular with diamond matrix built up on one end. This construction is similar to some grinding wheels. Diamond core drills have been previously used in metal matrix composites. However, additional improvements in drill motors, drills, and procedures yield better cutting efficiency and produce higher quality holes. Drill motor manufacturers have modified existing motors to achieve greater efficiency in drilling TMCs.

Multiple drill set-ups on a large TMC structure as shown in Figure 15. The aluminum drill template can hold several drills, which allows the operator to drill more than one hole at a time. Care is take to use standardized aircraft practices as much as possible. The diamond core drill produces excellent holes, and drilling tests conducted show hole variations on the order of 0.0021 inches in 4-ply material, 0.0030 inches in 15-ply laminates, and 0.0055 inches in 32 ply material. A photomicrograph of a typical

Waterjet Cut TMC Sample

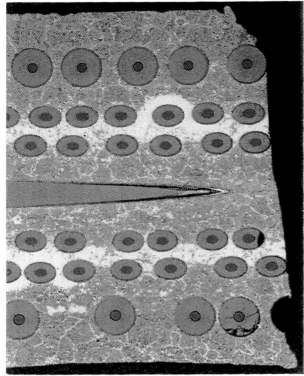

GP24-0422-29

Figure 7. Typical Edge of a Waterjet Cut TMC Laminate.

reproducible scale-up concepts have been developed. Fabrication of TMC structures requires specialized cutting techniques because of the highly abrasive nature of the material. Each cutting technique has advantages and disadvantages. However, most of the equipment required is commonplace in the aerospace industry, and can be adapted to produce quality parts.

diamond core drilled hole is shown in Figure 16.

Another structure built using TMC materials is the Lightly Loaded Splice Subcompnent, or LLSS, shown in Figure 17. This structure represents the splice of two fuselage sections at a frame station. Most of the cutting and drilling methods mentioned were utilized in the production of this structure. The skins and hats were cut with abrasive waterjet cutting, and the I-beam and splice plate were trimmed with the diamond cutting wheel. All fastener holes were drilled with the diamond core drill. The splice plate, shown in the foreground of Figure 17, has drilled and countersunk fastener holes. The complete assembled structure is shown in Figure 18.

Conclusions

A variety of techniques for cutting, trimming, and drilling of TMC components have been developed and succesfully demonstrated in the production of a variety of structural components. Reliable and

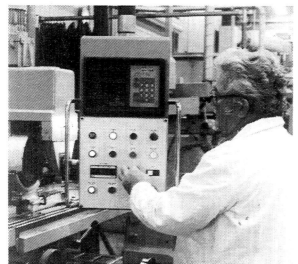

**Diamond Wheel
Mounted On A Horizontal Mill**

**Trimming Short Flange of
Curved I-Beam**

GP24-0422-21

Figure 8. Diamond Wheel Produces Excellent Straight Cuts

Diamond Wheel Produces Excellent Cut Edges

Figure 9. Typical Edge of a Diamond Wheel Cut TMC Laminate.

Machine Area

**Cutting Through Flange of
Canted I-Beam**

Figure 10. Wire Electrical Discharge Machining (EDM) Produces Complex Cuts in TMC Laminates.

TMC Spar For Stabilator Torque Box

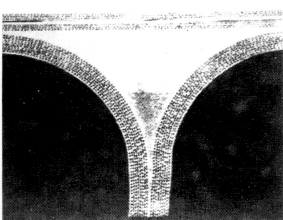

**Photomicrograph Shows Complete
Bonding Between TMC Components
and Ti-15-3 Filler**

Figure 11. TMC Spar Trimmed Using Wire EDM Method.

EDM Cut Sample

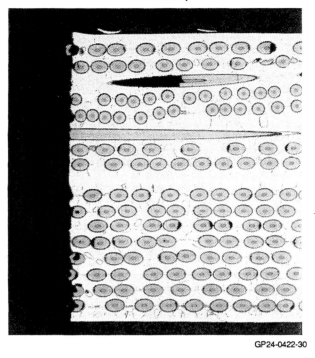

GP24-0422-30

Figure 12. Typical Edge of an EDM Cut TMC Laminate.

Substructure of TMC Stabilator Torque Box

GP24-0422-26

Figure 13. Extensive Cutting and Trimming Were Required to Fabricate the Stabilator Torque Box.

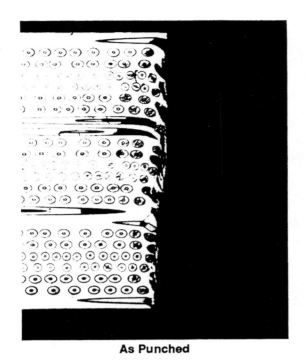

As Punched   **After Reaming**

GP24-0422-15

Figure 14. A 24-Ply TMC Laminate Punched and Reamed. Note Extensive Fiber Damage and Metal Smearing Visible on the As-Punched Specimen.

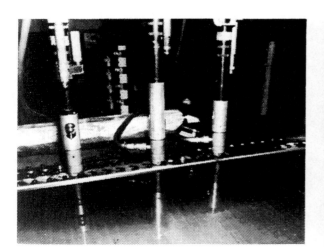

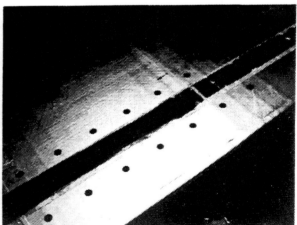

Uses Conventional Rigid Set-Up   **Close-Up of Drilled Holes**

GP24-0422-24

Figure 15. Diamond Core Drilling Adapts Well to Standard Aircraft Practices.

Diamond Core Drilled TMC Component

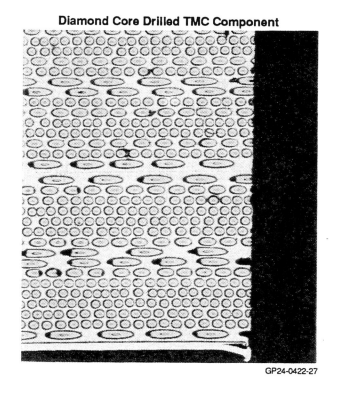

GP24-0422-27

Figure 16. Typical Edge of a Diamond Core Drilled TMC Laminate.

GP24-0422-25

Figure 17. Individual Components of the LLSS Trimmed and Drilled.

67

GP24-0422-14

Figure 18. Completed LLSS Assembly.

Proceedings of the ASM 1993 Materials Congress, Pittsburgh, Pennsylvania, October 17-21, 1993

Ultrasonic Machining of Ceramic-Matrix and Metal-Matrix Composites

R. Gilmore
Extrude Hone Corporation
Irwin, Pennsylvania

Abstract

Ultrasonic machining has emerged as an alternate machining method to grinding for applications areas in ceramics and composites because of its ability to machine such materials with little or no damage to the material and the advent of multiple axis ultrasonic machining systems. Today shapes of virtually any geometry can be successfully machined with ultrasonic techniques. Ultrasonic machining incorporates a tool vibrating at approximately 20 kHz and abrasives in a slurry mixture to perform intricate impact grinding of brittle materials. It is particularly useful in the machining of ceramics and ceramic-matrix composites that are not easily processed by conventional machining techniques. Even nontraditional machining methods such as EDM and laser may not be applicable to these composites because of low electrical continuity, complex geometry or detrimental effects to the workpiece surface. Ultrasonic machining offers precise control in the machining of ceramic-matrix composites with no damage to the material. Applications are currently being explored in the aerospace industry where cooling holes are being ultrasonically machined in ceramic-matrix composite turbine blades and metal matrix composite turbine components are manufactured with the aid of ultrasonic machining.

Of concern in broadening the applicability of composite materials is the requirement for components having higher accuracy, better surface finish, lower degrees of surface degradation and more complex geometry than ever before. Typical methods for processing composites today, including grinding, electrical discharge machining (EDM), laser and abrasive waterjet have limitations: grinding must be done with an expensive diamond wheel, a high concentration of microcracking often extending more than 25 µm deep may be produced and complex contours are not feasible; EDM is restricted to the machining of composites that have an electrical conductivity of 2×10^{-2} $(ohm/cm)^{-1}$ and composites which have been machined by EDM exhibit lower fracture strength, a thermally altered zone up to 50 µm and microcracking; laser machining requires extremely high power requirements which cause surface imperfections, and some composition changes or coatings may be needed to enable the material to be machined at all; and abrasive waterjet can cause excessive surface degradation and delamination.

Although other nontraditional machining processes can be used to machine composite materials, such processes typically will produce undesirable results in terms of surface and subsurface integrity. Ultrasonic machining of composites has a number of important advantages over these methods: conductive or nonconductive materials can be machined, material hardness is relatively unimportant and complex three-dimensional contours can be manufactured as quickly as simple ones. The process produces no heat affected zone and there are no chemical or electrical alterations on the workpiece surface, although the small impacts impart a shallow, compressive residual stress to the surface. It has been reported that this residual stress actually promotes an increase in the high cycle fatigue strength of the work material after ultrasonic machining.

Ultrasonic Machining Process

Ultrasonic machining incorporates a transducer, booster and ultrasonic tool, called a sonotrode, which vibrate at a frequency of approximately 20,000 cycles per second. A machining action occurs as the sonotrode vibrates the fine abrasive particles flowing throughout the machining gap and propels them against the workpiece material. The form tool itself does not abrade the workpiece the vibrating tool excites the abrasive grains in the flushing fluid, causing them to gently and uniformly wear away the material, leaving a precise reverse form of the sonotrode shape (Figure 1).

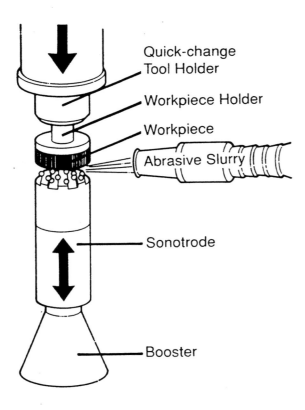

Fig. 1 - Schematic of the Ultrasonic Machining Process

Unlike thermal and chemical processes, USM is a mechanical material removal process applicable to both conductive and nonconductive materials and particularly suited to the machining of brittle materials such as graphite, glass, carbide, ceramics and composites. The uniformity of the sonotrode vibration limits the process to forming small shapes typically under 100 mm (4 inches) in diameter.

Although there are a number of variables that influence ultrasonic machining, the ones that have the greatest impact on machining performance include abrasive type and size, sonotrode material, frequency, surface area and static loading force. Optimization of these parameters is critical for close tolerance ultrasonic machining of composites.

The roughness of the ultrasonically machined surface is a function of workpiece material and abrasive type, size and circulation. Surface finish may be enhanced by using finer abrasives. Of course this will lower removal rates, so it is better to rough with larger abrasives and use the smaller abrasives for surface finish improvement only. Quite often the surface finish produced from the roughing operation is acceptable. Table I lists different materials that were machined with a roughing size (320 mesh) abrasive.

Table I. Surface finish produced in a variety of ultrasonically machined materials using 320 mesh abrasive.

Workpiece Material	Surface Roughness Ra (μm)
Graphite	1-2
Zirconia	0.75
Ceramic Matrix composites	0.70
Metal Matrix Composites	0.90

Vibraton Amplitude and Frequency

For optimum machining results the amplitude of ultrasonic vibrations should be adjusted in relation to the abrasive grain size. Ideally, the amplitude will be double the grain mean diameter. Tests have been conducted which verify that this optimizes feedrates. If the amplitude is too small, abrasive particles cannot enter the machining gap. Too large of an amplitude causes the grains to be incorrectly projected and can cause cavitation. A mixture of large and small abrasives may be used. In this case, the amplitude is adjusted to select which abrasives may enter the cut. This permits large abrasives to enter when the amplitude is high, therefore achieving higher removal rates. Conversely, only the very fine abrasives will enter the gap at the low amplitudes used for fine finishing.

Frequency mainly influences the maximum cross-sectional machining area. When the machining area

70

maximums are exceeded at a given frequency, unwanted transverse vibrations (rather than vertical vibrations). The typical frontal machining area possible at different frequencies is shown in Table II.

Table II. Relationship of frequency and machinable cross-sectional area.

Frequency	Frontal Area
10kHz	10,000 mm²
20 kHz	4,000 mm²
40 kHz	1,250 mm²

Composition of the Ultrasonic Tool

The main limitation of ultrasonic machining for composite machining has been the high tool wear associated with the process when using a high carbon steel sonotrode. However, with optimization of other parameters, even steel sonotrodes can produce relatively accurate machining

The sonotrode material must be selected in relation to its performance as well as its machinability. Sonotrode materials that have been tested include mild steel, high carbon steel, aluminum, titanium and diamond. In general, aluminum yields poor results due to high wear rates. High carbon steel gives a slightly higher feedrate than mild steel but exhibits the same wear. Titanium, while not good for metal matrix composites, yields the best results for ceramic matrix composites. Tools with diamond tips have good material removal characteristics and extremely low wear, but are difficult to machine conventionally.

Influence of Abrasives on the Process

Since it is actually the abrasives contained in the slurry that do the machining, they must be selected carefully based on the workpiece material and surface quality required. Typically, larger abrasive grain sizes yield higher cutting rates, but also a higher surface roughness. However, the abrasive grain diameter cannot be greater than the amplitude of the sonotrode_this would inhibit the injection of the abrasive grains to the machining gap.

Abrasive types commonly used in ultrasonic machining include aluminum oxide, silicon carbide, boron carbide and diamond. Ceramic matrix composites may be machined with silicon carbide or boron carbide, but metal matrix composites must be machined with boron carbide or diamond. Since the abrasive cost increases dramatically from silicon carbide to boron carbide to diamond, the least expensive applicable abrasive is normally used.

The abrasive grain diameter affects machining rate, overcut and surface roughness. When high surface quality is not required, 180 to 280 abrasives provide high cutting rates. For finer finishes, 320 to 600 mesh abrasive is recommended, and for super finishing, 1000 mesh or finer. For cuts requiring large amounts of material removal and a good surface finish, it is possible to rough with a large grain abrasive and finish with a finer abrasive.

Abrasive wear is an important factor in material removal and overcut. Abrasive grains begin to wear as soon as machining begins. Machining ceramic matrix composites with silicon carbide abrasive, material removal rates will degrade as the abrasive particles wear. Metal matrix composites tend to wear the abrasive at a higher rate. Therefore, when machining metal matrix composites, boron carbide should be used because it wears at a much slower rate than silicon carbide.

Machining Area Limitations

Equally important as other factors that influence removal rates and tool wear is the surface area of the tool. For small diameters, a higher feedrate is obtained, but with a smaller material removal rate. Also smaller diameters tend to have higher tool wear rates, perhaps because it is more difficult to inject abrasive grains to the gap, causing hammering of the tool on the workpiece. This unwanted effect can be overcome with a closed-loop force sensitive servo system which maintains accurate machining pressures. Another approach to minimize wear on smaller diameter tools is the use of diamond tipped tools on a rotary ultrasonic head. The optimum for small diameter drilling employs force sensing and diamond tipped tools. This approach yields the highest accuracy and removal rates while minimizing tool wear.

Typical machining rates for drilling holes with surface areas of 5 mm diameter and 10 mm diameter are shown in Table III.

Table III. Representative machining rates for a variety of materials via ultrasonic machining.

Material	Drilling Diameter - 5 mm		Drilling Diameter - 10 mm	
	Time (min)	Removal Rate (mm³/min)	Time (min)	Removal Rate (mm³/mi
Graphite	1	164	1.25	224
Ceramic Matrix Composites	3.5	39	5.6	50
Metal Matrix Composites	10	7.6	14	9.3
Zirconia	210	0.65	90	3.1

The Ultrasonic Machining System

The subassemblies that comprise an ultrasonic machining system include the machine tool, the generator, the slurry system and the operator controls. Precision mounting areas on the machine table and on the upper platen accommodate the sonotrode tool assembly and the electrode holder or an optional positioning table. The sonotrode tool assembly consists of a transducer, booster and sonotrode. The electronic generator powers the transducer, creating impulses that occur at a range of 19,500 to 20,500 Hz, and automatically adjusts the output frequency to match the resonant frequency of the tool, which varies according to the sonotrode shape and material. The transducer converts electrical pulses into vertical stroke. This vertical stroke is transferred to the booster, which may amplify or suppress the stroke amount. The modified stroke amount is then relayed to the sonotrode which contains the mirror image of the desired shape and serves as the actual tool in the process. The amplitude along the face of the tool typically falls in a 25 to 50 micron (0.001 to 0.002 in.) range. The vibration amplitude is usually equal to the diameter of the abrasive grit used.

The grit system supplies a slurry of water and abrasive grit, usually silicon or boron carbide, to the cutting area. In addition to providing abrasive particles to the cut, the slurry also cools the sonotrode and removes particles and debris from the cutting area. The overcut produced with USM is a function of the abrasive particle size (usually two times the particle diameter), as are the

surface finish and metal removal rates. Typical particle sizes range from 200 mesh, with an average particle size of 66 microns (0.0026 in.), to 800 mesh which has an average particle size of 11 microns (0.0004 in.). To maintain a constant temperature, an auxiliary chiller removes residual heat from the slurry as it returns to the tank.

The operator controls provide inputs for manual or automatic sequencing of operations. Controls include variable cutting force, ram position, speed control of ram movement, cycle timing, retract distance and flush timing. These controls may be manually activated for set-up or operated in an automatic mode for part processing. Machining parameters for multiple workpieces can be preprogrammed. A built-in CRT displays operational parameters including machine settings, Z axis position, distance-to-go and programming messages. A complete ultrasonic machining system is shown in Figure 2.

Figure 2 - SoneX ultrasonic machining system.

Areas of Application

The process is commonly used for drilling holes, slots and irregular configurations in ceramics and composites (Figure 3). Additional applications include machining of phased array radar components, cutting tool inserts, superconductors, wire draw dies and extrusion dies.

Figure 3 - A wide variety of ceramic components can be machined by ultrasonic means.

Penetration rates typically range from 0.25 mm (0.010 in.) per minute for high density workpieces to 1.5 mm (0.060 in.) for low density materials. Depending on the size of the abrasive grains used, metal removal rates can range from 5 mm^3 (0.0003 in.^{3}) per minute to 65 mm^3 (0.004 in.^{3}) per minute. The aluminum oxide accelerometer shown in Figure 4 was machined in a 30 minute cycle time.

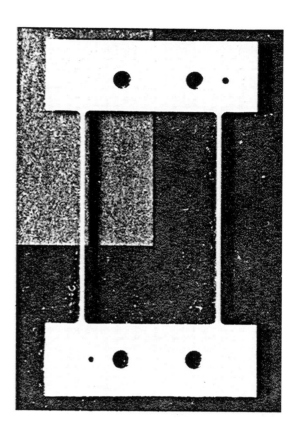

Figure 4 - Aerospace Application machined by ultrasonic machining.

The glass lens shown in Figure 5 is used in high altitude imaging. The entire form is ultrasonically machined in less than 1 minute. The process yields minimal radiusing on the face of the workpiece.

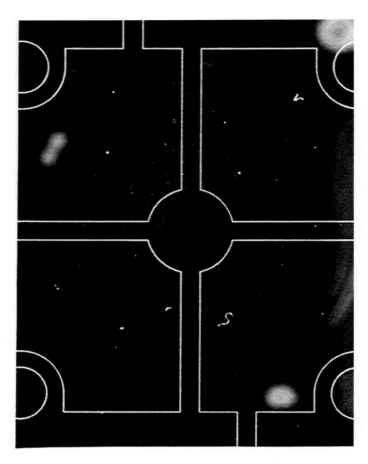

Figure 5 - Glass lens used in high altitude imaging.

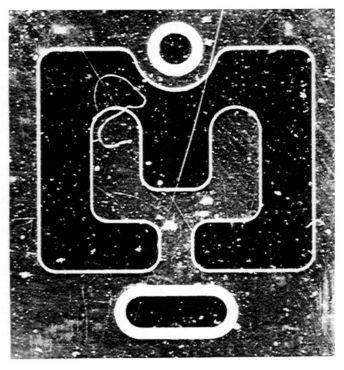

Figure 6 - Intricate shapes produce by multi-axis ultrasonic contour machining.

CNC control for contouring capabilities is currently under development. The glass strain gauge component shown in Figures 6 used a single point tool attached to a sonotrode. The 2 mm (0.080 in.) diameter diamond-tipped tool was mounted on a rotary ultrasonic head, spinning continuously as the workpiece was driven along the programmed path. The program repeats continuously as the tool sinks into the workpiece to a typical depth of 0.005 mm (0.0002 in.) per pass.

Slurry circulation is important to remove debris from the cut and to provide fresh abrasives to the machining gap. For hole drilling, a rotary ultrasonic head is often used. The rotary head enables contour machining with even wear distribution on the rotating tool. Deep cavities are processed more efficiently and more accurately. In addition, improved flushing capabilities result in better surface finishes.

Summary

Ultrasonic machining is a nontraditional mechanical material removal process applicable to both conductive and nonconductive materials and particularly suited to the machining of brittle materials such as composites, ceramics, graphite, glass and carbide. A nonabrasive form tool, called a sonotrode, attached to a transducer/booster combination vibrates at frequencies of approximately 20,000 cycles per second. A machining action occurs as the sonotrode vibrates the fine abrasive particles flowing throughout the machining gap and propels them against the workpiece material for drilling holes, slots and irregular configurations.

Abrasives used for machining composites include silicon carbide, which is used for the low hardness composites and boron carbide, which is typically used for the higher hardness composites. Slurry circulation is important to remove debris from the cut and to provide fresh abrasives to the machining gap. Penetration rates typically range from 0.25 mm (0.010 in.) per minute for high density workpieces to 1.5 mm (0.060 in.) for low density materials. Depending on the size of the abrasive grains used, metal removal rates can range from 5 mm^3 (0.0003 $in.^3$) per minute to 65 mm^3 (0.004 $in.^3$) per minute. The aluminum oxide piece shown in Figure 8 was machined in fifteen minutes. The process yields minimal radiusing on the face of the workpiece. Surface integrity depends on the workpiece material, abrasive size and flushing conditions. Hard ceramics yield slightly better surface conditions than soft ceramics with finishes as low as 0.4 µm R_a (16 µinch) feasible.

The ultrasonic machining process has a number of important advantages for ceramic and composite applications: conductive and nonconductive materials can be machined, material hardness is relatively unimportant, there are no chemical or electrical alterations on the workpiece surface and complex three-dimensional contours can be manufactured as quickly as simple ones. Recent developments in tooling and machine design have helped to establish the ultrasonic machining process as a way of satisfying tough manufacturing requirements economically and productively.

References

Barks, R. E., K. Subramanian and K. E. Ball, eds. *Intersociety Symposium on Machining of Advanced Materials and Components.* Westerville, OH: The American Ceramic Society, Inc., 1987.

Benedict, Gary F. *Nontraditional Manufacturing Processes.* Vol. 19 of *Manufacturing Engineering and Materials Processing Series.* New York: Marcel Dekker, Inc., 1987.

Department of Defense 1987 Machine Tool Manufacturing Technology Conference Proceedings. 1 - 5 June 1987. Report No. AFWAL-TR-87-4137. Vol. 4.

Drozda, Thomas J. and Charles Wick, eds. *Machining.* Vol. 1 of *Tool and Manufacturing Engineers Handbook.* 4th ed. Dearborn, MI: Society of Manufacturing Engineers, 1983.

Frederick, Julian R. *Ultrasonic Engineering.* New York: John Wiley & Sons, Inc., 1965.

Machinability Data Center. Vol. 2 of *Machining Data Handbook.* 3rd ed. Cincinnati: Metcut Research Associates Inc., 1980.

PRECISION MACHINING OF PLASMA SPRAYED CERAMIC COATINGS

S.Gowri, K.Narayanasamy, R.Krishnamurthy
Department of Mechanical Engineering
Indian Institute of Technology
Madras-600 036 India

Abstract

Industrial application of ceramic coated components require post-treatments like heat treatment, surface glazing, machining etc. To meet the demands like close tolerance, good surface finish and high efficiency in machining grinding, lapping, honing etc., are the precision machining methods adopted. In this study, the surface quality, grinding force, geometrical error, etc., were estimated for different machining conditions.

Since surface finish influences the friction and load bearing capacity of contact surfaces, for minimum wear and high load bearing capacity, super finishing of plasma sprayed coatings is essential.

Advanced ceramic coatings can be effectively machined by grinding with diamond or CBN wheel. The bonded abrasives and other process conditions could initiate and propagate cracks during grinding process. Lapping, the conventional free abrasive machining process, has been well investigated and practically applied to glass finishing. Chen et al, in 1991, have conducted studies on lapping of advanced ceramics. However, lapping of plasma sprayed ceramic coatings has not been carried out and it is required to understand the mechanism of material removal during lapping. The present work, hence, aims at obtaining data regarding more fundamental aspects of lapping of plasma sprayed ceramic coatings. Honing is a process for the finish machining of cylindrical surfaces with objective of improving their size, geometric form and surface quality . Since many of the plasma sprayed oxide ceramic coatings are finding wider industrial applications like cylinder liners, bearing races, etc., it is very much required to improve the surface quality, form, etc., by studying the machinability in case of honing of plasma sprayed ceramic coatings.

1. Grinding of Ceramic coatings

Experimentation

Using diamond and CBN grinding wheels, grinding trials were conducted on different ceramic { A (Al_2O_3), AT (Al_2O_3-TiO_2) and PSZ (ZrO_2-Y_2O_3) ceramic coatings } coated specimens surface grinding and (external) cylindrical grinding and internal grinding were carried out. The grinding conditions are as shown in Table 1.
The main object of the present study is to evaluate the behaviour of A, AT and PSZ ceramic coatings under different grinding conditions. The performance was evaluated by
     1. measuring grinding force
     2. measuring surface finish
The normal grinding force, Fn, and the tangential force Ft, were measured using Kistler piezoelectric crystal dynamometer. The ground samples were measured for different surface finish parameters such as Ra, Rt, Rz, Rmax, tp and surface profile, with perth-O-meter. Scanning electron micrographs (SEM) of the samples were taken with Jeol Scanning Electron Microscope.

Surface grinding

Ceramic (A,AT and PSZ) coated rectangular flat specimens were ground with diamond and CBN grinding wheels. The influence of depth of grinding (a) wheel velocity (v) on grinding forces and surface finish was evaluated. Since ceramics/ceramic coatings are known for the presence of isolated strength field over their matrix, surface damage, scatter in surface texture could be observed. It is known that during grinding of hard brittle materials, depending upon the intensity of stress and strength fields, material removal would be associated with either deformation (ductile) fracture or deformation associated with fracture [2] . As the deformation of material proceeds, the material strain hardness first followed by softening till such time the material attains energy for localized melting .The occurence of deformation, fracture could be visulaized by analogising grinding to an indentation process when the abrasive grain enters the ceramic surface, the ceramic material would be deformed and there would be flow of material around the indenting abrasive, with possible surface cracking. To understand this process, both normal and tangential components of grinding force were meausred.

Results and Discussions

Malkin in his text book on Grinding Technology, has reported that increase in grinding velocity would increase the temperature at the work-wheel interface. Fig. 1.1(a), 1.2(a) and 1.3(a) illustrate the typical variation of grinding force components with grinding speed. For all the three different ceramic coatings, change over in the force trend form three zones such as Za, Zb and Zc. At lower velocities, the grinding would have been dominated with plowing and higher order friction resulting in larger Fn component.

Za : Za corresponds to the velocity range of 5.7 m/s to 11.5 m/s in fig. At velocity of 5.7 m/s, the grinding would have been dominated with plowing and higher order friction resulting in larger Fn components.

Fig. 1.1(a) illustrates the effect of grinding velocity at different depths of grinding force Fn. The trend shows that with increase in velocity from 5.7 to 11.5 m/s, the magnitude of Fn decreases. The negative slope (decreasing trend) of the forming Za decreases with increase in depth of grinding. This explains the transition from ductile mode of grinding to brittle fracture mode. For a > 10 μm,the real contact zone width of wheel and workpiece increases. It enhances the brittle fracture of the surface asperities of the Al_2O_3 ceramic coatings.

Zb : Zone B defines the Fn variation in for the velocity range of 11.5 m/s to 15.7 m/s. Fn decreases with increase in sliding velocity. Degradation of diamond (diamond is stable upto 800°C in atmospheric condition)[Krishnamurthy et al] at this velocity range influence the grinding force. Due to the degradation (unstable) the force decreases.

Zc : Zone C corresponds to the velocity range of 15.7 to 31.5 m/s. Both the coated ceramic and the wheel are subjected to thermal degradation in this velocity range. Fracture associated with dominent deformation mode of grinding takes place and hence force increases with velocity and depth of grinding.

Fig. 1.1(b) shows the influence of velocity and depth of grinding on tangential grinding force (Ft) for grinding of alumina (A). Three different zones such as Za, Zb and Zc are observed in this case.

Za : In zone A, Ft increases with increase in velocity. At low velocity, ploughning of diamond wheel abrasives takes place and hence force is higher. With increase in velocity Ft increases largely for a = 10 μm and marginally increases beyond a = 20 μm. This shows that brittle fracture mode of grinding is marginally accompanied with ductile mode.

Zb: In zone b, Ft decreases with increase in velocity. This is due to the influence of thermally degraded diamond wheels Zc : In zone C, a = 30 μm is found to be critical, below which Ft decreases at high velocity and above it, Ft is found to be increasing with velocity. Beyond a = 30 μm, thermal degradation of both alumina and diamond in larger ductle mode of with fracture mode. F_t increase with increases in depth of grinding and speed. For a > 30 μm and v > 15.7 m/s, F_t increases. It is the indication of high thermal influence made alumina softened.

In Fig.1.1(a), it is observed that three different zones (Z_A, Z_B, and Z_C) indicating the relations between the normal grinding force and the grinding speed in grinding of alumina coating are existing. In Z_A the normal force is large at v = 5.7 m/s. At slow speed, plowing of diamond abrasives into the ceramic coating takes place resulting in deformation mode of material removal. Hence F_n is large. In Z_B, steady grinding takes place with increase in speed. Hence F_n reduces. In Z_C, higher grinding speed results in increasing the wheel-job interface temperature and both the diamond wheel and the alumina become unstable and hence F_n increases with speed from about 16 m/s to 31.5 m/s.

SEM analysis , as shown in Fig. 1.4, explains the mode of grinding (ductile, fracture and combination of these two). Fig. 1.2 shows the influence of grinding velocity at different depths of grinding on Fn and Ft for grinding of alumina-titania (AT) coating.

Za : In zone A, from Fig. 1.2, force at slow speed conditions is lower compared to grinding of alumina. Steady increase in Fn with velocity and with depth of grinding is observed in grinding of alumina-titania. The force trend is found to be generally similar to that of grinding of alumina coating but the initial plowing force is marginally smaller. With increase in speed (Zc), the force marginally increases. The presence of Titania improved the ductility of the coating and hence the force decreases in Za and Zb. In Zc, force is increasing with speed due to the thermal influence as it was observed in grinding of alumina coating.

It can be studied from Fig. 1.2 that the initial plowing, thermal influence, ductility of coating and metallurgical unstability of both the wheel and alumina-titania (AT) make variations in F_n with speed. At v = 15.7 m/s, F_n attains the lowest value for all cases of depth of grinding and hence it could be termed as critical velocity. Addition of titania in alumina shows marginal reduction in F_t compared with the force in grinding of pure alumina.

Fig. 1.3 illustrates the relation between grinding speed and force, F_n. Plowing of diamond abrasives into PSZ surface increases F_n at low speeds. Further increase in speed increases thermal effects and metallurgical changes take place i.e., $t \to m$ transformation takes place. Hence upto $v = 15.7$ m/s, F_n decreases. At higher speeds both diamond and PSZ become unstable and hence force increases.

Fig. 1.5 shows that surface finish of A, AT and PSZ ceramic coatings improved with increase in grinding speed using diamond wheel. At slow speed, due to plowing action of diamond grits into ceramic coating, force per grit increased (because of the smaller area of contact). Hence stress field increases and micro brittle fracture took place.

With increasing grinding speed, grinding becomes steady and the surface finish improves. From the gives figures, it can be understood that larger the speed and larger the depth of grinding, better is the surface finish with diamond grinding wheel. For a > 30 μm at higher grinding speed, plowing with fracture has taken place resulting in reduction in R_a. At higher speed and higher depth of grinding, rubbing and hence glazing could have happened resulting in improved surface finish. It can be claimed that titania in Al_2O_3-TiO_2 reduced porosity content of alumina and improved surface finish compared with that of alumina. Fig. 1.5 shows effect of grinding speed on R_a of the surface. At higher speeds and larger depth of grinding, better folding of surface asperities showed improvement in surface finish. Increase in speed at larger depth of grinding has led to $t \to m$ transformation which improved surface finish.

Surface finish of the ceramic coatings after grinding with CBN wheel is presented in Fig. 1.5. Being CBN thermally stable, marginal variations in R_a with grinding speed were observed. CBN grain flattening at larger depth of grinding and at higher speed gave better surface finish. X-RD pattern of ground PSZ with CBN has not shown remarkable variations in m/t value and it is similar to m/t ratios obtained in diamond grinding. It shows that there is limit for $t \to m$ transformable beyond certain limit of t content. The surface finish obtained with grinding of PSZ and AT using diamond wheel was better than that by CBN at higher speed and larger depth of cut. This might be due to the thermal instability of diamond at higher order working temperature and also due to the finer grit size of diamond compared to that of CBN.

2. Lapping of Plasma sprayed ceramic coatings

Experimentation

Ceramic coated samples were ground for the better surface finish and the thickness of the discs were measured using CMM. They were lapped under the conditions mentioned in Table 2. Since the surface roughness was not significantly affected by lapping pressure in case of flat lapping of ceramics with diamond abrasives [Chen et al], influence of lapping time and abrasive size on surface roughness was measured. Lapping plate material was cast iron. The process variables were lapping time ranging as 5, 10, 15, 20 and 30 minutes and the size of the lapping diamond abrasives. The Hi-Fin lapping oil was periodically sprayed to reduce friction during lapping. The lapped discs were ultrasonically cleaned and stored in desiccator. Stock removal (the loss of thickness) of the lapped discs was measured in μm and surface finish (R_t) was measured using Pertho meter. The results were given and discussed.

Results and Discussion

R_t, the peak to valley height of surface profile, can be used to define the surface roughness of any lapped surface [De Beer]. From the Fig. 2.1, it can be said that surface finish improves (R_t decreases) with lapping time. Lapped surface of Al_2O_3-TiO_2 (AT) ceramic gives better surface finish compared to that of PSZ and Al_2O_3 (A). The trend shows that beyond the lapping time of 30 minutes, AT and PSZ coatings will attain saturation in surface quality while Al_2O_3 coating will show further drop in R_t value and improvement in surface finish. The high degree of brittleness and higher porosity content of Al_2O_3 reduce the surface finish. Similar report made by Chen et al on lapping of monolithic Al_2O_3 ceramics confirms the observation. PSZ being more ductile and less porosity content than A coating has shown better finish. Similarly AT could have superior surface finish. Since lapping with diamond abrasives of size 6-8 μm give interesting result, stock removal (in μm) was measured for a series of lapping time for the three types of ceramic coatings and plotted in Fig. 2.2. Al_2O_3-TiO_2 ceramic coating attained saturation in stock removal beyond 20 minutes of lapping time. PSZ attained the same beyond this time and Al_2O_3 showed further stock removal with increase in time. Fig. 2.3 shows the influence of the size of the size of diamond abrasive on stock removal and surface roughness (R_t). It could be understood that the lapped surface was of better surface finish when lapped with 6-8 μm than that by abrasives of the other two sizes. The stock removal for lapping time of 15 minutes increased with increase in size of diamond abrasives. This result contradicts with lapping of metallic surfaces with diamond abrasives [3].

Since the porosity distribution is wider and the average size of pores ranged approximately from 0.1 to 3 μm, from Fig. 2.4 (SEM), the smaller sized grains of diamond got entrapped in the ceramic coatings and hence effective stock removal was not taking place. Hence the R_t value is higher and stock removal was low. During the process of lapping, the abrasive particles get anchored with the soft lapping plate (De Beers and Chen et al) when the small sized abrasives anchor themselves with the C.I. lapping plate. The protruding height of the grits from the lapping plate was smaller compared with that of larger sized grits. Hence the stock removal rate could be reduced.

Larger sized abrasives, remove larger amount of material and hence stock removal increases resulting in larger scratches on the surface. Also the larger sized grits might be broken as said, resulting in 'fresh' cutting edge formation which might result in surface scratches and hence the surface finish decreases. It can be concluded that 6-8 μm sized diamond can be possibly used to lap the plasma sprayed ceramic coatings . The stock removal is by higher amount brittle fracture in case of Al_2O_3 because of the higher % of porosity content and brittleness of Al_2O_3 also the diamond abrasive particle. This might be due to the fracture of diamond abrasives during lapping [Chen et al.].

3. Honing of plasma sprayed ceramic coatings

Experimentation

Cast iron rings of 100 mm in diameter were selected as substrate material since cast iron with plasma sprayed ceramic coatings are nowadays used as engine components. The rings were pretreated for plasma spraying as mentioned earlier. They were coated with NiAl bond coat and ceramics for total thickness of 400 μm. Green grit SiC wheel was selected to internally grind the plasma sprayed ceramic coated rings. The roundness error, R_a and R_t were measured with Perthen Form tester and perthometer. The average contact pressure of the honing stones exerted on ceramic surfaces was varied from 1 to 5 MPa, the speed was 1.5 m/s and the longitudinal feed was 30 mm/min., and the honing time were kept as process variables. In the expansion honing head, by adjusting the centre rod with nut and screw mechanism, the four honing sticks could be expanded with a regulable pressure. The thread length in the tightening screw was calibrated and used for the selection of contact pressure such as 1, 3, 5 MPa. The honing time was varied from 5 to 25 minutes in steps of 5 minutes. Kerosene was effectively supplied as coolant during honing. The honed specimens were ultrasonically cleaned. Both the surface finish (R_a and R_t) and the roundness error of the honed surfaces were measured. The micrographs of the honed surfaces were taken. The results were presented and discussed.

Results and discussion

Fig. 3.1 explains the influence of average contact pressure on R_t of the honed surface. At pressure of 3 MPa, the surface finish was better than that produced at pressure below and above 3 MPa. Effect of pressure on R_a of honed plasma sprayed ceramic layers is illustrated in Fig. 3.2. It is confirmed from Fig. 3.1 that pressure of 3 MPa gives better surface quality.

Fig. 3.3 shows the variations in R_t of the honed surface with honing time. Honing of the ceramic coatings has improved the surface finish with honing time. Specifically

Al_2O_3- TiO_2 and PSZ attained saturation in surface finish improvement in 15 minutes of honing time while Al_2O_3 has shown further improvement in surface quality with time at honing pressure of 3 MPa.

At low contact pressure, the stock removal rate was less than that at higher pressure conditions. Hence the surface quality was not highly improved. When pressure increased, stock removal rate increased and hence the surface quality was changed. At higher pressure conditions, surface quality is poor (R_t and R_a increase) because of the excess stock removal rate. Larger penetration of the diamond grits at higher pressure makes more number of scratches and hence the surface finish becomes poorer [H o hne L, 1991]. From the study, it has been understood that pressure of 3 Mpa is optimal.

Fig. 3.4 explains the roundness error of the ceramic coated C.I. ring at three different stages of processing such as 'as-sprayed condition', 'after grinding' and 'after honing'. The error measured in μm was larger in as-sprayed ceramic coatings than that in the other two conditions. Internal grinding of plasma sprayed ceramic coatings with SiC wheel reduced the error from that observed in as sprayed condition. The larger error in the as-sprayed condition of the plasma sprayed ceramic coatings might be because of the error in mounting the rings in the chuck for spraying. The error observed after grinding of the rings was of 3-lobe type and it was because of the grinding machine capability. Honing operation has shown only marginal reduction in roundness error but of 3-lobe type error. This might be because of the low stock removal and process features.

Stock removal in the beginning of honing was increasing and it attains stabilization after some critical time [DeBeer]. - in this study approximately 15 minutes for Al_2O_3 - TiO_2 and PSZ. But Al_2O3 showed improvement beyond this time. Beyond that time of honing, mere rubbing and polishing might occur but the porosity content and brittleness of the coatings would be the limiting factor for improvement in surface finish.

Conclusion

The critical velocity in grinding and depth of grinding of plasma sprayed ceramic coatings (PSCC) for the given set-up were experimentally estimated to be in the range of 15 to 16 m/s and 30 μm. Surface finish improved with grinding speed. For a=30 μm, the surface finish after grinding of AT ceramic coating was superior (R_a=0.62 μm) to that of alumina and PSZ coating (0.85 and 0.66 μm).

In case of lapping, diamond abrasives of 6-8 μm size were giving best surface finish compared to that by other two different sizes of abrasives for all cases of ceramic coatings. R_t values for A, AT and PSZ were 5.44, 4.25 and 5.2 μm respectively.

The critical pressure in honing of PSCC were

estimated to be 3 MPa. The surface finish (R_t) obtained at 3 Mpa for A, AT and PSZ were 7.3, 7.1 and 7.16 μm respectively. The roundness error after honing was found to be almost equal to 30 μm for all types of ceramic coatings. Honing after duration of 15 minutes showed saturation in surface finish and the R_t value for A, AT and PSZ were 7.6, 7.2 and 7.28 μm respectively.

Acknowledgement

The authors thank Mr. K. Kamban, Mr. Shanthakumar and other members of the Plasma unit of Carborundum Universal Ltd., for their help in preparation of samples.

References

1   I.Inasaki, Grinding of hard and brittle materials, Annals of CIRP, 36(2), 403-471,(1987)

2   Krishnamurthy and G.Rathnam, Grinding of transformation toughened Y-TZP Annals of CIRP, 40(1), 331-337, (1991)

3   Namba Y., Yamada Y., Tsuboi A, Unno K, Nakao H, Structure of Mn-Zn ferrite single crystals ground by ultraprecision surface grinder with various diamond wheels, Annal of CIRP, 41(1), 347-351, (1992)

4   De Beer's Hand book on Lapping with diamond abrasives, De Beer Diamonds, London, (1980)

5   Hohne, Ultraprecision Machining tutorial notes, II Int. conf. on Ultraprecision in Manufacturing Engg., Germany, (1991)

6   Chen. C., Saki. S., and Inasaki. I., Lapping of advanced ceramics, J. Materials and Manufacturing processes, 6(2), 211-226, (1991)

7   Precision Engineering Hand book, Vol.8, Macmillan, London, (1972)

Table 1   Grinding conditions

Machine	Tool & cutter grinding m/c
Type of grinding	Dry, Surface grinding
Wheel used	a. Diamond - BZ 1A1-100-6-1-6 grit 185
	b. CBN - B 120 RR 100 D-150-6 grit 120
Wheel speed	1100, 2200, 3000 & 6000 rpm
Depth of grinding	10, 20, 30 & 40 μm
Work feed	0.5 mm/s

Table 2   Surface Lapping conditions

Machine	Wentzky, Germany
Operation	Flat surface lapping
Lapping medium & abrasive	Hifin diamond compound
Diamond size	0.25-2, 6-8 & 10-14 μm
Lapping speed	0.30 m/s
Lapping pressure	52 kPa
Lapping time duration	2-30 min

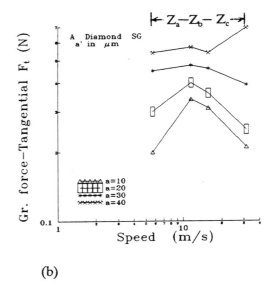

(b)

Fig. 1.1   Influence of speed on grinding force

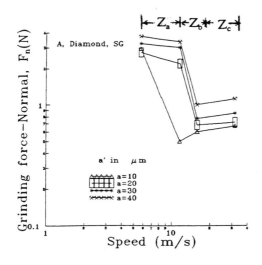

(a)

Fig. 1.1   Influence of speed on grinding force

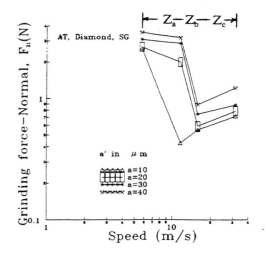

(a)

Fig. 1.2   Influence of speed on grinding force

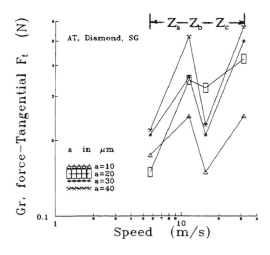

(b)

Fig. 1.2 Influence of speed on grinding force

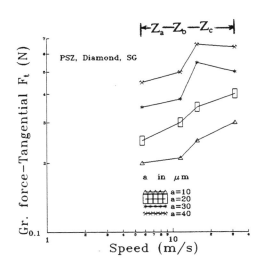

(b)

Fig. 1.3 Influence of speed on grinding force

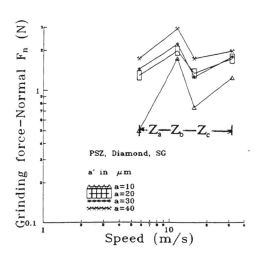

(a)

Fig. 1.3 Influence of speed on grinding force

Fig. 1.4 SEM of ground PSZ coated surface

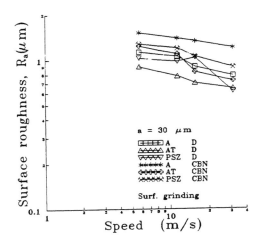

Fig. 1.5 Influence of speed on surface finish

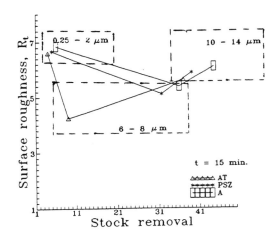

Fig. 2.3 Effect of grain size on stock removal and surface finish

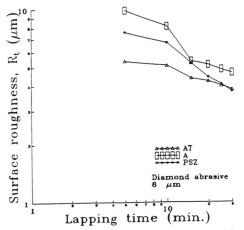

Fig. 2.1 Improvement in surface finish with time

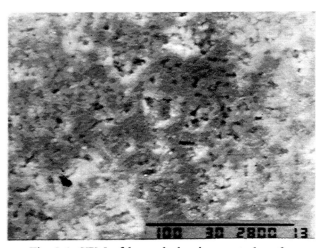

Fig. 2.4 SEM of lapped alumina coated surface

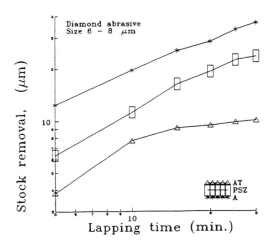

Fig. 2.2 Relation between stock removal & time

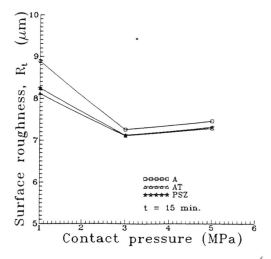

Fig. 3.1 Influence of pressure on surface finish (R_t)

84

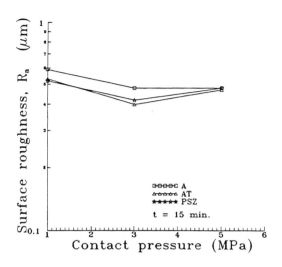

Fig. 3.2 Influence of pressure on surface finish (R_a)

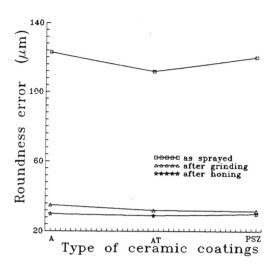

Fig. 3.4 Internal roundness error of ceramic coated rings

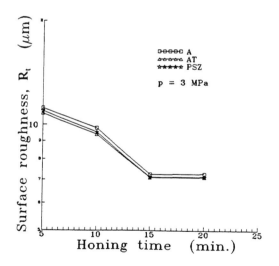

Fig. 3.3 Effect of honing time on surface finish

Proceedings of the ASM 1993 Materials Congress, Pittsburgh, Pennsylvania, October 17-21, 1993

Drilling of Kevlar Composites

S. J. Mander, D. Bhattacharyya
University of Auckland
Auckland, New Zealand

Abstract

Drilling operations in Kevlar aramid fibre reinforced plastics (KFRP) have previously relied upon the use of costly tooling and high drilling speeds. This paper shows that hole drilling in KFRP composites can be successfully accomplished using slightly modified HSS drill bits on standard drilling equipment without having to resort to expensive tooling and high drill speeds.

The technique of machining under localised cryogenic conditions has been successfully applied to the drilling operation, resulting in improved surface finishes and hole dimensional quality. The effects of various drilling parameters such as workpiece temperature, drilling speed and drill geometry on the machinability (in respect to drilling) of KFRP composites are presented and analysed.

THE DRILLING OF KEVLAR ARAMID FIBRE REINFORCED PLASTIC (KFRP) COMPOSITES has recently generated a considerable amount of interest from within the high performance yacht building industry particularly due to recent changes in the International Measurement System. These changes have seen the use of carbon fibres prohibited in the construction of the yachts hull, and as a result Kevlar fibres are being substituted for carbon fibres. This development has given rise to a need for a simple and inexpensive method of drilling KFRP laminates using existing drilling equipment commonly found in a boat builder's yard. While glass and carbon fibre reinforced composites can be drilled with reasonable success, Kevlar poses a problem with its higher toughness and flexibility. To date most literature [1-3, 11] recommends the use of tungsten carbide tooling in conjunction with very high rotational speeds, in the vicinity of 8,000 to 20,000 RPM. Previous research by the authors in the area of turning of KFRP composites has found that dramatic improvements in

machinability could be achieved by the novel technique of cryogenic machining [4] with a continuous application of liquid nitrogen (LN_2) on the workpiece while machining. This paper investigates the suitability of such cryogenic machining to the drilling process in KFRP laminates.

Drilling of KFRP is generally characterised by a poor fuzzy surface finish with a lot of loose, pulled out, and crushed fibres [5, 6]. Previous research has shown that in machining operations with KFRP, tools should maintain the fibres in tension in order to cut them by shearing [7]. For drilling operations it is, therefore, necessary to design the drill bit to cut the fibres towards the hole centre and shear at the diameter, so that the fibrils of fuzz caused by conventional tools, which start cutting the holes at the center and force chips against the hole walls, can be significantly reduced. Delamination (interlaminar crack propagation) is generally recognised as a major constraint in the drilling of fibre reinforced plastic (FRP) composites, severely affecting the composite's structural integrity. The concept of a critical thrust force at the onset of delamination [1] is generally accepted in the drilling of FRP composites. To predict the critical thrust force at the onset of delamination a recent study [8] developed the peel-up and push-out models at hole entry and exit repectively, using linear fracture mechanics and classic plate bending theory. Thrust being primarily a function of feed rate and tool geometry, it increases with feed rate. Regarding geometry, the chisel edge contributes significantly to thrust force and a model has been developed to describe the effects of these two variables on delamination in drilling [9].

In general it is also known that FRPs being poor conductors of heat, a better tool performance can be achieved by increasing the thermal conductivity of the tool [1-3], so that the cutting zone temperature is reduced. To this end tungsten carbide tooling is normally recommended for machining FRP composites. With a view to achieving economy and exploring the use of standard drill bits under certain conditions the drilling tests in this investigation have been performed with slightly modified HSS drill bits.

This paper presents the results of a series of drilling tests and the effects of various drill geometries and drilling speeds at room temperature and under cryogenic conditions. Tests have been carried out to determine the influence of negative drill point angles and varying drill helix angle on surface finish and the dimensional accuracy of the holes drilled. Superior surface finishes, and reduced fibre pullout at hole entry and exit faces, have been achieved when drilling under cryogenic conditions. It is generally accepted that drill wear affects the dimensional accuracy and surface finish of a drilled hole in metallic materials and as found in the turning of KFRP composites, surface finish may become the dominant factor in determining the tool life [4]. A series of drill wear tests have also been performed, under both drilling conditions, with the optimum drill geometry arrived at during earlier tests. Surface finish and hole roundness errors have been measured to give an indication of relative drill life at room temperature and at cryogenic temperature.

Experimental Details

Drilling tests were performed on a drill press fitted with automatic feed using 10 mm diameter HSS twist drills with various negative drill point angles and helix angles. Various drilling speeds, commonly available on general drilling equipment, were used to study hole surface finish and drilling forces. The feed rate was kept low (0.1 mm/rev), in line with recommendations made by Tagliaferri et al. [10]. Drill forces were measured during the period of drilling using a Kistler (9273) 2-D tool force dynamometer. A view of the equipment setup is shown in Fig. 1.

Layers of Kevlar K-285 (crow's foot weave)/ADR240 epoxy were hand laid to obtain 0°/90° panels. The nominal laminate thickness was 6 mm with a fibre volume fraction of 36%. A short series of drill wear tests were performed using Kevlar KA-060/ADR240 epoxy hand laid to give a continuous unidirectional (0°) panel. The nominal laminate thickness of the unidirectional panel was also 6 mm, but had an increased fibre volume fraction of 55%. Both laminates were autoclave cured at 45° C for 15 hours and post-cured at 65° C for 8 hours as recommended by the epoxy supplier.

For each main test, a series of four sub-tests were performed. Each sub-test consisted of five holes. Values for surface finish and drilling forces were recorded and an average value calculated. The drill bit was re-sharpened between sub-tests. The four mean sub-test results were then averaged again to give a single test value. This procedure was adopted to remove any spurious results due to inconsistencies arising from manually grinding the drill bits.

The modified drill geometries were achieved by re-sharpening standard HSS drill bits on a Jones Shipman 310T Tool and Cutter grinder. All drills were ground with a 10° clearance angle and straight lip. The drill web was kept to a minimum by grinding to a point. An example of the drills used is shown in Figure 2.

The surface finish of the hole walls was measured using a Surtronic-3 with a diamond stylus at cut-off and traverse lengths of 0.3 mm and 1.75 mm respectively. Surface finish measurements were made at 60° intervals about the circumference, and an average value obtained. The stylus was consistently moved against the direction of drill feed and as suggested by König et al. [1], the average roughness values (Ra), rather than peak-to-valley measurements, were used for surface finish comparison. A more detailed study of the hole surface finish was carried out with the aid of a Phillips scanning electron microscope (SEM 505). Evidence of delamination at the exit area of the drilled hole was performed visually with the aid of an optical microscope at 10x magnification. A summary of experimental details is given in Table I.

To assess the magnitude of error for surface finish and drill force measurements, multiple readings were taken and the errors based on the mean values were ± 4% and ± 6% respectively.

The tests were carried out at ambient temperature and at low temperature to investigate the suitability of the method of cryogenic machining to the drilling process. The technique of cryogenic machining involved generating sufficient pressure within the ewer to pump LN_2 at a flow rate of 0.2 - 0.3 l/min. through a 3 mm nozzle. The outlet tube was attached to the drill press bed in such a manner that the LN_2 sprayed on the workpiece in the vicinity of the hole being drilled.

Table I Summary of experimental details.

Machine:	Ibarma 30-CA 1.5 HP drill press fitted with automatic feed	
Drills:	HSS Twist Drills double fluted. Diameter 10 mm.	
Drilling parameters:	Drilling speed:	643 RPM, 941 RPM, 1344 RPM
	Feed rate:	0.1 mm/rev
	Helix Angle:	Slow 29°
		Fast 57°
	Point Angle:	-6°, −10°,−20°
	Clearance angle:	10°
Work piece temperatures:	Room Temperature	
	Cryogenic - Continuous pouring of LN_2	
Work piece materials:	Kevlar K-285 /ADR240 epoxy (0°/90°) fibre vol. fraction 36%.	
	Kevlar KA-060/ADR240 epoxy unidirectional (0°) fibre vol. fraction 55%.	
	nominal panel thickness 6 mm.	

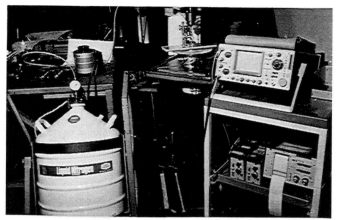

Fig. 1   View of equipment setup

Dimensional accuracy of the holes drilled at room temperature, and under cryogenic conditions, was investigated with the aid of a Nikon profile projector. For comparison, a series of holes were drilled in 6 mm aluminium plate with the same drill, drill speed and feed rate. The dimensions were measured and compared to those of the holes in the KFRP laminate. The assessment of hole dimensional accuracy was based on the deviation of the drilled hole diameter ΔD,

where $\Delta D = d - D$;   d= maximum diameter
                                                        D= drill diameter

A gauge of hole roundness error f_k was also determined using

$$f_k = \frac{1}{2}(d_{max} - d_{min})$$

where d_{max}, d_{min} are maximum and minimum diameters.

A series of drill wear tests were conducted on the high fibre volume laminates mentioned earlier. Two wear tests were executed, each consisting of eighty holes, drilled under ambient and cryogenic conditions. Hole wall surface finish and hole roundness error (f_k), were obtained at regular intervals to give an indication of drill wear.

Fig. 2   Example of drills used in experiments. Left a fast helix drill, right a slow helix drill. Both with -20° point angle. For comparison a standard HSS drill is shown in the centre

Results and Discussion

Drilling Speed. The main objective of this work is to establish appropriate simple methods for drilling holes in KFRP composite plates without having to resort to high drilling speeds or expensive tooling presently recommended in literature [11]. Initial tests have been performed using a HSS drill bit with a helix angle of 57° (Fast Helix) and point angle of -10° to investigate the effects of drill speed on hole quality. Backing has been provided at the drill exit side in the form of 6 mm Perspex strips. These tests have been carried out at room temperature.

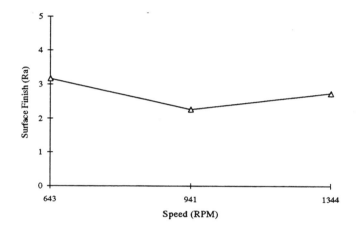

Fig. 3   Surface finish of hole wall at various drilling speeds. Drill: HSS Fast Helix, drill point angle -10°

It is evident from the results, Figure 3, that the drill speed has little influence on the surface finish of the hole wall; however, a slight improvement in surface finish at 941 RPM is noted. The rest of the drilling tests were performed at 941 RPM as speeds close to this are commonly available on hand held power tools.

Drill Geometry. Having established a satisfactory drilling speed, tests have been performed in order to determine a suitable drill geometry. The effect of drill point angle and helix angle are also investigated. Negative drill point angles are used ranging from -6° to -20°. All drills have been ground with a 10° clearance angle and the tests have been performed at room temperature and with the use of LN_2. Figure 4 shows the surface finish of the holes as a result of the differing drill point angles. As with variations in drilling speed, there is little difference in hole wall surface finish with varying drill point angle. However, there is a large difference in surface finish shown between those tests conducted at room temperature and those performed with LN_2.

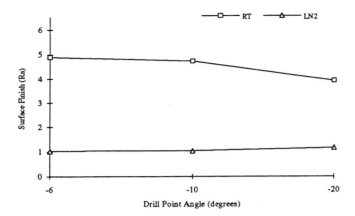

Fig. 4 Hole wall surface finish at varying drill point angles at room and cryogenic conditions. Drill: Fast helix

As reported previously [4], a peculiarity in turning of KFRP is the remnant of uncut fibres left, generally at the end of the machined portion. This is also evident in the drilling of KFRP, as shown in Figure 5a. The length of these uncut fibres reduces with increasing negative drill point angle. This is applicable for drilling operations at both room and cryogenic temperatures. In an effort to minimise these uncut fibres, a thin layer of resin (approximately 0.5 mm thick) was applied to the plates on both sides prior to drilling and left to cure. This cured resin rich layer was completely effective in eliminating all uncut fibres leaving a clean hole entry face, as shown in Figure 5b. The authors suggest that this is a simple solution to avoid fuzzy uncut fibres at the hole entry point. It has also been observed that the unidirectional fibre laminates are more likely to exhibit uncut fibres at the hole entry and exit faces. It is, therefore, recommended that when unidirectional laminates require drilling, the designer should consider including a single layer of KFRP woven cloth on each side of the laminate to ensure a clean hole entry/exit.

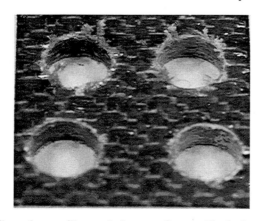

Fig. 5a View of uncut fibres at hole entry: front and back show holes using-20° and -6° point angle; holes under cryogenic conditions on the left and at room temperature on the right. Drill: Fast Helix

It is generally excepted that in machining of KFRP high rake angles result in better machined surface finish. To investigate whether this is applicable to drilling of KFRP as well, drill tests were performed with slow helix (helix angle 29°) and fast helix (helix angle 57°) drills. At room temperature there is little difference in surface finish between fast and slow helix drills, as shown in Figure 6. However, when LN_2 is used, there is a marked difference in surface finish with the fast helix drill giving a consistently better result. This is consistent with the previously reported improved values obtained with higher rake angles [4].

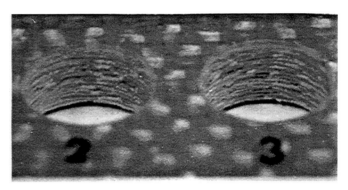

Fig. 5b View of hole entry with a cured resin rich layer. Note absence of uncut fibres at hole entry face. Drill: Fast helix, -20° point angle. Drilled at room temperature

The large difference in surface finish between fast helix and the slow helix drills when LN_2, is used, Figure 7, as opposed to little, if any, difference observed at room temperature can be attributed to several factors discussed later in the paper. It should be noted that the surface finishes are better for both the fast and slow helix drills when LN_2 is used, as opposed to those obtained at room temperature.

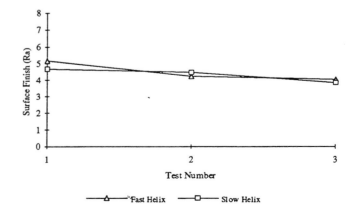

Fig. 6 Hole wall surface finish with varying drill helix angle at room temperature. Drill:-20° point angle.

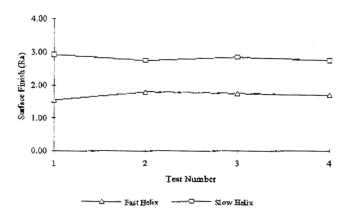

Fig. 7 Hole wall surface finish with varying drill helix angle under cryogenic conditions. Drill:-20 point angle

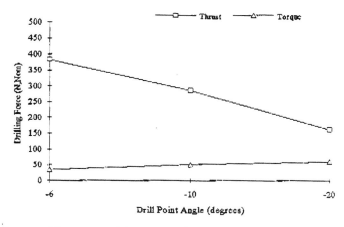

Fig. 8 Drilling forces with varying drill point angle under cryogenic conditions. Drill: Fast helix HSS

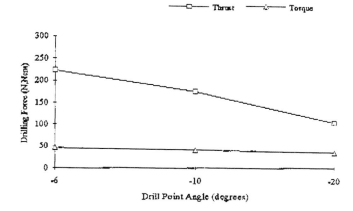

Fig. 9 Drilling forces with varying drill point angle at room temperature. Drill: Fast helix HSS

Fibre pull out and free deflection of fibres before failing in a tensile mode are common features of KFRP machining as reported by Santhanakrishnan et al.[6]. It is reasonable to suggest that due to difference of thermal expansion co-efficients of the resin and the fibre (epoxy: 80-100 x 10^{-6}/°K and Kevlar: about -4 x10^{-6}/°K and 50 x 10^{-6}/°K in longitudinal and transverse directions respectively) a compressive stress is induced on the fibre, producing a clamping force. This combined with the epoxy becoming stiffer in the cryogenic range [12], would result in the fibres being held in a more rigid fashion, thereby reducing the fibre deflection. This would, in turn, help change the failure mode from one of bending induced rupture to that of shear failure. A higher helix angle gives the effect of a higher rake angle resulting in a cleaner cut, as is evident from micrographs presented later in the paper. However, at room temperature the fibres are able to deflect away from the tools cutting edge and indications of a tensile failure mode due to bending with some shear failure are evident. Under these conditions the variation in rake angle due to changing helix angle is expected to have minimal effect on the failure mechanism.

Drilling Forces. It is generally recognised that in drilling fibre reinforced composites, drilling forces subject the laminate to the risk of delamination (interlaminar crack propagation), which threatens the structural integrity of the composite. Clearly it is preferable to keep the drilling thrust forces to a minimum to avoid any risk of delamination. To this end drilling forces were measured with various drill point geometries at room temperature as well as with the use of LN_2. The results are shown in Figures 8 and 9.

In both instances drill thrust force decreases with increasing negative drill point angle. This suggests that in practice, a high negative drill point angle would reduce the risk of delamination. The use of LN_2 results in higher thrust forces which are to be expected due to the increased hardness of the epoxy matrix in the cryogenic range. However, there is little change in torque results.

Surface finish. As found in the turning of KFRP, the temperature of the workpiece strongly influences its surface finish [4]. Figure 3 clearly demonstrates that this also applies to the drilling of KFRP. Comparing results from Figures 4, 6, and 7 it can be seen that workpiece temperature has more influence on surface finish than the other drilling parameters.

However, it must be noted that in using Ra values, little account is taken of the exposed fibres at the hole wall surface. It was clearly evident from visual inspection that the machined surfaces exhibited more fuzzy texture at room temperature than those produced at cryogenic temperatures. Figures 10(a) and (b) show the scanning electron micrographs of hole wall surface finish obtained at room and cryogenic temperatures with a fast helix drill, and a -20° drill point angle. Cryogenic conditions produce a superior surface finish with negligible exposed uncut fibres. Figures 12(a) and (b) show hole wall surface finish at the two drilling temperatures using a slow helix drill, and a -20° drill point angle, whereas Figures 11(a) and (b) show the results with a fast helix drill with -6° drill point angle.

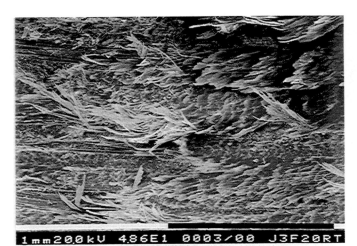

Fig. 10a Surface finish at room temperature. Drill: Fast helix HSS; -20° drill point

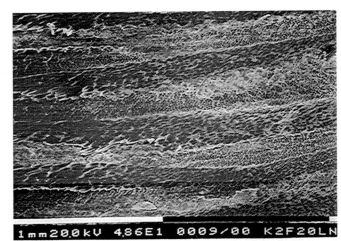

Fig. 10 b Surface finish at cryogenic temperature. Drill: Fast helix HSS;-20° drill point

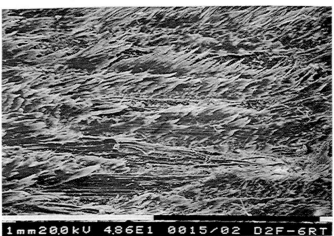

Fig. 11a Surface finish at room temperature. Drill: Fast helix HSS; -6° drill point

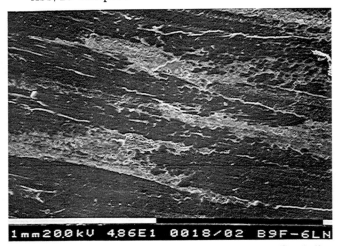

Fig. 11b Surface finish at cryogenic temperature. Drill: Fast helix HSS;-6° drill point

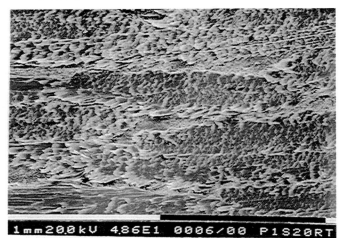

Fig. 12a Surface finish at room temperature. Drill: Slow helix HSS; -20° drill point

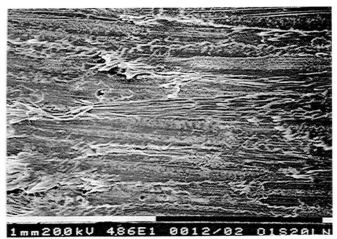

Fig. 12b Surface finish at cryogenic temperature. Drill: Slow helix HSS;-20° drill point

Comparing Figures. 10(a), 11(a) and 12(a) there is little apparent difference in surface finish of the hole walls at room temperature when using drills with different helix angles or drill point angles; the micrographs all show similar amounts of exposed uncut fibre ends. However, comparing Figure 10(b) with Figure 12(b) it is evident that the hole wall surface finish is improved at cryogenic temperatures by using a higher drill helix angle. On the other hand it appears from Figures 10(b) and 11(b) that drill point angle has little influence on the hole wall surface finish.

Dimensional Accuracy. As machining operations on cured parts are always performed towards the end of a production sequence, these operations are of particular importance. An unsatisfactory machining operation can result in a part being rejected, resulting in wastage and increased part costs. In drilling operations the dimensional accuracy is important for various reasons, notably bearing stress considerations and fit limitations for fasteners. A series of holes were made under both temperature conditions, to check the hole roundness error and dimensional deviation errors. For comparison, a series of tests were also performed in aluminium alloy plate of the same thickness as the KFRP laminate. The results are shown in Figures 13 and 14.

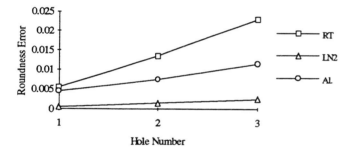

Fig. 13 Roundness error of a 10 mm hole at room temperature and cryogenic conditions. Drill: Fast Helix HSS, -20° point angle

Both Figures 13 and 14 show that holes drilled under cryogenic conditions are better dimensionally than those drilled at room temperature. It is also interesting to note that in both cases cryogenic conditions produce dimensionally

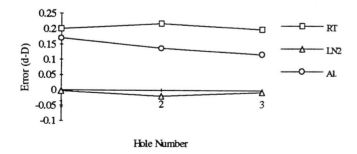

Fig. 14 Deviation error of a 10 mm hole at room temperature and cryogenic conditions. Drill: Fast Helix HSS, -20° point angle

better holes than those drilled in the aluminium plate. This suggests that more accurately drilled holes are possible under these conditions than are commonly obtained when drilling an aluminium alloy plate. This may require designers to re-think certain aspects of a design in future if adopting the methods recommended in this paper.

Drill Wear. As previously reported, tool wear is greatly reduced in the machining of KFRP, when performed under cryogenic conditions [4]. Tool wear itself may not be a limiting factor in determining tool life and surface finish may become the dominant factor. As the main interest of this work is to establish a simple method of drilling KFRP laminates, two short series of wear tests have been performed at both drilling temperatures on a unidirectional laminate. Hole surface finish and dimensional accuracy are recorded, as these parameters are usually of more interest to the designer, and are easily determined. Note that the surface finish of a hole in a unidirectional laminate is dependent on the correspondence of fibre direction and drill cutting edge [5]. For this reason surface finish has only been measured at 0° and 180° to the fibre direction (positions where the fibres are cut perpendicularly by the drill). This accounts for the slightly better surface finish results, Figure 16, than those reported in the earlier sections (for example Figures 4 and 7).

It becomes apparent from both Figures 15 and 16 that when drilling at room temperature hole quality starts to deteriorate after a relatively short period (eighty holes), while drilling under cryogenic conditions over the same number of holes shows little, if any, deterioration taking place. It should also be noted that the hole roundness error under cryogenic conditions is unchanged over the test duration while at room temperatures the roundness starts to diminish with a large amount of scatter in the results.

Concluding Remarks

It can be concluded from this study that KFRP laminates can be successfully drilled with fast helix HSS drill bits, by modifying the drill geometry to give a high negative drill point angle, and an increased clearance angle. By using these modified HSS drill bits, drilling operations have been performed at markedly reduced drilling speeds than previously suggested. The technique of cryogenic machining, which is achieved by continuously applying LN_2 to the workpiece, can be applied successfully to drilling operations resulting in improved hole wall surface finish, dimensional quality and increased tool life. The improved machinability under cryogenic conditions can be explained in terms of workpiece temperature.

The characteristic deficiency of KFRP laminate drilling operations which leave the hole entry and exit faces with

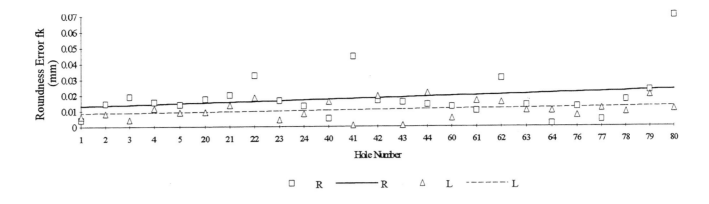

Figure 15   Roundness error f_k trend over eighty holes under both drilling conditions. Drill: Fast helix HSS, -20 degree point angle; speed 941 RPM

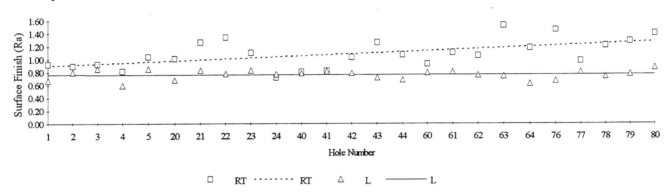

Figure 16   Hole wall surface finish trend over 80 holes under both drilling conditions. Drill: Fast helix HSS, -20 degree point angle; speed 941 RPM

uncut, fuzzy and protruding fibres, can be negated by applying a thin layer of resin on the surface of the laminate in the immediate vicinity of the drilling operation. The authors recommend that when unidirectional laminates require drilling, the designer should consider the inclusion of a single layer of KFRP woven cloth on both sides of the laminate to ensure the elimination of protuding and uncut fibres about the hole entry and exit areas.

Acknowledgment

The authors wish to acknowledge the help received from Messrs B. N Fullerton, P. Selby, and F.T.H. Kwee during the course of this study. They are also grateful to High Modulus (NZ) Ltd. for providing materials and facilities.

References

1   König, W., Wulf, C., Grass, P., and Willerscheid, H., Annals CIRP, 34(2), 536-48 (1985).

2   Sakuma K. and Seto M., Bulletin JSME, 22(163), 107-14 (1979).

3   Sakuma K. and Seto M., Taniguchi, M. and Yokoo, Y., Bulletin JSME, 28(245), 2781-88 (1985).

4   Bhattacharyya, D., Allen, M.N., and Mander, S.J., Processing and manufacturing of composite materials, Srivatsan and Chandrashekhar ed., ASME PED/MD 49/27, 133-47 (1991).

5   König, W., Grass, P., Annals CIRP, 38(1), 119-124 (1989).

6   Santhanakrishnan, G., Krishnamurthy, R. and Malhorta, S.K., J. Mech. Working Technology, 17, 195-204 (1988).

7   Doerr, R., Greene, E., Lyon, B. and Taha, S., Development of effective machining and tooling techniques for Kevlar composites, Tech. Rep. #AD-A117853 (1982)

8   Ho-Cheng, H. Dharan, C.K.H., ASME Trans. J. Engng. Ind., 79, 236-39 (1990).

9   Jain, S. and Yang, D.C.H., Processing and manufacturing of composite materials, Srivatsan and Chandrashekhar ed. ASME PED/MD, 49/27, 37-51 (1991).

10   Tagliaferri, G., Caprino, G. and Diterlizzi, A., Int. J. Mach. Tools Manufact., 30(1), 77-84 (1990).

11 Penzelli, R., Cutting and machining of Composite
    Materials based on Aramid Fibres, Tech. Rep. Du
    Pont de Nemours. Geneva, Switzerland. (Private
    communication).
12 Hartwig, G., Adv. Cryog. Eng., 24, 17-36 (1978).

Proceedings of the ASM 1993 Materials Congress, Pittsburgh, Pennsylvania, October 17-21, 1993

Milling Force Prediction for Fiber Reinforced Plastics

H. Y. Puw, H. Hocheng
National Tsing Hua University
Hsinchu, Taiwan, R.O.C.

Abstract

This paper presents a mechanistic model for the force prediction in milling of composite materials. The concept of chip load is used to obtain the relation between force and cutting conditions. Planing tests are adopted to investigate the directional mechanical response of the fiber-reinforced plastics. The specific cutting force K_T and K_R are closely related to chip thickness and cutting velocity. The second stage of this model is the prediction of the milling force based on force components from two fiber orientation considering the directional properties. Experimental results agree with the proposed model for unidirectionally reinforced carbon/PEEK. Since burr is a serious problem while milling carbon/epoxy, experimental results illustrate large deviation from the proposed model and further modification is needed.

IN THE APPLICATION OF composite materials, such as aircraft structures or machine elements, some accurate surfaces for bearing mounting or adhesive joints are required. Precise machining has to be performed to guarantee the dimensional stability and interface quality. However, the experience acquired from metal cutting can not be transplanted to the fiber-reinforced plastics without considering the peculiar material response to machining. Some pioneering works came from the extension of the research on machining of plastics,since one major matrix materials is polymer [1]. In the seventies, a few paper discussed the machining of composites [2,3,4]. Rough surface finish is attributed to the characteristics composition of composites, such as fiber ends. Precision tooling like diamond is suggested,while HSS tool suffers extreme wear thus should not be used for composite removal. Carbide instead can be an alternative. Miner and Mackey studied the complexities of the machining of the two-phase composite materials and concluded that not only new concepts of tooling but also different realms of cutting conditions are needed [5].

Koplev is the first who declared that chip formation in composite removal is a process of serial material fractures [6]. He and co-workers described the machined surface as a function of machining orientation relative to fiber axis [7]. These are valuable works, which show different cutting mechanism from that of metals. Inoue and Kawaguchi reported the cutting mechanism in grinding process in terms of failure of yarns[8]. The topography of the ground surface was correlated to the direction of yarns. Sakuma point out that there is a strong correlation between the rapid rising of the cutting temperature and the existence of the critical speed causing drastic tool wear [9]. He also compared the different tool wear in cutting CFRP and GFRP based on their physical and mechanical properties [10]. Santhanakrishnam reported that the machined surfaces of CFRP is better than KFRP. He also discussed the mechanisms of material removal,tool wear and cutting forces during machining [11].

For milling operation, limited reference can be found. Some tool and machine builders reported range of suggested cutting conditions with large variance[12,13]. Hocheng & Puw paid attention to the fiber orientation affecting cut edge,surface finish and cutting force,and suggested the milling parallel to the fiber axis [14].

Fiber-reinforced plastics contain two phases of materials with drastically distinguished mechanical and thermal properties,which brings in complicated interactions between matrix and reinforcement during machining and hinders sound analysis of the cutting forces. The material anisotropy made by fiber reinforcement heavily influences the chip formation and other machinability indices during machining. In this paper, an approach to the force prediction of carbon/PEEK carbon/Epoxy and carbon/ABS in milling considering their directional properties is proposed. The existing milling force prediction for metals will be first introduced followed by the prediction for unidirectionally reinforced plastics.

Model of Force Prediction

Various cutting mechanisms develop during machining of composites majorily as a function of the fiber axis in reference to the cutting direction. Tool geometry such as rake angle exerts relatively secondary effects. The cutting mechanism in action determines the momentary cutting forces. Researchers have investigated into these cutting mechanisms since last decade [6, 8, 15].

Koplev et.al. observed the difference between cutting parallel and perpendicular to the fiber axis. It represents two basic cutting mechanisms -shearing in perpendicular direction and buckling in parallel direction, hence different cutting forces are required. Consequently,one suggests to predict the cutting forces by composition of two systems resulted from cutting parallel and perpendicular to the fiber axis.

The goal of this research is to develop a model for the prediction of the force in end milling for fiber-reinforced plastics. The authors extend the concept of chip load to deal with the anisotropic cutting mechanisms of composite materials. The approaches for metal and composites based on the concept of chip load in predicting milling force is illustrated in Fig.1.

In metal cutting, material removal is done by shear deformation in front of cutting tool. The prediction of milling force is based on the chip load on cutter. Martellotti examined the geometrical tool-work relationship in milling and showed that the true cutting path both for up and down milling is trochoid [16,17].

This research initiates the chip load calculations.

Koenigsberger and Sabberwal proposed that the instantaneous cutting force are proportional to the sectional chip area [18]. Fig.2 shows the three-dimensional view of an end mill with the chip load elements on the flutes of the cutter. The periodic variation of the chip section causes pulsations of the cutting force. Sabberwal also showed that cutting forces can be predicted by considering the tangential component proportional to the chip load, and the radial component proportional to the tangential force [18]:

$$DFTN = K_T * B * t_c \qquad (1\text{-}a)$$
$$DFRAD = K_R * DFTN \qquad (1\text{-}b)$$
where
  DFTN:tangential force
  DFRAD:radial force
  K_T and K_R: constants of proportionality
  B: width of cut
  t_c: chip thickness

The chip thickness(t_c) can be approximated by $t * \sin(\alpha)$ where t is the feed rate, α is the angular position of the cutter. The specific cutting force K_T varies with the chip thickness,
$$K_T = C(t_c)^P \qquad (2)$$
where P=-0.3.

Planing experiment is adopted to investigate the fundamental specific

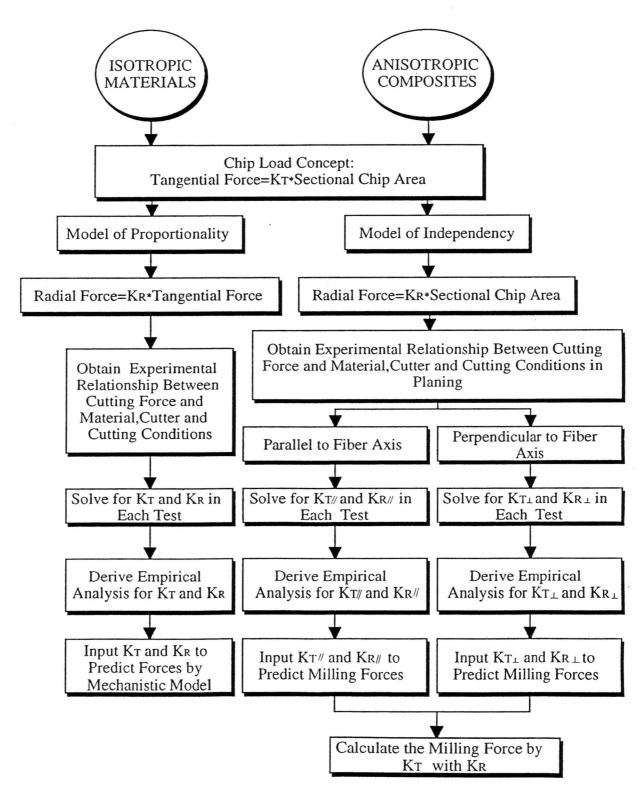

Fig. 1 Comparison of Algorithm of Milling Force Prediction for
Metals and Directionally-Reinforced Composites

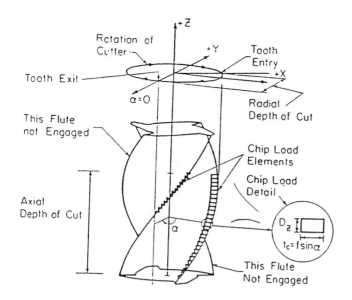

Fig.2 End Mill with Chip Load Elements   (Kline,1982)

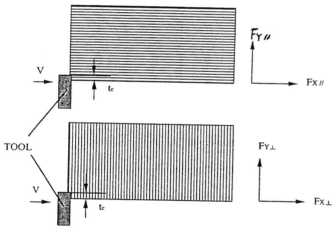

Fig.3 Planing Experiment of Unidirectionally
Reinforced Plastics.

forces $K_{T//}, K_{R//}, K_{T\perp}$ and $K_{R\perp}$. Fig.3 shows the planing operation, which can be considered as milling with a cutter of infinite radius. $F_{//}$ and $F_\perp$ are the cutting forces in planing parallel and perpendicular to the fiber direction. Label x and y represent the force component parallel and perpendicular to the tool speed(V) respectively. By selecting cutting speed of 1, 3, and 6

m/min,chip thickness from 0.01 to 1 mm and width of cut of 2, 5 and 10 mm, one obtains the empirical expressions of the major forces in x- and y-direction.

(I).for cutting parallel to fiber axis
$$F_{x//}=K_{T//}*B*t_c \qquad (3)$$
(II).for cutting perpendicular to fiber axis
$$F_{x\perp}=K_{T\perp}*B*t_c \qquad (4)$$

The short fiber-reinforced thermoplastic ABS is considered near isotropic,and is studied for comparison.
$$F_{xO}=K_{TO}*B*t_c \qquad (5)$$

One recognizes that the major specific cutting force K_T is also the specific cutting energy defined by input cutting power (F_x*V) divided by volume removal rate $(V*B*t_c)$. As to the orthogonal force,two models are proposed and later examined with experimental results.
(1). Model of Proportionality
$$F_{Y//}=K_{R//,1}*F_{x//} \qquad (6a)$$
$$F_{Y\perp}=K_{R\perp,1}*F_{x\perp} \qquad (7a)$$
and $F_{YO}=K_{RO,1}*F_{xO} \qquad (8a)$

For cutting parallel and perpendicular to carbon/PEEK and carbon/epoxy, and cutting carbon/ABS respectively. The model assumes that K_R's are determined by tool geometry only.

(2). Model of Independency
$$F_{Y//}=K_{R//,2}*B*t_c \qquad (6b)$$
$$F_{Y\perp}=K_{R\perp,2}*B*t_c \qquad (7b)$$
and $F_{YO}=K_{RO,2}*B*t_c \qquad (8b)$

The model proposes that K_R's vary with cutting conditions and do not remain constant for one tool geometry, since various mechanisms of chip formation may develop at various chip configuration (chip thickness and width of chip) resulted from cutting conditions .

The above algorithm apply the concept of chip load to predict cutting force in planing of composites . The specific cutting force(K_T's and K_R's) is found closely correlated to chip thickness and cutting velocity [19].

As shown in Fig.4, the instantaneous milling forces can be calculated by instantaneous chip load composed of F_{X*} and F_{Y*}(* represents //, $\perp$, or o) from planing test. Noticing the variation of chip thickness with angular position, one can calculate F_{X*} and F_{Y*} variation of chip thickness with angular position, one can calculate F_{X*} and F_{Y*} by Eq's (3) to (8) respectively, where $t_c = t \sin\theta$.

(I) milling parallel to fiber axis
$$Fx=Fx_{//}*\cos\theta+Fy_{\perp}*\sin\theta \quad (9)$$
$$Fy=Fy_{//}*\sin\theta -Fx_{\perp}*\cos\theta \quad (10)$$
(II) milling perpendicular to fiber axis
$$Fx=Fx_{\perp}*\cos\theta+Fy_{//}*\sin\theta \quad (11)$$
$$Fy=Fy_{\perp}*\sin\theta -Fx_{//}*\cos\theta \quad (12)$$
For carbon/ABS
$$Fx=Fxo*\cos\theta+Fyo*\sin\theta \quad (13)$$
$$Fy=-Fxo*\sin\theta+Fyo*\cos\theta \quad (14)$$

Experimental Results

Fig 5 shows the results of milling experiment for carbon/PEEK. The agreement between the predicted force using proposed algorithm and the measured force is satisfactory. Fig.6 shows very close agreement between the predicted and measured forces for carbon/ABS. The thermoplastic composite material is ready to deform plastically. Consequently, one can well predict the milling forces of these materials by extending the mechanistic model to anisotropic analysis.

Fig.7 shows large difference between the prediction force and the measured force. Large amount of fracture in chip formation and the produced burrs exert additional influence on the cutting force. Some modifications are needed to compensate the deviation, which is a function of cutting conditions and materials properties.

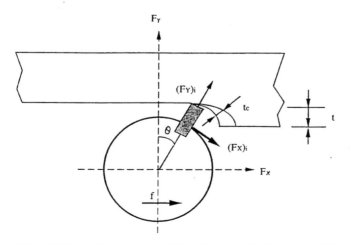

Fig.4 Milling Experiment of Unidirectionally Reinforced Plastics.

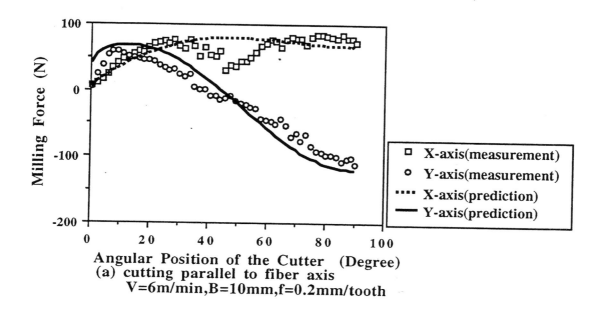

(a) cutting parallel to fiber axis
V=6m/min,B=10mm,f=0.2mm/tooth

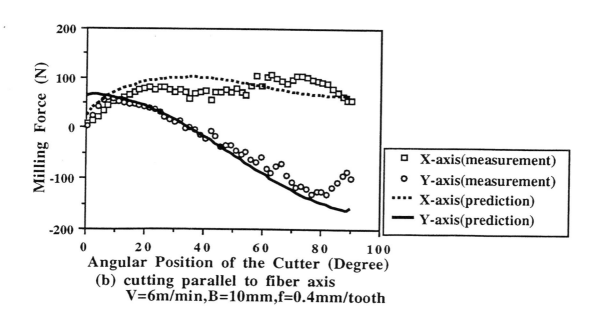

(b) cutting parallel to fiber axis
V=6m/min,B=10mm,f=0.4mm/tooth

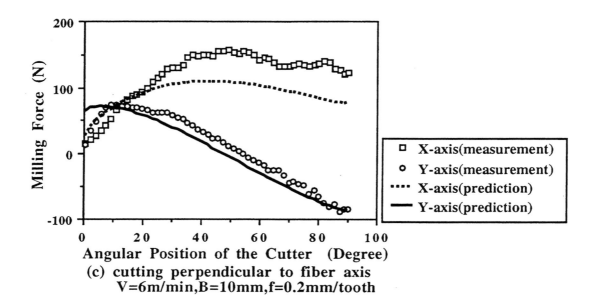

(c) cutting perpendicular to fiber axis
V=6m/min,B=10mm,f=0.2mm/tooth

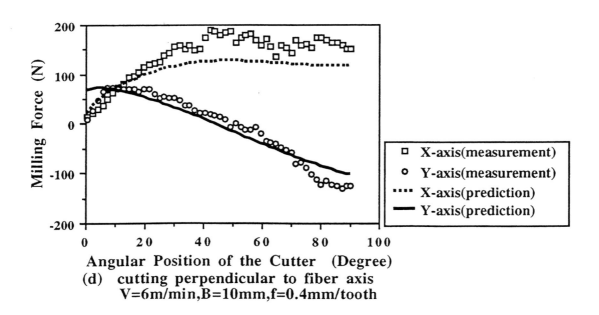

(d) cutting perpendicular to fiber axis
V=6m/min,B=10mm,f=0.4mm/tooth

Fig.5 Milling Force of Carbon/PEEK.

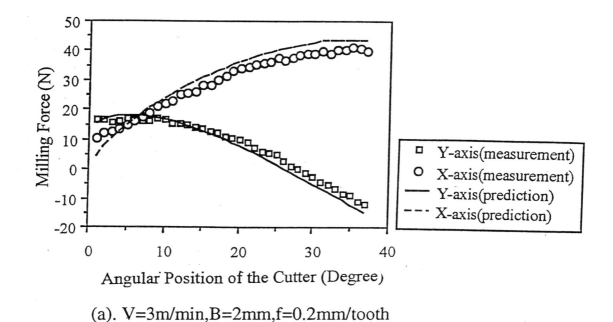

(a). V=3m/min,B=2mm,f=0.2mm/tooth

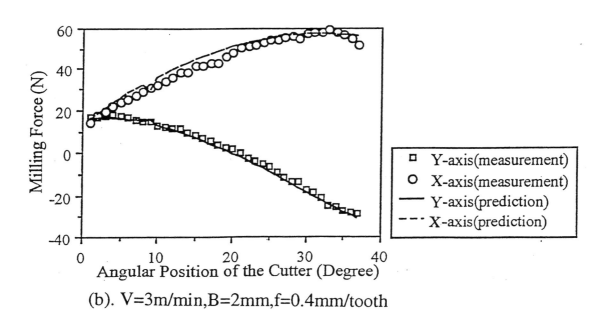

(b). V=3m/min,B=2mm,f=0.4mm/tooth

Fig.6 Milling Force of Carbon/ABS.

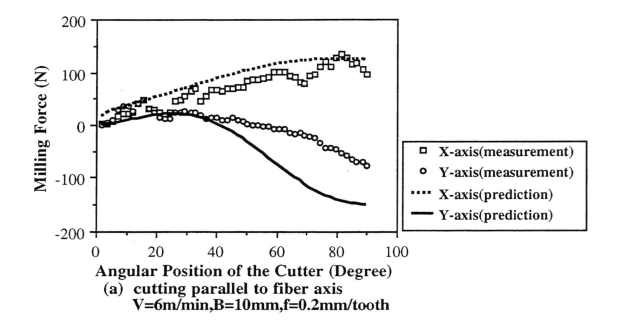

(a) cutting parallel to fiber axis
V=6m/min,B=10mm,f=0.2mm/tooth

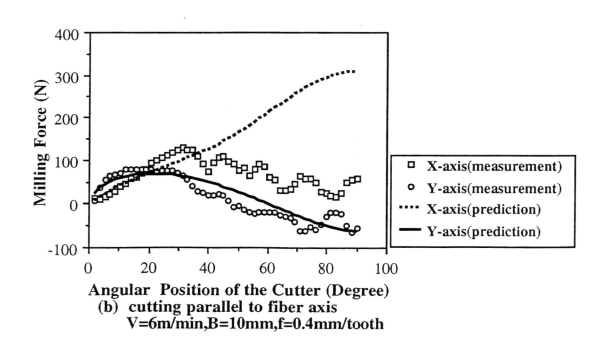

(b) cutting parallel to fiber axis
V=6m/min,B=10mm,f=0.4mm/tooth

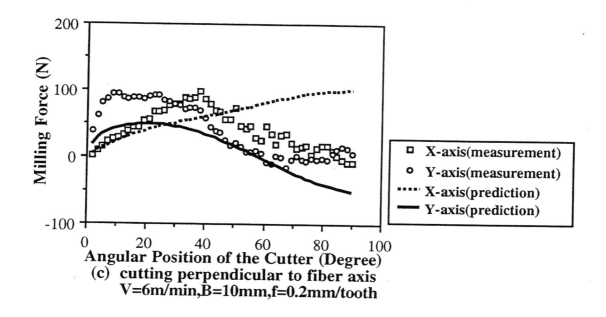

(c) cutting perpendicular to fiber axis
V=6m/min,B=10mm,f=0.2mm/tooth

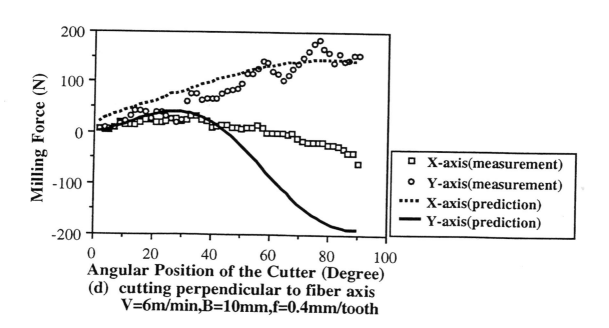

(d) cutting perpendicular to fiber axis
V=6m/min,B=10mm,f=0.4mm/tooth

Fig.7 Milling Force of Carbon/Epoxy.

Conclusions

This paper presents the development of an anisotropic mechanistic model for the prediction of force in end-milling. With directional reinforcement, the model of chip load is extended to two-dimensional. Planing of unidirectionally fiber-reinforced plastics is adopted to investigate the correlation between cutting force and chip load. The specific cutting forces (K_T and K_R) represent the cutting parallel and perpendicular to fiber axis respectively. For the orthogonal specific cutting force (K_R), the conventional model of proportionality is suitable for isotropic materials, while the model of independency is appropriate for anisotropic materials. Experimental results agree with the proposed algorithm for both carbon/ABS and carbon/PEEK while further modification is required for carbon/epoxy.

Acknowledgment

This research is supported by the grant from National Science Council, Republic of China, under contract #NSC81-0422-E007-14.

Reference

1. Kobayashi, A., 1967, <u>Machining of Plastics</u>, Mc-Graw-Hill, New York.
2. Doran, J.H., & Maikish, C.R., 1973, Composite Materials in Engineering Designed, ASM, pp:242-250.
3. Friend, C.A., Clyne, R.W., & Valentine, G.G. ,1973 , ibbd.,pp:217-224
4. Marx, W., and Trink, S., 1978, Tech Rep, #AD-B034202.
5. Mackey, B.A., 1980, Plastic Engineering , pp.22-24.
6. Koplev,A., 1980, Proc 3rd ICCM , pp.1597-1605, Paris.
7. Koplev, A., Lystrup, A., & Vorm, T.,1983, Composites,Vol.14,pp.371-376.
8. Inoue, H and Kawaguchi,I, 1990, Journal of Engineering Materials and Technology , July, Vol.112, pp:341-345.
9. Sakuma, K.,and Seto, M.,1981, Bulletin of JSME, Vol.24 ,No.190, April ,pp:748-755.
10. Sakuma, K., Seto, M., and Taniguchi, M.,1985, Bulletin of JSME, Vol.28, No.245, November , pp:2781-2788.
11. Santhanakrishnan, G., Krishnamurthy, R., and Malhotra, S.K. ,1988, J. Mech. Work. Technology,17,pp:195-204.
12. Wiendl, J., and Reimann, W., 1987, Werkstatt und Betrie, Vol.120 ,No.3, pp.189-197.
13. McGinty, M.J., and Preuss, C.W. ,1985, ed. by Sarin, V.K., Am Soc Metals, pp:231-243.
14. Hocheng, H., and Puw, H.Y., 1991, in Processing and Manufacturing of Composite Materials ,112 ASME Winter Annual Meeting, Atlanta, USA,pp.65-76.
15. Kameeda, T, 1989, Proceeding of the 16th North American Manufacturing Research Conference ,p:216-221.
16. Martellotti,M.E., 1941, Transactions ASME , Vol.63 ,p:677
17. Martellotti,M.E., 1945, Transactions ASME ,Vol.74, p:233
18. Sabberwal, A.J.P., 1961/62, Annals of CIRP, Vol.10, No.3,p:197
19. Kline, W.A., Devor, R.E., and Lindberg,R.L.,1982,Int.J.Mach.Tool Des. Res, Vol.22,No.1,p:7-22.

FLANK WEAR AND SPALLING OF CERAMICS DURING MACHINING OF POLYMERIC COMPOSITES

G.Santhanakrishnan[*], R.Krishnamurthy[**] and S.K.Malhotra[*]

[*]FRP Research Centre, [**]Manufacturing Engineering Section
Indian Institute of Technology, Madras 600 036 INDIA.

Abstract

Higher strength to weight ratio, greater resistance to chemical and associated wear and relative easiness in fabrication have enhanced the application range of polymeric composites. Among the polymeric composites Glass Fibre Reinforced Plastics (GFRP) and Carbon Fibre Reinforced Polymer (CFRP) are popular ones. Though most of the products of polymeric composites are moulded, to overcome the shrinkage problems and also to attain a desired near nett-shape configuration, polymeric composites have to be machined. Due to varying degree of fibre content and also their orientations in the matrix, considerable difficulties are encountered during machining. The cutting tool is subjected to fluctuation in force, vibration of the tool tip and also thermal shock. This may result in normally severe flank wear; also in chipping and spalling of the cutting tool over the cutting zone. This paper presents data on flank wear and associated phenomena during machining of polymeric composites with ceramic and ceramic coated tools.

DURING MACHINING OF COMPOSITES, the contact surface with the cutting tool and work material is subjected to conditions promoting intense adhesion, and plastic deformation and abrasion over a portion of cutting tool. This will result in different forms of wear; among them flank wear is important one, in that it has got a bearing on effective depth of cutting and consequently the work piece dimensions. Usually it is distinguished by formation of a bright land presenting a strap wear. This land-formation could be associated with abrasion[1,2], small scale/discrete or localised deformation of asperities over the tool flank, possible dissolution - diffusion and glazing. Fig.1 illustrates a schematic illustration of forms of tool wear and associated mechanism. It is seen that with the increasing cutting velocity, abrasion, diffusion, and deformation due to thermal plasticity effects become pronounced indicating that most of the mechanism of the tool wear were thermal dependant. Polymeric composites being poor conductor of heat, most of the mechanisms are operative during machining of composites. In the following sections of the paper the observations of tool wear are presented.

Experimental

Filament wound tubes of GFRP and CFRP have been machined using coated cemented carbides and oxide ceramic cutting tools. Machining trials were conducted in a high speed, precision, VDF lathe. The cutting conditions are presented in Table-1. For understanding the wear of cutting tools and associated mechanisms, worn out portions of cutting tools were observed in a scanning electron microscope.

Result and Discussions

Flank Wear on Black Ceramics. During machining of FRP composites the cutting tools were exposed to severe abrasive environment. Earlier trials using cold compacted white Al_2O_3 tools indicated sudden chipping and catastrophic failures. This is attributed to the poor fracture - rupture strength (FRS) characteristics. The hot pressed black ceramic tools (70% Al_2O_3 + 30% TiC) have superior FRS value and thermal properties owing to the particulate reinforced micro structure. Such tools performed better; however, they exhibited broad flank wear. Fig.2 illustrates typical flank wear observed on black ceramic tools. As seen in the figure the worn-out cutting tool presented a flank with glossy texture with localised pull out of material.

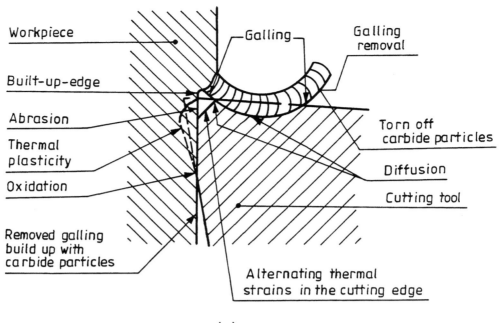

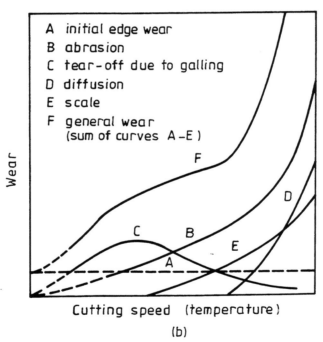

Fig.1 Schematic representation of (a) Causes of wear
(b) Wear as a function of cutting speed [3]

During machining the just machined work surface will slide past the flank surface establishing an intense adhesion contact pair. During this contact it is likely that the hard TiC particles may get transferred to work surface, and during subsequent sliding these particles will promote localised adhesion within be TiC present over the flank surface and consequent pull out of material from the same. This situation is similar to the performance of P-type carbides while machining cast iron. During machining of cast iron, an abrasive material, the TiC particles for P-type tools get transferred to work surface and subsequently resulting

110

Table 1 - Machining Conditions

- Machine

VDF Lathe
Spindle speed   :   140 - 5600 rpm (stepless regulated)
Motor power   :   20Kw

- Work Materials

GFRP -	Tubular section	132.0 mm OD 91.0 mm ID.
CFRP -	"	120.0 mm OD 97.5 mm ID.
Resin -	Epoxy	Ciba Geigy LY556
	Hardener	Ciba Geigy HT772
Fibres -	E-glass Roving, Epoxy compatible - 2240Tex.	
	Carbon Roving, BESFIGHT 6.4 μ filament dia 6000 fibres/tow.	

- Tool Material

	γ	α	λ	χ	β	r
Ceramics	-6	6	-6	75	90	0.8
P30, K20 cemented Carbides Coated with TiN/TiC	-6	6	-6	75	90	0.8

- Cutting conditions

Right hand turning
Cutting speed   :   V m/min. 12.5 to 200
Feed rate   :   s mm/rev. 0.025 to 0.15
Depth of cut   :   a mm 1.5

- Environment   - dry

in some attrition and gouging wear. On the contrary plain K-type carbides exhibited smoother flank wear without any attrition and material pull-out from the flank surface. Apart from attrition wear, the localised pull out of material can be due to discrete small scale plastic deformation of the asperities on the tool flank and consequent tearing. Schematic illustration of small scale deformation and tearing is given in Fig.3.

Further, the poor thermal conductivity of GFRP would have also aggravated the flank wear. Thus, for machining of GFRP an ideal cutting tool will be a plain grade of cemented carbide tools with better thermal properties. This was observed in the better performance of K-type carbides while machining GFRP material [4].

Influence of Wedge geometry on performance of coated carbides. GFRP composites were machined with hard but relatively tougher grade of TiN coated cemented carbide tools. During the machining trials, TiN coated tools with the coating on 90° wedge angle of the substrate subsequently exhibited chip notching, primary grooving over the depth of cut line zone (dcl). Continuous sliding of chip on the rake face, rubbing of the outer most diameter of the work surface over the primary cutting edge usually result in high order contact temperature. Consequently the coating becomes thermally softened and tends to spread over the flank portion. On excessive spreading, coating peals off associated with chip notching and grooving. This is seen in Fig.4. Thus for improving the performance of coated tools, it is necessary to control the substrate deformation so that the deformation and spreading tendency of the coating can be minimised. Hence, cutting tools with modified wedge (substrate geometry) was tried out. Unlike the 90° wedges the modified wedge consisted of 20° negative land of 200 μm width, followed by a positive land of 150 μm

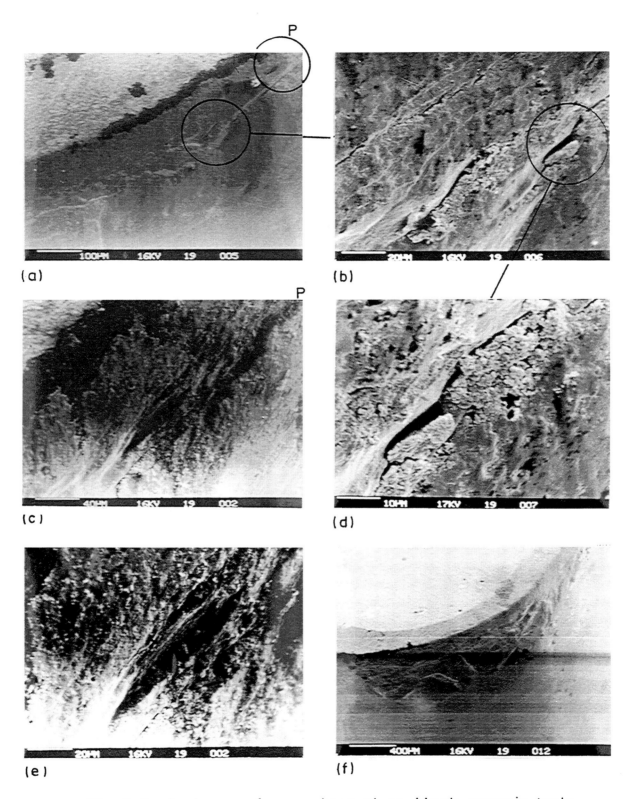

Fig. 2 Typical wear forms observed on black ceramic tools
during machining of GFRP

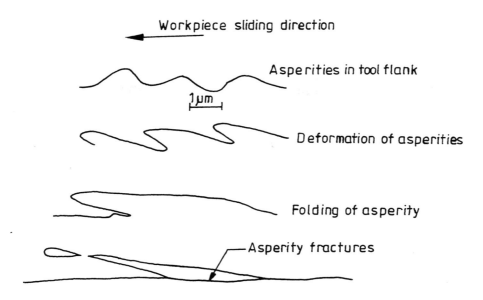

Workpiece sliding direction

Asperities in tool flank

1 μm

Deformation of asperities

Folding of asperity

Asperity fractures

Fig. 3 Typical schematic of small scale discrete asperity deformation and tearing [1]

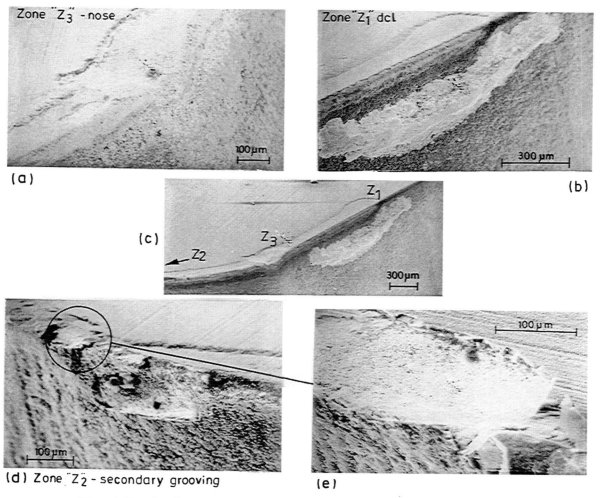

Zone "Z_3" - nose

(a)   100 μm

Zone "Z_1" dcl

(b)   300 μm

(c)

Z_1

Z_3

Z_2

300 μm

(d) Zone "Z_2" - secondary grooving

100 μm

(e)   100 μm

Fig. 4 Typical wear observed on TiN coated tool during GFRP machining

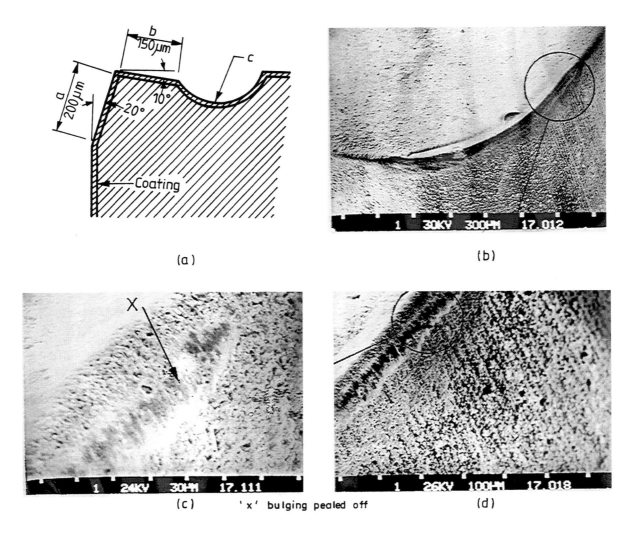

(a)

(b)

(c)   'x' bulging pealed off   (d)

Fig. 5 Typical wear of TiN coated tool with modified wedge

and a chip breaker groove. This modified wedge when coated over exhibited enhanced resistant to deformation there by the coated tool performed better. The enhanced wear resistance of the TiN coated tools with modified wedge is illustrated in Fig.5. It is seen that unlike in the case of TiN coated on 90° substrate, the tool exhibited minimum and relatively smooth flank wear land, with reduced chipping and flaking of the coating. The better performance of these tools can be attributed to the improved resistant to deformation of substrate materials and also enhanced resistance to withstand fluctuating loads normally encountered during machining of GFRP composites.

Influence of type of substrate on wear of coated carbides. During machining of composites, most of the heat of friction during machining has to be transmitted through the cutting tool. This result in thermal loading of the coated layer; the

thermo-mechanical phenomenon associated with frictional heating could significantly influence the wear of coating. Usually, the higher order contact temperature (associated with machining) will result in (thermo mechanical) compressive stresses and consequent plastic flow of coating material. On release of the thermal loading, the coating will experience tensile residual stress, inducing cracking of the coating material. Once the crack is initiated due to cumulative stressing by way of continuous machining, the coating will exhibit a progressive failure such as chipping, spalling and the like. The occurrence of cracking and subsequent failure of the coating is largely due to thermal gradient and the mis-match between the deformation characteristics of the coating and substrate material. Thus, the wear of hard coating during machining of composites can be controlled by selecting a proper substrate material for the cutting tool.

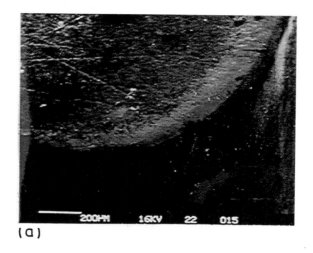

(a)

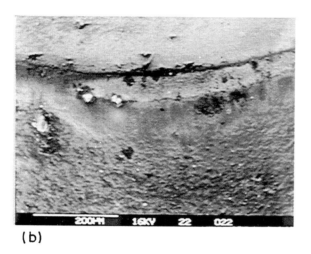

(b)

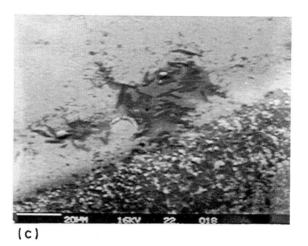

(c)

Fig. 6 Primary notching and secondary grooving on TiC coated
P-type substrate tool

During machining trials conducted on CFRP composites with TiC coated tools with P and K type of substrates, it was observed that the tool with P type substrate exhibited secondary grooving, chip notching and thermal cracking while tools with K type substrate exhibited small flank wear without any chipping or grooving. Fig.6 illustrates typical observation of tool wear with P type substrate. Secondary grooving chip notching can be observed. Smooth flank wear of TiC coated K type substrate tools is illustrated in Fig.7. Thus it is seen that apart from coating, the type of substrate also influences the tool wear.

Conclusion

From the study on flank wear of cutting tools while machining FRP composites, it was found that type of substrate, and the wedge geometry of the substrate influenced the performance of coated tools.

Compared to traditional 90° wedge, the substrate with a wedge of -25° x 200 μm land when coated with TiN exhibited better performance with smoother flank wear and absence of chipping of the coating.

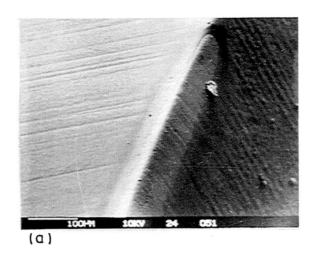

(a)

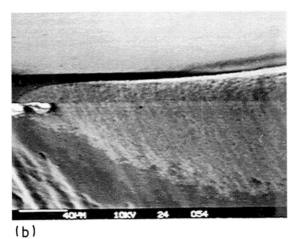

(b)

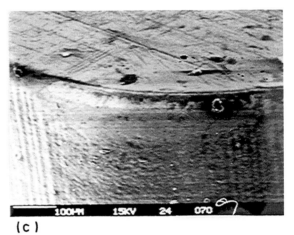

(c)

Fig. 7 Smooth flank wear with almost nil primary and secondary grooving - Ti C coated K-type substrate tool

- Between the P and K type (cemented carbides) substrate, TiC coated tools on K type exhibited better performance.

Even, particulate reinforced black ceramics (Al_2O_3+TiC) tools exhibited broad flank wear of glossy texture with localised pull out of material from the flank surface.

References

1. Dearnley,P.A. "Rake and flank wear mechanisms of coated and uncoated cemented carbides", The Singapore Production Engineer, V2, p.27-59 (1985).

2. Everstine,G.C. and Rogers, "A theory of machining of fiber reinforced materials", Jl.Composite Materials, V5. p.94-106 (1971).

3. Schintlmeister,W. "Cutting tool materials coated by chemical vapour deposition", Wear, V100 p.153-169 (1984).

4. Santhanakrishnan,G. "Investigations on machining of FRP Composites and their tribological behaviour", Ph.D. thesis, IIT Madras (1990).

Proceedings of the ASM 1993 Materials Congress, Pittsburgh, Pennsylvania, October 17-21, 1993

An Investigation into the Drilling of Glass Fibre Reinforced Liquid Crystal Polymer Using Pulsed Nd:YAG Laser

Y. H. Zhang
Nanjing Aeronautical
Institute
PRC

W. S. Lau, T. M. Yue
Hong Kong Polytechnic
Hong Kong

L. Chiang
Chen Hsong Machinery
Co. Ltd.
Hong Kong

Abstract

Theoretical and experimental investigations of Nd:YAG laser drilling of liquid crystal polymers with and without glass fibre reinforcements were conducted. Theoretical model for quantitative prediction of the dimensions of the laser drilled hole has been established. The effects of pulse energy, duration, power intensity as well as the number of pulses on the depth of the drilled hole were demonstrated. The theoretical analysis has been verified by experiment. SEM examinations of the drilled holes revealed the possible removal mechanism of the glass fibre reinforced composite material during laser processing.

GLASS FIBRE REINFORCED LIQUID CRYSTAL POLYMER (LCP) COMPOSITES are newly developed material gaining popularity in industry owing partially to the low viscosity of the material which enables injection moulding to be performed with ease. More importantly, the inherent preferred orientation of the extended molecular structure can be tailored to offer many distinct properties like excellence shock and impact resistance which are actually superior than many other types of glass fibre reinforced engineering resins. However, previous works have shown that the machinability of such materials was poor when using conventional techniques [1-6]. Though, water jet cutting can normally yield a clean cut surface, it still presents the problem of breaking the chain structure of the moulded parts. Clearly, laser cutting is an alternative which has the advantages of no tool wear, high cutting speed with no breaking of chain structure [7-10]. Previously, both continuous and pulsed laser have been employed to machine glass and kevlar composites as well as other polymer based materials. However, despite of their great potentials in

success machining of these exotic materials, there remain few studies on the theoretical analysis of laser machining of polymer based composites. It is obvious that in laser processing of polymer composites, the matrix material and the filler material will be removed via different modes, thus making the whole analysis to be not simple. Nevertheless, in order to achieve high quality and high productivity with laser cutting, it is necessary to establish the theoretical basis on the machining process. This paper presents a drilling analysis on a LCP composite which enables the depth of cut to be related to the various laser parameters.

Theoretical Background

In laser drilling of polymer based composites, it is assumed that the material of the hole is removed through decomposition, ejection of melt and perhaps vaporization. Since, the disintegrate temperature of the filler is normally much higher than that of the matrix material they will be removed via different ways. Nonetheless, it can be assumed that the average energy needed for removing an unit micro-volume of the composite material is constant. Assuming, also, the heat to be quasistationary and ignoring the interaction between the expelled material and the incident beam.

Furthermore, in single pulse drilling the "machined" hole is considered to have a depth h and consists of m equal-spaced layers, with each layer takes a time of τ_i (i from 1 to m) to disintegrate. Taking the power intensity at the centre of the laser beam to be I_i at the depth of ih/m, then:

$$\sum_{i=1}^{m} \tau_i = \tau \qquad (1)$$

$$kSI_i\tau_i = SC_m\frac{h}{m} \qquad (2)$$

$$I_i R_i^2 = I_0 R_0^2 \qquad (3)$$

$$R_i^2 = R_0^2 + (\theta \frac{i}{m} h)^2 \qquad (4)$$

where τ is the single pulse duration, S is the micro-area, K is a parameter which relates to the laser absorptivity of the material, R_i and R_0 are the laser spot radii at the position ih/m below the focal plane and at the focal plane respectively, C_m is the average energy required for removing an unit volume of the material, and θ represents the laser beam divergence. Hence,

$$\tau_i = \frac{C_m h}{k I_0 R_0^2 m}[R_0^2 + (\theta \frac{i}{m} h)^2] \qquad (5)$$

$$\sum_{i=1}^{m} \tau_i = \frac{C_m h}{k I_0 R_0^2}[R_0^2 + \frac{1}{m}(\theta h)^2 \sum_{i=1}^{m}(\frac{i}{m})^2] \qquad (6)$$

$$\tau = \lim_{m \to \infty} \sum_{i=1}^{m} \tau_i$$
$$= \frac{C_m h}{k I_0 R_0^2}[R_0^2 + \frac{1}{3}(\theta h)^2] \qquad (7)$$

when $R_0 \ll \theta h$, and taking W to be the laser power for a single pulse then equation (7) can be reduced to:

$$h = [\frac{3 k I_0 R_0^2 \tau}{C_m \theta^2}]^{\frac{1}{3}}$$
$$= [\frac{6 k W \tau}{\pi C_m \theta^2}]^{\frac{1}{3}} \qquad (8)$$

Thus, from equation (8), the relationship between the depth of cut and the number of pulses can be established:

$$h_n = [\frac{6 k W n \tau}{\pi C_m \theta^2}]^{\frac{1}{3}}$$
$$= h_1 n^{\frac{1}{3}} \qquad (9)$$

Now, according to the nature of a Gaussian beam:

$$I(r,z) = I(0,z) \exp(\frac{-2 r^2}{R^2}) \qquad (10)$$

$$R^2 = R_0^2 + (\theta z)^2 \qquad (11)$$

$$I_0 R_0^2 = I(0,z) R^2 \qquad (12)$$

where $I(0,z)$, $I(r,z)$ and R represent the power intensity at the center, the intensity at a distance r from the center and the beam radius at the depth of z respectively. Since, the maximum depth, h_{ex}, is reached when the threshold power intensity, I_t, is established at the end of the n_{ex}th pulse, substituting Eq.(11) and (12) into (10), and recognizing that $I(0,h_{ex}) = I_t$, the following result is obtained:

$$h_{ex} = \frac{R_0}{\theta}[\frac{k I_0}{I_t} - 1]^{\frac{1}{2}}$$
$$\approx \frac{R_0}{\theta}[\frac{k I_0}{I_t}]^{\frac{1}{2}} \qquad when I_0 \gg I_t \qquad (13)$$

and the number of pulses needed for maximum depth drilling can then be written as:

$$n_{ex} = [\frac{h_{ex}}{h_1}]^3$$
$$= \frac{\pi R_0^3 k^{\frac{1}{2}} C_m}{6 W \tau \theta}[\frac{I_0}{I_t}]^{\frac{3}{2}} \qquad (14)$$

To verify the validity of the above equations, a series of experiments have been carried out.

Experiment

An unreinforced LCP which was a wholly aromatic copolyester and the corresponding glass fibre reinforced LCP which contains 30 volume percent of glass fibre were used in this study. The specimens having a dimensions of $150 \times 73 \times 1.2 mm$ were prepared by injection moulding with a mould design in a such way that the extended chain of the orientated molecules were along the longitudinal axis of the specimen.

Laser drilling was conducted on a pulsed Nd:YAG laser with pulse duration ranging from $2 ms$ to $12 ms$, frequency from 5 to $60 Hz$ and pulse energy from $4J$ to $40J$. The laser system was set up to give a theoretical focal spot radius of $0.04 mm$ and the beam divergence of $0.1225 rad$.

For both single pulse and multipulse drilling, two flat specimens were carefully clamped together and holes were drilled along the parting line between the two clamped faces, with the incidence beam set perpendicular to the fibre orientation. A coaxial air jet of pressure of $0.2 MPa$ was utilized in all the experiments.

Results and Discussion

Single Pulse Drilling. Figures 1 and 2 compare the experimental results of the relationship between the depth of the drilled hole and the pulse energy to that as predicted by equation (8) for the reinforced and unreinforced material respectively. Equation(8) presents the fact that in single pulse drilling the depth of the drill is a function of the product of the laser power and the pulse duration. This implies that the final depth of the hole does not depend explicitly on the power or the duration of the laser pulse but rather the total energy alone. However, results presented in Figure 1 and Table 1 indicate differently: an increase in pulse duration from $2ms$ to $12ms$ resulted in a 15% increase in the depth of the hole, i.e. the longer the duration, the deeper would be the hole.

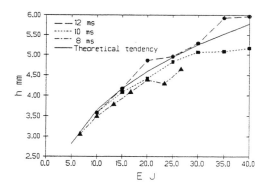

Figure 1. Depth of hole vs. laser output energy with various pulse durations: 8, 10 and 12 ms. Theoretical tendency curve is derived from Eq.(8).

Table 1. Effect of pulse duration on the depth of the drilled hole, with a constant energy output.

Energy output 8 J/pulse					
τ ms	2	4	6	8	10	12
h mm	3.05	3.23	3.22	3.22	3.41	3.46

The discrepancy found between the theory and the experiment is believed due to the fact that in the proposed model effects like the interaction between the laser beam and the disintegrated material is largely ignored. Clearly, a longer pulse duration would mean a reduction in the power intensity of the beam, and correspondingly the volume of the disintegrated material will be reduced. In other words, with less disintegrated material involved in the screening process a higher power intensity could have obtained at the bottom of the hole, and hence an increase in the depth of the hole.

Figures 3 and 4 simply illustrate the effect of pulse energy on the depth of the hole of the reinforced material: within the range of study a higher pulse energy always yield a deeper hole and is according to equation (8).

Multipulse Drilling. The relationship between the depth of the hole, h_n, and the number of pulses is presented in Figure 5, and the experimental results obtained are very close to that as predicted by Equation (9) of which h_n is a function of h_1, i.e., the depth of the hole drilled by a single pulse and n, the number of pulses. As the parameters k and C_m deduced from Eq.(9) were calculated by using the measured value h_1 which would be less than that obtained in the ideal condition where no interactions between the beam

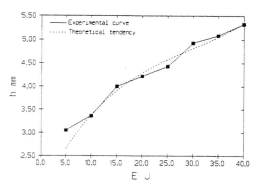

Figure 2. Depth of hole vs. output energy with pulse duration = $12ms$ for the unreinforced material.

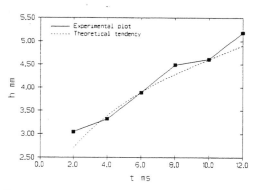

Figure 3. Effect of pulse duration on depth of hole with constant power intensity $I = 99.5 \times 10^6$ W/cm^2 of the reinforced material.

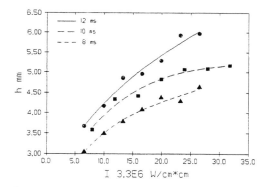

Figure 4. Relationship between the depth of the hole and the power intensity for different pulse durations of the reinforced material.

and the disintegrated material is assumed. As a result, the achievable value of h_n was underestimated and caused the theoretical tendency curve to be displaced below that of the experimental data. Moreover, this is an accumulative effect, therefore, as the number of pulses increases, the bigger will be the differences between the two curves. Nevertheless, there is no doubt that the depth of the hole that can be reached in practice can not be greater than the true theoretical value because of the screening of the irradiance and other influences which occur in reality.

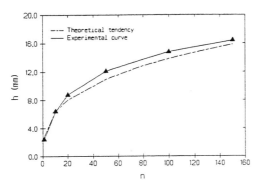

Figure 5. Depth of hole vs. number of pulses of the reinforced material with $E=5J$, $\tau=4\ ms$.

SEM Analysis. Figures 6 and 7 show the surface features of a multipulse drilled hole of the reinforced and the unreinforced materials respectively. As for the reinforced specimen in position near the bottom of the hole, fractured glass fibers are found in the melted back matrix surface. This phenomenon is likely due to the fact that the melting and the disintegration temperature of the glass fibre is much higher than that of the matrix itself, and the energy reaching the bottom of the hole is not high enough to disintegrate the fibres entirely. This effect causes the glass fibers to stand out of the melted back matrix. Subsequently, the protruded fibers can be easily cracked by stresses which can be generated either by the flux of the gas jet and/or by means of thermal effects. The fragmented fibers will then be expelled from the hole, and some of the fractured fibre stems are shown here in Figure 6(a).

Considering the situation at the mid-height of the hole, SEM photo Figure 6(b) shows that both the matrix and the glass fibers were disintegrated. This indicates that at the middle position the incident energy is high enough to disintegrate both the matrix and the glass fibers. Looking now at the entrance regions of the hole where glass fibers resemble a mushroom morphology. This is likely due to the prolong exposure of laser radiation in this region causing the matrix material to be melted and expelled by the assistance of the gas jet; but on the other hand, the energy is only high enough to melt the fibre into droplets.

The Physical Constant of I_t, k and C_m. Undoubtedly, the three parameters I_t, k and C_m are the key figures required for predicting not only the depth of the laser drilled hole but are also the material constants vitally important for the determining of the entire profile of the hole. However, it is considered to be difficult to obtain these three parameters from a theoretical point of view based on the known physical and chemical properties of the material. In the present proposed model it is assumed that the three parameters do not change with the drilling conditions. This assumption appears to be valid as was verified by the good agreement between the calculated and the experimental results.

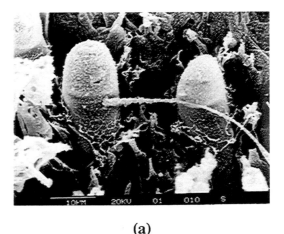

(a)

(b)

(c)

Figures 6(a-c). SEM photos of a drilled hole in the reinforced material with 10 pulses, $E=5J$, $\tau=4ms$, (a) bottom, (b) mid-height, and (c) mouth regions.

Conclusion

This investigation proved that quantitative analysis of

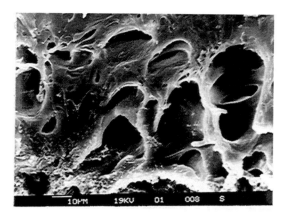

Figure 7. SEM photo of a drilled hole in the unreinforced material with 10 pulses, $E=40J$, $\tau=12ms$.

Nd:YAG laser drilling of liquid crystal polymer and its composite is achievable. From the study, it can be concluded that:

1. The theoretical equations developed are considered to be reasonable for determining the depth of the laser machined hole, processed by using both single and multipulse conditions.

2. The depth of the hole are primarily controlled by the total energy of the laser pulse, but can be affected slightly by changing the pulse duration.

3. In the case of the reinforced material, the surface morphology of the drilled hole appears differently at various sections of the hole. This phenomenon is considered to be attributed to the uneven energy distribution in the hole and the interaction between the gas jet and the disintegrated material.

4. Glass fibers in polymer based composites can be disintegrated via vaporization, by the actions of the gas jet and other disintegrated products generated during laser processing.

Reference

[1] Ho-Cheng, H., Dharan, C. K. H., Machining Composites Presented at the Winter Annual Meeting of ASME, Chicago, IL, USA Nov 27-Dec 2, 1988.

[2] Obraztsov, I. F., Tomashevskii, V. T., Mechanics of Composite Materials, v 23 n 4 p486-493(Jan 1988).

[3] A. Di Ilio, V. Tagliaferri, F. Veniali, J. Mach. Tools Manufact. v 31 n 2, p155-165(1991).

[4] T. Nagao, Y. Hatamura, Annals. CIRP 37, 79 (1988).

[5] N. L. Hancox, IN Handbook of Composite Materials, v 4, Fabrication of Composites (Edited by A. Kelly and S. T. Mileiko), p1-44, North-holland, Amsterdam(1983).

[6] W. KÖnig, P. Graß, Ch. Wulf and H. Willerscheid, Annals. CIRP 34(1985).

[7] N. Ryklin, A. Uglov, A. Kokora, "Laser Machining and Welding," Ergamon Press, (1978).

[8] C.Y Jiang, W.S Lau, T.M. Yue and L. Chiang," On the Maximum Depth and Profile of Cut in Pulsed Nd:YAG Laser Machining," To be Published in Annals. CIRP 42, (1993).

[9] A. Di Ilio, V. Tagliaferri, I. Crivelli Visconti, LAMP'87, Osaka, Japan(May 1987).

[10] Chryssolouris, G. Sheng, P. Choi, W. C., Machining Composites Presented at the Winter Annual Meeting of ASME, Chicago, IL, USA Nov 27-Dec 2, 1988.

Proceedings of the ASM 1993 Materials Congress, Pittsburgh, Pennsylvania, October 17-21, 1993

Drilling of Partially Stabilized Zirconia with Ultrasonic Machining

C. Cruz
Universidade Federal de Uberlandia and CNPq
Brazil

K. P. Rajurkar, B. Wei
University of Nebraska
Lincoln, Nebraska

Abstract

This paper reports the results of ultrasonic drilling of Partially Stabilized Zirconia (PSZ). The performance measures considered in this experimental research include material removal rate, feed rate, and surface roughness. A state-of-the-art machine with both conventional ultrasonic (USM) and rotary ultrasonic (RUM) machining capabilities was utilized. A comparison of material removal rates (MRR) obtained for Alumina and PSZ under the same conditions is also presented. A fracture toughness study was done to help gain an insight into how these processes affected surface integrity. This paper also includes some suggestions for improving the machining of PSZ in future research.

ZIRCONIA-BASED CERAMICS have shown a dazzling development recently. Until a decade ago, zirconia would not have been considered a candidate as an engineering ceramic because its polymorphism can lead to large strains and self-fracturing. It has always been used in refractories and the glass industry. Progress in the study of the crystallography and, in particular, the mechanism of the phase changes, has placed this material in the forefront of ceramic applications [1]. The development of so-called Partially Stabilized Zirconia (ZrO_2 PSZ), which contains dimorphous (monoclinic and tetragonal) crystals, has led to the achievement of a high value of toughness (at least 10 $MN/m^{3/2}$) [2]. This has not been observed in other ceramics [3]. ZrO_2(PSZ) is especially useful in more demanding environments due to its increased strength and thermal shock resistance by the stress generated from the dimorphous structure. Because high densities can be achieved at moderate temperatures, the solid artifact contains large amounts of metastable tetragonal modification which not only results in very high toughness and modulus of rupture but, even more significantly, bestows an excellent resistance to crack initiation. The fine powders needed to ensure metastability lend themselves well to forming by cold isostatic pressing or to conventional slip casting. Examples of ZrO_2(PSZ) applications include cutting tools, cutters, ball mill balls, nozzles, dies, and sleeve parts [2]. As a lightweight material with a low coefficient of friction, it is being used in wire drawing dies, in diesel engines as cylinder liners, as complete turbocharger components, and as a toughening agent in other ceramic systems [1].

The improved toughness that makes ZrO_2(PSZ) ceramics attractive from a product performance standpoint poses a great challenge on machining process when precise size and shape are required. As often observed in machining ceramics, existing machining processes have rather limited capabilities in meeting the demanding requirements of tight tolerances, low cost, and high reliability [4]. For instance, conventional machining of ceramics can be up to 80% of the total manufacturing cost in many cases [5]. On the other hand, ceramics are often highly sensitive to microscopic defects. As a result, parts rejected as faulty account for no less than 50% of the present cost of ceramic components [1]. With an increased toughness in such ceramics as ZrO_2(PSZ), more machining difficulties are expected. There is an acute need in studying alternative machining technologies which are capable and cost-effective. Among different traditional and nontraditional machining processes, Ultrasonic Machining processes hold promise in providing a great ability to process hard and brittle materials with desired performance in surface integrity, precision, and material removal rate [5-8]. Low cutting pressures found in USM cause little surface damage and, therefore, insignificant strength reduction. Two types of ultrasonic processes exist - the conventional Ultrasonic Machining (USM) and Rotary Ultrasonic Machining (RUM). Figure 1 shows the schemes of the two processes.

(a)

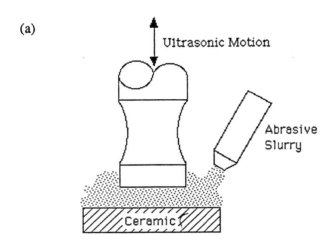

(b)

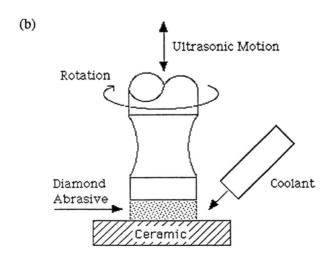

Fig. 1 - Schematic view of ultrasonic machining processes (a) USM (b) RUM

In USM, the tool vibrates ultrasonically in the direction of the tool feed. The abrasive slurry is pumped in the gap between the tool and the workpiece. Material removal occurs when the abrasive grits suspended in the slurry are propelled by the impact from the vibrating tool and strike the workpiece. RUM is generally the same as USM except that a rotating tool electrode is used. In some RUM systems the rotating tool is impregnated with diamond abrasives while others still use slurry carrying abrasive grits. While both processes have proven to be effective in drilling and even milling operations if the material is brittle rather than ductile, most of the available reports indicate that RUM is more versatile and efficient than conventional USM [9].

The study presented in this paper attempts to extend application of the ultrasonic processes to machining $ZrO_2(PSZ)$ which is known for its superb toughness. Experiments were conducted at different parameter levels on a state-of-the-art ultrasonic machine. Comparative studies were carried out both between RUM and USM of $ZrO_2(PSZ)$, and are contrasted with the results from machining an Alumina (Al_2O_3) ceramic, which is less tough than $ZrO_2(PSZ)$. Process characteristics (material removal rate, feed rate, and surfaces roughness) were examined and discussed along with a strength test that helps give an insight into the surface integrity of the machined surfaces.

Experiments

The experiments were conducted on an Extrude Hone SoneX ultrasonic machine which has both USM and RUM capabilities. The workpiece material is Mg-PSZ (97% ZrO_2, 3% MgO), and Al_2O_3 (96% pure) produced by the Hot Pressure (HP) process. The dimensions of these test pieces and the ultrasonic tools are described in Figures 2 and 3, respectively. Experimental conditions used in this experiment are shown in Table 1. Three key parameters were selected: abrasive size, tool vibration amplitude, and pressure, with each parameter having two levels. The parameter combinations were classified as *Moderate* or *Aggressive* for the convenience of analysis. It should be noted that the parameters of abrasive size and amplitude are strongly related, since a larger abrasive size requires a larger amplitude.

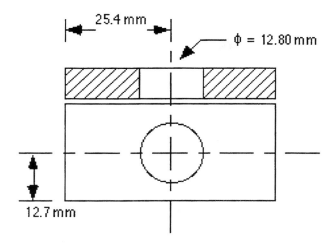

Fig. 2 - Workpiece dimensions.

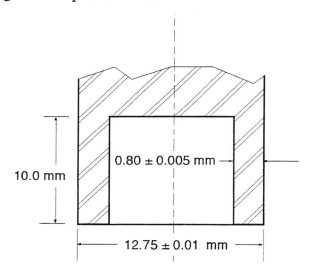

Fig. 3 - General tool dimensions.

Table 1. Qualitative Machining Conditions

USM & RUM (1000 RPM) Machining Conditions				
Parameter	Conditions			
	Moderate		Aggressive	
	M +	M -	A -	A +
Abrasive Size	320 mesh	320 mesh	150 mesh	150 mesh
Amplitude (µm)	20	20	40	40
Pressure (MPa)	0.35	0.46	0.35	0.46

The tool vibration frequency in both USM and RUM was fixed at 20 Khz and the tool rotation speed in RUM was held at 1000 rpm during machining. A 40% concentration (by weight) of B_4C abrasive slurry was supplied at a constant flowrate of 44 ml per second at all test levels. The total number of samples used in this study were 16 (that is, [2 materials] x [4 conditions] x [2 processes]).

Surface roughness of workpieces before machining was measured and the results were R_a = 0.75 µm for Alumina and R_a = 0.20 µm for Zirconia. The effects of the experimental machining conditions, especially the abrasive size, will be related to the surface roughness values after machining.

Evaluation criteria in this experiment include Feed Rate (FR), Material Removal Rate (MRR), Surface Roughness (SR), and Flexural Strength (FS).

Results and Discussions

Material Removal Rate and Feed Rate. The MRR for each test condition is obtained by measuring the weight of the workpiece before and after machining. Figures 4 and 5 show the measured MRR for RUM and USM of both Alumina and the ZrO_2(PSZ). From the two figures, it can be found that MRR is higher in the case of RUM compared to MRR in USM for both ceramic materials. RUM shows an MRR improvement of about 2-5 times that of conventional USM when using the Aggressive conditions. These values agree with other published results [10,11]. It is also clear that the MRR is higher for Alumina compared to PSZ when employing either process.

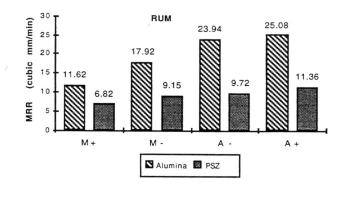

Fig. 4 - Material removal rates for Alumina and PSZ at different power levels of RUM.

125

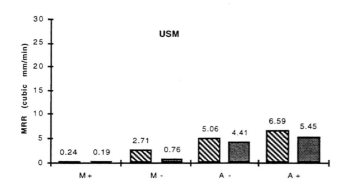

Fig. 5 - Material removal rates for Alumina and PSZ at different power levels of USM.

This can be seen in Table 2, where the ratios of MRR's for each treatment are obtained from figures 4 and 5.

Table 2. Ratios of material removal rates

	MRR Alumina / MRR PSZ			
Process	M+	M-	A-	A+
RUM	1.7	2.0	2.5	2.2
USM	1.3	3.6	1.2	1.2

It is apparent that RUM generally produces a greater MRR improvement than USM when comparing the chosen workpiece materials. However, when employing the Moderate M- condition, USM yields a greater difference in MRR between the two materials. This may be a sign of a threshold energy that needs to be applied in the MRR of PSZ. This also suggests the existence of multiple material removal mechanisms even when conventional USM is used [11]. This, of course, will need to be supported by further study of the actual material removal mechanism(s).

The feed rate considered in this work is measured in μm/cycle, where one cycle refers to the average of 11 seconds from which 8 seconds contribute to machining and the remaining 3 seconds is non-working time when the debris from the working zone is flushed away by the slurry. The feed rate measurements (taken at 8 second

intervals) were made by reading the digital indicator of the machine that indicates the actual position of the tool tip. The feed rate values are recorded for USM only at Aggressive (both A- and A+) conditions due to the difficulty in machining at Moderate conditions, whereas feed rate was recorded for all four conditions in the case of RUM. The comparative difference can be easily seen when looking at MRR as shown in the previous Figure 5.

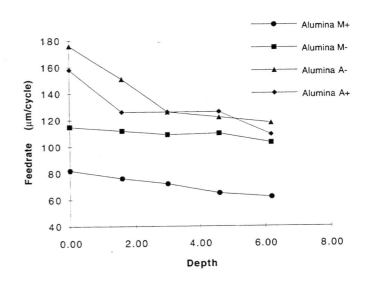

Fig. 6 - Feed rates for Alumina at different machining conditions of RUM.

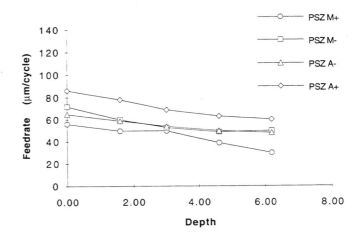

Fig. 7 - Feed rates for PSZ at different machining conditions of RUM.

126

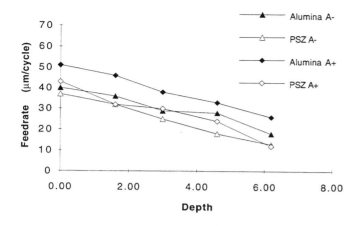

Fig. 8 - Feed rates for Alumina and PSZ at aggressive levels of USM.

From the Figures 6, 7 and 8, it is clear that the feed rate values are higher in the case of RUM compared to those of USM for both Alumina and PSZ. It is also apparent that the values of feed rate are decreasing with increasing depth. One of the more probable reasons for this effect is the change in effective pressure on the cut face. A change in cutting forces at the front of the cut will result due to the increased abrasion between the sides of the tool, slurry, and sides of the workpiece. In other words, the pressure applied to the tool is being transferred in a less efficient manner. Another probable reason for this declining feed rate may be that at increasing depths more of the workpiece "cut-out" is in the tool, adding to frictional forces. Also, an accumulation of slurry may find itself inside this area with constricted flow. The actual effect of this is difficult to consider because of the work cycle referred to previously.

By looking at Figure 6 for Alumina and Figure 6 for PSZ, it can be seen that the feed rate values are higher for Alumina than the less brittle PSZ. By comparing the Aggressive machining conditions for USM, it can be found that USM behaves similarly as RUM but at a slower feed rate and, consequently, a lower MRR. In comparing Figure 8 with the Aggressive data from Figures 6 and 7, one can catch a hint of a faster decline in feed rates when USM is used. Generally, the Aggressive feed rates drop to 70% at the end of the cut when RUM is used on these ceramics, but the drop is about 50% when USM is used

with the same Aggressive machining conditions.

Surface Integrity. Surface Integrity was studied in terms of surface roughness of the hole and fracture strength of the sample after machining. The surface roughness was measured in terms of R_a using a Mahr Perthen profilometer (Model C3A). The fracture strength was measured by a 3-point bending test using the Instron machine as shown in Figure 9.

Fig. 9 - Instron machine for 3-point bending test.

The results of the measured surface roughness are shown in Figures 10 and 11, and the Fracture Strength results are shown in Figure 12.

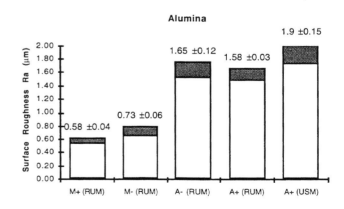

Fig. 10 - Surface roughness of Alumina by RUM and USM.

From figures 10 and 11, it can be found that surface roughness, R_a (µm), obtained for Alumina is higher compared to PSZ for different conditions using both RUM and USM. These Figures also indicate that the surface roughness obtained by conventional USM is higher than RUM.

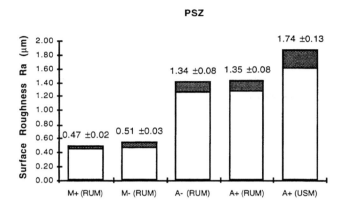

Fig. 11 - Surface roughness of PSZ by RUM and USM.

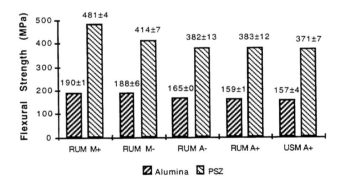

Fig. 12 - Flexural strength for Alumina and PSZ by RUM and USM.

This may be explained by the added rotation motion that acts on the sides of the cuts. This rotary motion, along with the slurry, provides a gentle machining condition that may have a polishing effect. As shown in Figure 12, the Flexural Strength of both materials decreases as the machining conditions switch from Moderate to Aggressive. This figure also suggests that RUM is less damaging to the surface compared to the USM process, since the flexural strengths of the materials machined by RUM are higher than the materials processed by USM at the same Aggressive condition.

Summary and Conclusion

Based on the experimentation done in this study, the general findings can be listed as follows:

1. The feed rate and MRR for both PSZ and Alumina are higher when using RUM than when using USM.
2. The feed rates and MRR for Alumina are higher than those for PSZ when using the same machining conditions.
3. Surface roughness values resulting from the RUM process are lower than the values from the conventional USM process.
4. The flexural strength of these ceramic materials processed by RUM is higher than the flexural strength provided by USM at the same conditions.

In summary, RUM promises to be superior to conventional USM in many respects but this study and related work show that both have their advantages. Combining both of these processes in stages will allow a machining environment having the benefits of both ultrasonic processes by simply modifying existing systems with the additional geometric motion of rotation. Adding this feature to existing equipment can only expand a unit's capabilities.

Acknowledgments

The authors would like to thank Extrude Hone Corp. (Irwin, PA) for the use of its facilities in this study. The authors also thank Associated Ceramics Technology (Sarver, PA) for providing ceramic workpieces. Assistance from Dave Diaz, Nooka S. Reddy, and Tom Grant of Nontraditional Manufacturing Research Center of University Nebraska-Lincoln in preparing the manuscript is highly appreciated.

References

[1] McColm I. J., "Ceramic Hardness", Plenum Press, New York (1990).

[2] Shigeyuki Somiya, "Advanced Technical Ceramics," Academic Press, Inc. (1989).

[3] Muller, J. I., American Ceramic Society Bulletin, 61, No. 8, 588-590 (1982).

[4] Stinton, D.P., "Assessment of the State of the Art in Machining and Surface Preparation of Ceramics," ORNL/TM - Report 10791, Oak Ridge National Laboratory, Tennessee, Nov. 1988.

[5] Sheppard, L. M., Machining of Advanced Ceramics, Advanced Materials and Processes Inc. Metal Progress 12/87.

[6] Deepak, Prabhakar and Haselkorn, Michael, Transactions of NAMRI/SME, Volume XX, 211-218 (1992).

[7] Cruz, C., Kozak, J., and Rajurkar, K.P., Annuls of X-CBCIMAT, Campinas Brazil, December, 1992.

[8] Gilmore Randy, International Manufacturing Technology Conference'90, Nontraditional Machining Chicago, Illinois, SME (1990).

[9] Komaraiah, M., MANAN, M. A., Narasimha Reddy, P., and Victor, S., Precision Engineering, Vol. 10, No. 2, 59-65, April, 1988.

[10] Kainth, G. S., Nandy, Amitav, Singh, Kuldeep, International Journal of Machine Tools, Vol. 19, 33-41 (1979).

[11] Komaraiah, M. and Narasimha Reddy, P., International Journal of Production Research, Volume 29, No. 11, 2177-2187 (1991).

Production Drilling Models for a Composite Material

H. R. Leep, D. L. Herde
University of Louisville
Louisville, Kentucky

Abstract

The objective of this research was to develop mathematical models which predict tool wear based on measured cutting forces. Machining parameters which were considered included cutting speed, feed rate, and workpiece hardness. This project established a procedure which could be extended to other machining processes, workpiece and tool materials, and cutting tool geometries. Drilling of composite materials is extremely important in the aerospace, automotive, electronic, and recreational products industries. The abrasive nature of composite materials makes them very difficult to machine. Blind holes, 6.35 mm (0.250 in.) in diameter, were drilled into an aluminum matrix composite containing 16-vol% alumina particles. This 6061 aluminum alloy composite was hardened and tempered to a T6 condition. Carbide-tipped drills and a synthetic cutting fluid with a 5-wt% concentration were used. In addition to varying the three machining parameters, the thrust along and the moment about the vertical axis of the drill were measured. The statistical analysis considered the five main factors. Drilling thrust, cutting moment, and workpiece hardness were significant in all three tests. Cutting speed and feed rate were significant in the model which combined all three tests with different speed/feed combinations and variations in workpiece hardness.

A COMPOSITE MATERIAL could be defined as "a material made from any two or more organic, inorganic, or metallic materials (1)." Structural composites are normally classified as being either a metal matrix composite (MMC) or a polymer matrix composite (PMC). Aluminum is a common matrix material for producing a MMC. The aluminum matrix material can be reinforced with fibers, whiskers, or particulates. Figure 1 shows different types of composite materials. By selecting the proper matrix material, reinforcing material, and manufacturing technology, it is possible to produce a MMC to meet specific design requirements (2).

In addition to the aluminum matrix material, magnesium is used as the basis for other commercially-popular MMC products. Other important matrix materials include titanium and copper alloys.

Casting, extrusion, rolling, and forging can be used to process a particle-reinforced MMC material (3). However, certain precautions must be exercised when working with this material. Pressures used to extrude a particle-reinforced aluminum must be higher than those used to extrude an unreinforced aluminum. Also, a particle-reinforced aluminum must be gently stirred during processing to prevent alumina reinforcing particles from precipitating (4).

Practically all surface metal treatments which are applied to unreinforced aluminum and magnesium alloys can be applied to finished MMC parts. Cook and Mohn successfully demonstrated that several of these treatments could be used (5).

When drilling a MMC material, a drill with a standard 118-degree included angle at the point can be used. The two major forces exerted on this type of twist drill include a linear thrust along the axis of rotation and into the workpiece, and a torsional moment about the axis of rotation (6).

A catastrophic event during machining, such as tool failure, can cause the machine tool to be damaged or scrapping of expensive finished workpieces (7). These events can be avoided by implementing an adaptive control system which requires real-time collection and analysis of data.

Several research projects involving the machining of composite materials have been conducted. Miller tested different point geometries of drills to be used in mass

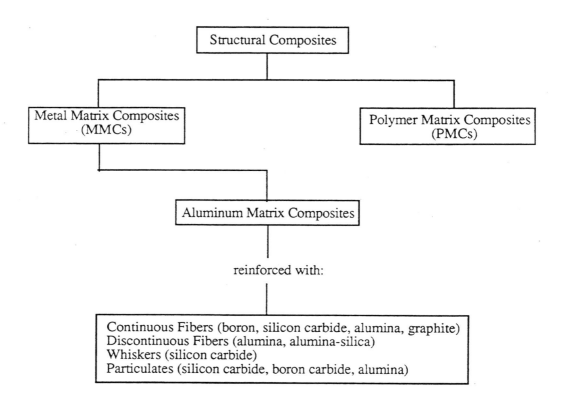

Fig. 1 - Different types of structural composite materials

production. The criteria were drill life and hole quality (8). Zieser also studied several drill-point geometries for carbide-tipped or solid-carbide drills used to machine extremely abrasive or hard materials (9).

Lambert examined the relationships involved in drilling composites. Some of the factors studied included tool life, drilling thrust, cutting moment, cutting speed, and feed rate (10). Rahdhakrishnan and Wu were interested in determining the best time to replace drills used to machine composites. They were able to relate hole quality to thrust, moment, speed, and feed (11).

Brun, Lee, and Gorsler conducted research on the turning of a 6061 aluminum matrix containing SiC particles. They were able to relate tool wear to the hardness of the tool materials, and recommended the use of polycrystalline diamond tools to reduce the number of required tool changes (12).

Tool-wear models based on measured cutting forces were developed by Leep and Peak for drilling a medium-carbon steel with a 9.525-mm (0.375-in.) drill and a titanium alloy with a 6.350-mm (0.250-in.) drill (13). Leep and Foley also generated tool wear models for the same workpiece material used in this study and solid-carbide drills with multifaceted

points (14).

In a similar study, Geary developed tool-wear models for a medium-carbon steel, a titanium alloy, and copper at different temperatures. All tests were run dry. Results from the study showed thrust to be significant in all models. Moment was significant in the models for the medium-carbon steel at the ambient temperature and the titanium alloy at the ambient temperature using a relatively high speed and a relatively high feed. The elevated temperature of the medium-carbon steel caused reductions in accumulated wear, average thrust, and average moment. Elevating the temperature of the titanium alloy produced a large reduction in the average moment (15).

The major objective of this research was to develop relationships which predict tool wear from measured cutting forces while drilling an aluminum matrix composite material containing Al_2O_3 particles. The cutting speed and feed rate were varied in order to generate predictive models for carbide-tipped drills with a diameter of 6.35 mm (0.250 in.). Regression analysis was used to develop the relationships between tool wear and drilling thrust, cutting moment, and workpiece hardness. A secondary objective was to determine the outer edge of the envelope associated with the cutting conditions for the tool geometry, tool material, and workpiece material used in this project.

Experimental Work

The tests were conducted on a computer numerical control (CNC) milling machine. This machine tool had a positioning accuracy of ±0.0203 mm (±0.0008 in.) and a positioning repeatability of ±0.0076 mm (±0.0003 in.). A computer-assisted part-programming system was used to develop the tool path for drilling the hole pattern. Programmed feed rates were easily changed with the editor.

A MMC, consisting of a 6061 aluminum matrix with 16-vol% Al_2O_3 particles, was used as the workpiece material. This material was hardened and tempered to a T6 condition. Cylindrical blanks were prepared from extruded bar stock which had a diameter of 5.08 cm (2.00 in.). The finished height of each cylinder was 3.175 cm (1.250 in.).

The hole pattern consisted of 19 holes with 12 holes on the outer circle, six holes on the inner circle, and one hole in the center. A total of 38 holes were drilled into each cylinder, with 19 on the top and 19 on the bottom. Each blind hole was 6.35 mm (0.250 in.) in diameter and 12.70 mm (0.500 in.) deep to the shoulders of the drills. The minimum wall thickness between holes was 3.175 mm (0.1250 in.). Before drilling the test holes, the 19 hole positions were center drilled to minimize flexing of the test drill.

The drilling sequence skipped around the hole configuration to eliminate any heat build up during the drilling operation. Only the holes on the inner circle were used when recording cutting-force and tool-wear measurements. This procedure was followed in order to eliminate the effects of any radial variations in workpiece hardness.

The average surface hardness of the MMC material was 64.9 HRC. This average hardness was based on the hardness next to the 47 test holes on the cylinders used for the three tests.

Carbide-tipped, jobber-length, twist drills, with a standard 118-degree included angle, were used to drill the MMC material. The drill diameter was 6.35 mm (0.250 in.). Drills with straight flutes were tried in the preliminary study, but they had a tendency to break after drilling only a few holes when the recommended cutting conditions were tried.

A commercially available synthetic cutting fluid was used at a concentration of 5 wt%. The tradename of this cutting fluid was CIMTECH®400 (Cincinnati Milacron). The synthetic lubricant in the concentrate of this cutting fluid was recommended for heavy-duty machining and grinding operations, including those on MMC aluminum alloys.

Molmans and Compton reported that an early version of this heavy-duty synthetic cutting fluid was compared to a heavy-duty cutting oil, heavy-duty soluble oil, and heavy-duty semisynthetic cutting fluid in an extensive international laboratory and in-house machine tool testing program (16). The field test results indicated that in drilling, turning, and grinding operations performed on several different types of steel, the heavy-duty synthetic cutting fluid was superior to the other three cutting fluids.

Tool wear on the multifaceted drills was measured with a toolmaker's microscope. This microscope had a magnification factor of 30X, and the digital readouts displayed the stage movements within an accuracy of 0.001 mm. Accumulated tool wear was measured every 3 to 16 holes during the first 101 holes of a test, or until the drill failed. Then, if the test were continued, measurements were usually taken every 19 holes. Tool wear was measured along the margin at the outside end of each cutting edge. Each time tool wear was measured, the average of the measurements associated with the two cutting edges was recorded.

The drilling thrust along and cutting moment about the z-axis were measured using a dynamometer with piezoelectric crystals in the platform. The forces in the x-y plane were minimized by center drilling first. A data acquisition system (DAS) converted the electrical charges from the dynamometer into information processed by a computer. Analog signals from the dynamometer were amplified before being converted into digital signals.

Software was developed for collecting and processing the raw data from the dynamometer. A routine was written to smooth the curves representing thrust and moment. After observing the curves for thrust and moment from the first few holes drilled, the following parameters were selected: threshold, jump, and smooth. These parameters were monitored for changes and adjusted accordingly. Each curve was smoothed by eliminating the points before and after the drilling process. The "threshold" level was chosen as approximately 50% of the thrust or moment from the section of the curve where drilling started. The "number of points to jump" was the number of sample points to skip after the threshold value was crossed. This parameter eliminated the points before the "linear" section of the curve. The "number of points to smooth" specified the data points to be included in the calculation of the average thrust or moment.

Each test was continued until enough holes were drilled to develop an accurate model, tool wear reached a critical stage, or the drill failed. The development of relationships which predicted tool wear from measured cutting forces was the primary objective of this study.

The three drilling tests were performed at various speeds and feeds. The following cutting conditions were used for the three tests to determine the models:

Test 1: Low Speed of 88.9cm/s (175 ft/min) and High Feed of 0.381 mm/rev (0.015 in./rev).

Test 2: High Speed of 101.6 cm/s (200 ft/min) and Low Feed of 0.229 mm/rev (0.009 in./rev).

Test 3: High Speed of 101.6 cm/s (200 ft/min) and High Feed of 0.381 mm/rev (0.015 in./rev).

These speeds and feeds were also used to determine the outer edge of the envelope associated with the cutting conditions.

Results and Discussion

Results from the drilling tests were analyzed using the Statistical Analysis System (SAS) computer software package. The analysis included data from tool-wear, cutting-force, and surface-hardness measurements. Measurements were taken through the 234 holes drilled in Tests 1 and 2, and 101 holes drilled in Test 3. Some of the test results are summarized in Table I.

Regression analysis was used to develop three models from the test results for the machining parametric combinations of low speed/high feed, high speed/low feed, and high speed/high feed. Three other models were developed by pooling the data from the two tests at high speed, the two tests at high feed, and all three tests with variations in speed and feed to help explain the observed variance in tool wear.

The dependent variable was tool wear while the independent variables were drilling thrust, cutting moment, and workpiece hardness. These variables were used to develop each model using the main effects, square terms, and first-order interactions. When the data were pooled, cutting speed and feed rate were added along with the new square terms and first-order interactions.

SAS was used to perform the multiple classification analysis of variance (ANOVA) of the raw data. This procedure aided in determining which independent variables were significant at the 0.05 level. Using the backward elimination procedure, or backward regression, factors which were not significant were removed from each model, and a new model was generated. Backward regression began with all expected effects in the model, the model was then evaluated, and the least-significant effect was removed. Each time the model was evaluated, the least-significant effect was removed until all remaining effects were significant at the 0.05

level. The significance of the model and the sources of variation were determined by using an F-test, and the coefficient of multiple regression (R^2) was used to determine the percentage of variation in tool wear that could be explained by the independent variables.

The following nomenclature was used in developing the regression equations:

W = accumulated tool wear, mm
T = thrust along the z-axis, N
M = moment about the z-axis, N-cm
H = Rockwell hardness of the workpiece, HRB
S = cutting speed, cm/s
F = feed rate, mm/rev

Criteria used to select the "best" models are summarized below:
1) The model was significant at the 0.05 level.
2) The independent variables were significant at the 0.05 level.
3) The coefficient of multiple regression was greater than 0.80 when possible.
4) The number of independent variables was reduced as much as possible.

Table II shows a summary of the significant main effects in each model. The values of R^2 are also presented.

These results can be compared to the results obtained by Leep and Foley. They used the same workpiece material, drill diameter, and cutting fluid.

However, they used solid-carbide drills with multifaceted points. As in five of the models developed in this project, drilling thrust was significant at the 0.05 level. When Leep and Foley pooled the data from their three tests, they also found that the drilling thrust and cutting speed were significant at the 0.05 level.

These results can also be compared to those obtained by Leep and Peak. They used the same cutting fluid, but developed a model for a medium-carbon-steel workpiece and a 9.525-mm (0.375-in.) high-speed steel (HSS) drill with conventional-point drill geometry and a model for a titanium-

Table I. Summary of some drilling test results

Test No.	Cutting speed cm/s (ft/min)		Feed rate mm/rev (in./rev)		No. of holes	Comment
1	88.9	175	0.381	0.015	234	Wear = 0.161 mm (0.00634 in.)
2	101.6	200	0.229	0.009	234	Wear = 0.193 mm (0.00760 in.)
3	101.6	200	0.381	0.015	115	Drill shattered

Table II. Summary of significant main effects

Cutting conditions	Significant main effects	R^2
Low speed/high feed	T,M,H	0.63
High speed/low feed	T,M,H	0.97
High speed/high feed	T,M,H	0.81
High speed	T,M	0.84
High feed	M,H,S	0.71
All three tests	T,M,S,F	0.83

alloy workpiece and a 6.35-mm (0.250-in.) cobalt HSS drill with split-point drill geometry. Drilling thrust in these models was also significant at the 0.05 level.

Conclusions

The following conclusions were drawn from the results of the drilling tests using 6.35-mm (0.250-in.) carbide-tipped drills and an aluminum matrix composite containing 16-vol% alumina particles as the workpiece material. All six models were significant at the 0.05 level. The four models which incorporated high cutting speed had R^2 values greater than 0.80. Two models which incorporated high feed rate had R^2 values of 0.63 and 0.71. The effect of cutting moment was significant at the 0.05 or 0.10 levels in all six models. The effect of drilling thrust was significant at the 0.05 level in five models. The effect of workpiece hardness was significant at the 0.05 or 0.10 levels in four models. Cutting speed and feed rate were significant at the 0.05 and 0.10 levels, respectively, in the model for all test results.

Acknowledgment

The authors greatly appreciate the financial support provided for this research project by the National Science Foundation (EPSCoR Grant 87-57 # 13) through the University of Kentucky Research Foundation. We are grateful to Mr. Charles T. Lane, a materials engineer with Duralcan USA, a Division of Alcan Aluminum Corporation, for donating the MMC material. We also wish to thank Mrs. Linda A. Tarrence for typing the manuscript.

References

1 Lambert, B.K., Carbide Tool J., 19, 31-4 (1987).

2 Zweben, C., Carbide Tool J., 20, 7-10 (1988).

3 Hains, R.W., P.L. Morris and P.W. Jeffrey, in Proceedings Int. Symp. on Advanced Structural Materials, Montreal, Canada, 28-31 August 1988, pp 53-60.

4 "DURALCAN™ A Promise Fulfilled!" Duralcan USA, San Diego, California (1990).

5 Cook, J.L. and W.R. Mohn, "Engineered Materials Handbook," p 897, ASM International, Materials Park, Ohio (1987).

6 Friedrich, M.O., R.O. Burant and M.J. McGinty, Manuf. Eng., 83, 29, 31 (1979).

7 Mazoff, J., Mod. Mach. Shop, 62, 66-76 (1989).

8 Miller, J.A., Am. Mach. Autom. Manuf., 131, 70-1 (1987).

9 Zieser, W., Tool. Prod., 52, 64-6 (1986).

10 Lambert, B.K., Cutting Tool Eng., 39, 20-2 (1987).

11 Rahdhakrishnan, T. and S.M. Wu, J. Eng. Ind. Trans. ASME, 103, 119-25 (1981).

12 Brun, M.K., M. Lee and F. Gorsler, in Proceedings Int. Conf. on Wear of Materials, Vancouver, Canada, 14-18 April 1985, pp 539-44.

13 Leep, H.R. and M.A. Peak, Int. Coll. on Tribology 2000, Esslingen, Germany, 14-16 January 1992, pp 23.4-1 through 3.

14 Leep, H.R. and V.R. Foley, in Proceedings Int. Seminar and Applications Forum on a Systems Approach to Machining, Cincinnati, Ohio, 4-5 May 1993, pp 105-10.

15 Geary, Sr., C.R., "Effects of Workpiece Temperature on the Machinability of Metals," p 61, M.Eng. Thesis, Department of Industrial Engineering, University of Louisville, Louisville, Kentucky (1991).

16 Molmans, A.H.M. and M. Compton, Int. Coll. on Synth. Lubricants and Operational Fluids, Esslingen, West Germany, 10-12 January 1984, pp 40.1-5.

M. Mehta and A.H. Soni

Hole Quality, Drilling, Assessment and Integrity Issues in Graphite Fiber Reinforced Composite

Laminates: A Generalized Approach

An integrated drilling process development methodology has been proposed to address the diverse issues and factors influencing the quality of holes in production and repair of composite laminates. The approach has been applied and demonstrated on PMR-15/gr composite laminates. A simple index of fastener hole damage assessed from non-destructive tests on drilled panels has been developed, together with a set of accept/reject criteria.

Proceedings of the ASM 1993 Materials Congress, Pittsburgh, Pennsylvania, October 17-21, 1993

Hole Quality, Drilling, Assessment and Integrity Issues in Graphite Fiber Reinforced Composite Laminates: A Generalized Approach

M. Mehta, A. H. Soni
Environmental Research Institute of Michigan
Ann Arbor, Michigan

Abstract

The drilling and assurance of high integrity fastener holes in polymer matrix composite laminates presents numerous challenges to manufacturers and repair technologists alike. The generation of acceptable holes is based on a combination of material, process, tooling and inspection issues. The assessment of "acceptable" quality of holes, however, has yet to become an exact science due to the complexity of these interactions. An integrated drilling process development methodology has been developed to address these issues in a systematic manner.

The paper also discusses the application of the proposed methodology to a machinability test program undertaken with PMR-15/gr laminates, which included the identification of optimum drilling process and tooling conditions for fastener holes. Hole quality was first assessed visually, then measured using both geometric and processing response parameters, and finally validated by use of ultrasonic C-scans and photomicrographic sectioning. Based on C-scan image enhancements of damaged areas in panels, a simple index for measuring structural integrity of drilled holes was developed, called the "damage ratio".

COMPOSITE MATERIALS have been engineered to offer very high strength-to-weight and stiffness-to-weight ratios, to withstand high temperatures and be corrosion resistant - attributes which increase their attractiveness as metal substitutes in the aerospace industry. Despite a strong desire to utilize composites in fabrication of structural products, use of these materials has been limited primarily because of the lack of process models, lack of widely distributed property and processing databases, and the absence of rapid and efficient manufacturing techniques (1). Due to these shortcomings, newer aircraft structural

parts using organic matrix composites are often overdesigned to compensate for the scatter in material properties and possible undetected damage during manufacture or in-service - a practice which contributes in large part to the high cost of fabrication of composites, which, in turn, has prevented their widespread use, as well as severely impacted an already recessed raw materials supplier base.

Machining is an essential finishing process on many near-net-shape manufactured composite laminate parts. Unlike metals, for which standard, validated machining practices and quality requirements are well documented, the machining of fiber-reinforced polymer composites often is a trial and error process (2, 3) due to a lack of adequate technology and tooling. The problem is far from trivial as the machinability relations developed for metals are not known to apply in this case, making it necessary to establish different machining and tooling regimes, commensurate with their physical properties and desired finish quality. The assessment of "acceptable" quality holes has yet to become an exact science. A number of issues have contributed to this 'technology void'.

The aim of the present research was to develop an integrated hole drilling, testing and acceptance methodology, and thereby provide a more comprehensive evaluation of the processing, tooling, materials and quality mechanisms involved during drilling of carbon fiber reinforced polymer matrix laminates. Using PMR-15/gr as the test material, the research addresses a long-felt need for development of a test methodology which directly relates information on machinability of a composite with service performance and integrity of the structure. Such an integrated test methodology, if available, would permit a more realistic appraisal of the consequences of departure from non-optimality in hole fabrication. It needs to reconcile hole performance requirements with the tooling and process parameters involved, as well as address the technology for assessing hole quality. In addition to development of process automation, the availability of detailed information on the machinability and damage tolerance of PMR-15/graphite and similar composite laminates would promote their application in primary and secondary composite structures. This paper attempts to facilitate such information transfer by applying the proposed methodology for developing a set of accept/reject criteria for fastener holes in PMR-15/gr laminates.

Key Issues and Industry Concerns

The **material and process related problems** encountered in drilling of carbon fiber reinforced thermoset PMC laminates include (4):

- surface delamination,
- internal inter-ply delamination,
- splintering and fraying,
- fiber/resin pullout,
- high, localized heat generation in tool and workpiece, causing debonding between fiber and resin,
- abrasive wear on tooling, and
- creation of hazardous dust.

The adverse effect on tool life, and hence, cost, is already well known. Tool life that is 1/100 of that for drilling comparable holes in ferrous metals is commonly encountered (5).

Many of these process and quality problems are directly traceable to the use of **non-optimal cutting tool designs and machining conditions** (6). Current drill designs being applied by industry for drilling composites, were originally developed for metal removal applications, and do not take into account the differences in properties of the homogenous and non-homogenous work materials (7). The majority of drilling operations on critical airframe and aeroengine composite parts are carried out using variants of the conventional high speed steel twist drill, invented by Samuel Morse. Only in recent years have airframers and cutting tool manufacturers begun developing tool geometries specifically for drilling of composite laminates. An improvement in cutting tool design and process conditions can yield gains far in excess of those obtained through a change to a premium tool material such as polycrystalline diamond (PCD), whose cost can be quite prohibitive, apart from its high susceptibility to damage).

The mechanism of interaction between the tool and the composite laminate during drilling is not completely known since the available experimental and theoretical investigations are few, and have not been strictly addressed to this goal. More importantly, perhaps, the impact of process and quality anomalies on in-service performance of drilled holes has not been addressed in sufficient detail to build contractor confidence in the use of fasteners for assembly and repair of composite laminates. There is a clear need in the industry for a realistic process and quality specification which defines the limits of acceptable hole quality for laminates reinforced with carbon fibers.

Current hole quality standards being applied to composite laminates were adopted directly from existing standards and specifications for metals, with little regard for the obvious mechanical and rheological differences between the materials. Additionally, it has not been conclusively investigated to what extent process specifications applicable to graphite/epoxy and boron/epoxy laminates may apply to other thermoset resin composites. Since it is known that PMR-15 resin has physical and chemical properties far different from those of epoxy, it is likely that the qualifying standards for machined components may be significantly different too, particularly in situations requiring endurance at high temperatures. As there is little engineering test data and service experience on aircraft parts made from structural composites, industry has chosen to overdesign parts, establishing rather stringent hole quality requirements for all such composites. It has not been substantiated yet in case of PMR-15/graphite whether present process and geometric tolerances are tight or lax. The development of a customized, accurate process and hole quality specification for this thermoset would benefit industry by way of increased confidence in use of fasteners for repair, reduced assembly fabrication/ machining cost, and economy of effort. This, in turn, would encourage greater substitution with PMR-15/gr among composite repair technologists, and vendors of aerospace components. Many of the issues involved in hole drilling for mechanical repair of PMR-15/gr laminates have been addressed in Reference (8).

Hole quality assessment and classification in laminates is virtually unreliable at present, except with use of expensive and time-consuming techniques. In the present investigation, an attempt has been made to correlate important non-destructive test information yielded about a hole (as by ultrasonic C-scans) to the actual static and dynamic load carrying ability of the hole. A method using non-destructively measured parameters of hole quality has been applied to the assessment and classification of drilled hole quality achievable over a wide range of machining conditions explored.

Integrated Process Development Methodology

The holemaking quality concerns and issues highlighted above are highly coupled with one another. It would be considerably difficult, if not impossible, to address any one issue independent of the others. Hence, an integrated machinability-cum-structural integrity-assessment and testing strategy has been developed to address the industry concerns raised above. Illustrated in Figure 1, it consists of three main components:

(1) **Machinability Testing:** Optimization of the process of generation of fastener holes in a composite laminate by methods and tools that result in 'acceptable' holes is the first component of the generalized methodology for drilling process development in composites.

(2) **Structural Integrity Testing:** This consists of damage tolerance testing to study the extent to which composite structures are tolerant of the type of flaws introduced by the machining process, and techniques for extending the structural life of these parts. It would be most beneficial to determine the minimal flaw sizes achievable in the manufacturing process, through the development and use of optimal tool geometries in machining, yet keeping processing costs at a minimum.

(3) **Quality Assessment:** All toughness-improvement developments in PMC engineered materials depend on meaningful and reliable measures of machinability and damage tolerance specific to composite laminates. This is sufficient justification for inclusion of hole quality assessment methods in the integrated methodology. Unfortunately, there has been little coordination between test-methods and standardization groups, resulting in an absence of universally standardized test methods in the composites industry (9). Until universally standardized tests are adopted by the industry, however, testing of composites will have to continue with the existing array of destructive and non-destructive methods.

The above approach is demonstrated in fastener hole drilling process development for PMR-15/gr composite, a high temperature resistant thermoset laminate.

Application to PMR-15/gr Laminates

Study Objectives: The main objectives of the program were to evaluate drills having different geometric configurations, and assess the quality trade-offs from use of non-optimal tooling when generating fastener holes in PMR-15/gr laminates.

The effectiveness of current non-destructive evaluation of drilled laminates by the ultrasonic C-scan technique was also studied, and area measurements used for obtaining more conclusive quality data by use of innovative quantitative image processing techniques.

Experimental Methods: A machinability test program was designed to evaluate four special purpose drills having different geomteries. Hole quality was assessed by performing geometric measurements and non-destructive evaluations on drilled panels. The results of the assessment were substantiated by performing a systematic series of static and residual mechanical property tests on hole anomalies in the composite.

Machinability Screening Tests and Measurements: PMR-15/gr test panels were fabricated from 16 plies of [0,90] woven graphite prepreg into laminates, with a total average thickness of 5.2 mm (0.204 in). They were ultrasonically C-scanned prior to machining.

A 2^4 factorial experiment was designed to investigate the following test variables identified from a literature review as being important in drilling, with blocking on drill geometry: cutting speed, feedrate, use of cutting fluid, and use of exit side backup. The levels of these factors for one drill test block are shown in Table 1.

Three solid carbide drill geometries were evaluated for their ability to produce acceptable hole quality: the dagger drill, 8-facet split point drill, and 4-facet standard Master drill, shown in Figures 2 through 4. Their performance was compared with that of the NAS 907 'J' high speed steel split point twist drill frequently used in composite repair operations, shown in Figure 5. The 4-facet Master drill is a stocked tool crib item used for drilling shallow holes in tough, difficult-to-machine superalloy and titanium sheets; the dagger drill was originally developed at McDonnell-Douglas Co. as a modification of the spade drill for machining epoxy/boron and epoxy/graphite laminates; and the 8-facet drill is a variant of the 4-facet Master drill which combines the free-cutting features of the split-point twist drill with a long taper angle of about 24 degrees at the shoulder, in an attempt to distribute torque and thrust over several cutting edges. A summary of the test conditions is shown in Table 2.

The panels were drilled on a Tongil TNV80 CNC machining center with a maximum spindle speed of 8000 rpm; a Kistler drill dynamometer was used in conjunction with a PC-based data acquisition and signal processing system to collect data in real-time at a sampling rate of 2048 bytes/sec. A dust collection system was assembled to exhaust the fine powder from the dry machining tests. Whereas none of the carbide drills reached the 0.254 mm (0.01 in). localized tool wear criterion, a new NAS 907 drill was required for each test condition investigated, since it underwent excessive wear. At each of sixty-four test conditions (with two replicates), the axial thrust force and torque were recorded in-process, using the equipment setup shown in Figure 6. Several hole geometry measurements were made off-line using a Bowers' digital bore gage to obtain data on hole diameter and roundness, and a Talysurf[R] Profilometer to measure the surface finish.

After the drilling tests, each hole was visually assessed, as illustrated in Table 3. Finally, the drilled laminate panels were ultrasonically C-scanned to further characterize hole quality and panel damage. Both, through transmission (TT) and time-of-flight (TOF) scans were performed to identify the extent and depth locations of damage, respectively, in the laminate. Sample through transmission C-scans of holes drilled by the carbide dagger (least panel damage) and the NAS 907 HSS-J (greatest panel damage) are shown in Figures 7 and 8, respectively. Sample photomicrographs prepared for corresponding holes are shown in Figures 9 and 10.

Hole Periphery Damage - A Proposed Index: For each hole, the actual internal panel damage area was measured as a digitized thresholded[1] pixel count using the Image Pro II[R] image processing software based on data from a TT C-scan of a drilled panel, representing the portion of laminate panel which attenuated greater than 80% of the input ultrasonic signal. A pixel count was taken of the digitized damaged area (using a special software feature), where one pixel is equal to 0.40 mm^2 (0.00625 in^2) of damaged panel. The count also provided information on the repeatability of panel damage for each process condition replicate.pixel count was determined for each hole in a test panel. To facilitate statistical data processing, the pixel counts, P1, from thresholded C-scans were transformed, to variables expressing hole periphery damage areas and damage ratios:

i.e., Hole Peripheral Damage Area,
$$D_{MAR} = (P1 \times 0.40 \times 0.40) \text{ mm}^2$$
Assuming average hole diameter,
$$D_{AVG} = 6.35 \text{ mm } (0.2500 \text{ in}),$$
Average cross-sectional area of a drilled hole,
$$A_{AVG} = II (D_{AVG})^2/4$$
$$= II (6.35 \times 6.35)/4 \text{ mm}^2$$
or $A_{AVG} = 31.67 \text{ mm}^2 (0.0491 \text{ in}^2)$

We define the index **Damage Ratio, D_{RAT}** as the ratio of Hole Peripheral Damage Area to Nominal Drilled Hole Area, as shown in Figure 11.
i.e., $D_{RAT} = D_{MAR} / A_{AVG}$
Using this parameter as a measure of hole quality, it is possible to develop an index for comparison of holes of approximately identical diameters having different peripheral damage characteristics; or even holes of different

diameters. A 6.35 mm (0.25 in) diameter hole with a damage ratio of 3.6 (say) has greater peripheral damage than a hole with damage ratio of 1.4.

In order for the technique to apply, it must be assumed, within reasonable limits of panel thickness, that the drilling damage is two-dimensional. As advantages, the damage measurement technique is direct and not affected by fiber orientation as are other damage indices such as w_d, the width of delamination, proposed by Konig and Grass (10) the measurement of which requires destructive sectioning of holes.

Results and Discussion: The data generated were subjected to parametric statistical analyses (4) to determine the effect of each machining parameter on the final quality of a hole measured as internal damage. In the analysis of variance, drill type emerged as the factor having the greatest influence on hole quality. This information was correlated with other measured hole quality response variables. Deciding on 'optimum' drilling conditions on the basis of geometric measurements alone is quite complicated; there are many criteria that may be involved in such a decision, depending on the intended application of the drilled hole (production-related assembly fasteners, repair, heat exchange, etc.). Each application demands a certain level of acceptability based on either geometric accuracy or appearance, or both.

Criteria for Optimal Drill Selection: Following criteria were adopted for drill selection and fastener hole quality assessment:

1. Minimum entrance/exit-side delamination/breakout around hole;
2. Minimum density of matrix microcracking in hole periphery;
3. Minimum measured damage area at hole periphery (indicated by Through-Transmission, Time-Of-Flight C-scan), P1 and D_{MAR};
4. Minimum thrust force,
5. Minimum torque,
6. Minimum hole surface roughness,
7. Minimum hole oversize variations,
8. Minimum hole out-of-roundness variations, and
9. Minimum hole damage ratio, i.e., D_{RAT}.

Using these criteria, a summary of visual assessment results is provided in Table 3, and statistical results in Table 4.

Drill Performance: Overall, the cutting performance of the dagger drill was found superior to the other drills, especially over the NAS 907 HSS drill, as was evidenced by the extent of damage imaged in ultrasonic C-scans (Figures 7 and 8). The closest hole size control was achieved using the dagger and eight-facet drills. The 4-facet Master drill and NAS 907 HSS-J drill tended to produce slightly larger holes. The dagger drill exhibited lowest mean thrust forces at all test conditions, whereas the NAS 907 recorded the highest average thrust force and

---

[1] "Thresholding" is an image processing treatment of digitized data which permits the extraction and display of a specific range of damage in the laminate according to the panel's ability to attenuate the input sonic signal; in this case, the range of interest was 80% - 100% signal attenuation, indicating moderate to severe damage areas only, which are shown in dark contrast relative to other less damaged portions.

torque to accomplish the same cut. The NAS 907 drill tended to produce a greater proportion of out-of-round holes than any of the solid carbide tools. Over the conditions tested, the least peripheral hole damage (measured as D_{RAT}) was accomplished with the dagger drill (D_{RAT}=1.96); the 8-facet drill ranked second; the NAS 907 drill produced greatest extent of panel damage (D_{RAT}=3.43). Surface roughness scattered greatly, and could not be correlated to the machining test conditions. Surface finish generated by the dagger drill was the least sensitive to feedrate and speed variations. Cutting speed effect on thrust force and panel damage was not significant for any of the drills tested, though the feedrate was found to be highly correlated with thrust force and peripheral panel damage area. Backup use, while it restricted push-out delamination, did not significantly reduce internal panel damage, as was evidenced from ultrasonic C-scans of drilled panels; this was particularly true for drills with large point angles; backup use also increased the required thrust force. Use of coolant is not recommended due to excessive thrust forces recorded during its use with drills of small point angles (i.e., dagger and 8-facet).

Validation by Structural Integrity Testing: While all holes in the Screening Tests were found acceptable based on geometric measures according to current hole quality and dimensional specifications of size and roundness, the acceptance of holes drilled by the NAS 907 HSS tools, based on ultrasonic C-scan imagery of the peripheral damage, clearly presents a dilemma to the repair technologist, as shown in Figures 7 and 8. *How does one decide if internal damage resulting from use of the NAS 907 drill geometry is within acceptable quality limits, and will not deleteriously affect fastener hole performance under load?*

To answer this question, it was necessary to compare the performance of these holes with that of the baseline quality holes with least peripheral panel damage, such as produced by the dagger. The various geometric nonconformities (oversize and out-of-roundness) tested in static loading were replicated to simulate defects of greater severity than obtained during the machining tests. The peripheral panel damage test coupons of the composite were maintained at the same damage severity levels as experienced in the machinability test phase.

Machining Damage Tolerance Tests: Four types of hole damage situations were simulated in specially prepared test coupons of PMR-15/gr, based on the indications of hole quality in the drill machinability Screening Tests:
(1) baseline acceptable holes, 3 coupons, ($D_{RAT} < 1.5$);
(2) oversized holes, 3 coupons;
(3) out-of-round holes, 3 coupons; and
(4) severely delaminated holes, 4 coupons ($D_{RAT} > 5.0$).
The effects of these possible anomalies were

investigated at room temperature by subjecting prepared coupons of PMR-15/gr to (1) "open-hole" static tension test, (2) static compression test and (3) residual compression test following 500,000 cycles of reverse-cycle fatigue at 50% of ultimate compressive strength. SACMA-prescribed test methodology was followed during the static tests (11,12). An MTS 810 material testing machine was used for testing of coupons together with a SACMA test fixture.

Structural Integrity Test Results: (Refer to Table 5).

The least data scatter in ultimate strengths of PMR-15/gr coupons was observed in the Open-Hole Static Tension Tests. Of the three hole anomalies investigated, the delamination hole condition produced the most significant tensile strength degradation from baseline conditions, with values ranging from an average of 2.3% to a maximum value of 7.8% - not statistically significant.

In the Open-Hole Static Compression Tests, again, the delamination anomaly caused the largest degradation in strength relative to baseline hole quality, with the average difference being about 10%, reaching a maximum of 20%. In case of the out-of-round and oversize anomalies, the strength reductions averaged 10.9% (maximum 20%), and 4% (maximum 19%), respectively. In general, the data scatter was fairly high for control specimens, the baseline and oversize holes, but low for the delaminated and out-of-roundness anomalies.

In the Open-Hole Residual Compression Tests, the delamination anomaly produced the greatest average reduction in residual strength from baseline holes, about 14.35%, with a maximum value of 25.3%. This was followed by a mean of 4.75% strength reduction for oversize holes (maximum difference = 13%), and a less significant difference for the out-of-round defect which averaged 2.5% (maximum = 15%). With the exception of the delamination anomaly, the residual strengths for all other hole conditions were, in general, equal to or greater than nonfatigued specimen static compression strengths.

Drilling Process and Quality Specification for PMR-15/gr: Based on this study, a drilling process and quality specification for PMR-15/gr laminate used in bolted repair applications would include the following recommendations:

Tool: 883 grade solid carbide dagger or eight-facet drill
Cutting speed: 156 m/min (500 fpm)
Feedrate: 0.0508 mm/rev (0.002 ipr)
Conditions: Dry, without exit-side backup
Acceptable peripheral panel damage
(based on ultrasonic C-scan): $D_{RAT} < 2.0$
Hole diameter tolerance: 0.0762 mm (0.003 in)
Out-of-round tolerance: 0.0254 mm (0.001 in)

Conclusions

It is clear from the machinability and structural integrity tests that high speed steel tools are not suited for drilling PMR-15/gr laminates, either on the basis of their drill geometry or cutter material. At all drilling conditions investigated, the heat generated melted and severely abraded the cutting edges of the NAS 907 drill, yielding severe 'peel-up' and 'push-out' delamination (13). The damage tolerance tests substantiate the finding (from C-scans of machined panels) that the resulting quality of holes is unacceptable, being more likely to cause premature failure of bolted joints under cyclic loading than geometric non-conformities.

Of the carbide drills tested, the dagger and 8-facet drills produce holes of superior quality in PMR-15/gr, simultaneously holding tight dimensional tolerances even at abusive drilling conditions. These conclusions on hole quality parameters are valid within the limits of the factors tested.

The research conclusions warrant a significant change in current philosophy and methodology of qualification of composite structures: i.e., the reduction of dependence on fasteners (and, hence, drilling processes) for joining composites. Where fastener use is unavoidable, a reduction in the risk of generating flawed holes is recommended through selection of optimal tooling and process conditions. An integrated methodology for hole generation, assessment and proof-testing as the one discussed in this paper would greatly facilitate the implementation of these recommendations.

Acknowledgements

The authors gratefully acknowledge the support provided by Systems Support Division, Wright Laboratory Materials Directorate, WPAFB, Ohio under Air Force Grant F33615-89-C-5609; GE Aircraft Engines, Cincinnati, Ohio; and Metcut Research Associates Manufacturing Technology Division (a division of Institute of Advanced Manufacturing Sciences), Cincinnati, Ohio. The technical direction provided by Mr. Theodore J. Reinhart, Mr. Robert B. Urzi, Mr. Neal Ontko and MSgt. Bryan Cramer of the Wright Laboratories is also acknowledged.

References

1. Reinhart, T.J., and L.L. Clements, "Composites Engineered Materials Handbook", edited by T.J. Reinhart, Vol.1, ASM, 1987, pp.1-12.

2. Hickey, J., Modern Machine Shop, March 1987, pp.84-90.

3. Beard, T., Modern Machine Shop, April 1989, pp.74-85.

4. Mehta, M., Doctoral Dissertation, University of Cincinnati, Cincinnati, OH, 1993.

5. Hough, C.L., Lednicky, T.E., and Griswold, N., J. Testing and Eval, JTEVA, Vol.16, No.2, March 1988, pp. 139-145.

6. Gindy, N.N.Z., Int. J. of Prod. Res., Vol.26, No.8, 1988, pp.1317-1327.

7. Miller, J.A., American Machinist and Automated Manufacturing, October 1987, p. 70-71.

8. Mehta, M., Reinhart, T.J., and Soni, A.H., Proc., ASM Symposium on Machining of Composites, ASM/TMS Materials Week, November 1992, pp.113-126.

9. Baker, H., Adv. Mats. and Proc., July 1990, pp.39-43.

10. Konig, W. and P. Grass, Proc. CIRP, August, 1989.

11. SACMA Recommended Test Method for Open-Hole Tensile Properties, SRM 5-88.

12. SACMA Recommended Test Method for Open-Hole Compression Properties, SRM 3-88.

13. Ho-Cheng, H., and Dharan, C.K.H., Proc. ASME Conf. on Machining of Composites, 1988.

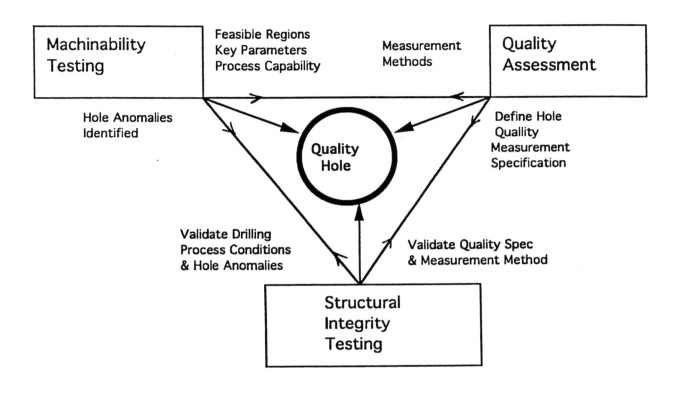

Figure 1. Integrated Hole Testing Methodology for Composite Laminates

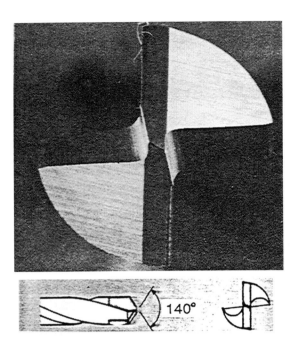

Figure 2. The Solid Carbide 4-Facet Standard Master Drill

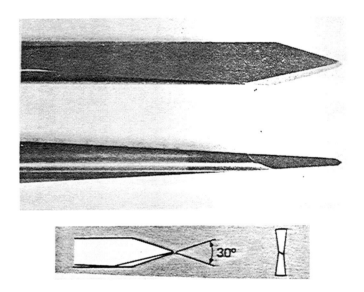

Figure 3. The Solid Carbide Dagger Drill

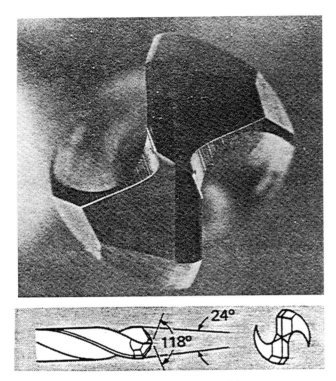

Figure 4. The Solid Carbide 8-Facet Drill

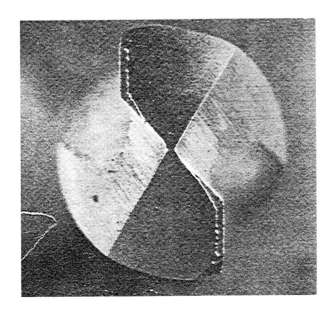

Figure 5. The NAS 907 HSS 'J' Split-Point Drill

Figure 6. Machinability Test Setup for Dry Machining

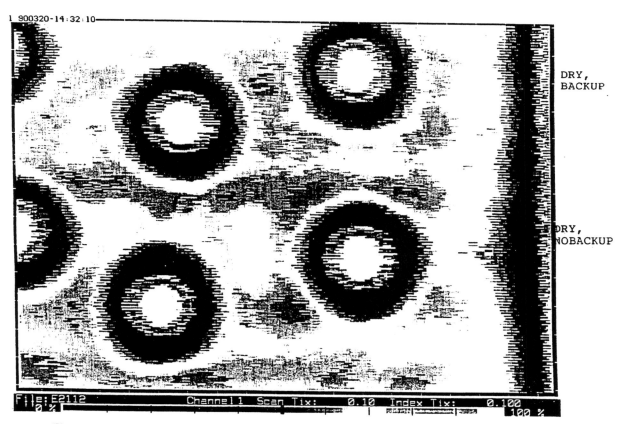

Figure 7. TT C-Scan of Least Damaged Holes Made by the Dagger at Optimal Process Conditions: Speed 156 m/min, Feedrate 0.0508 mm/rev, Dry, Without Backup

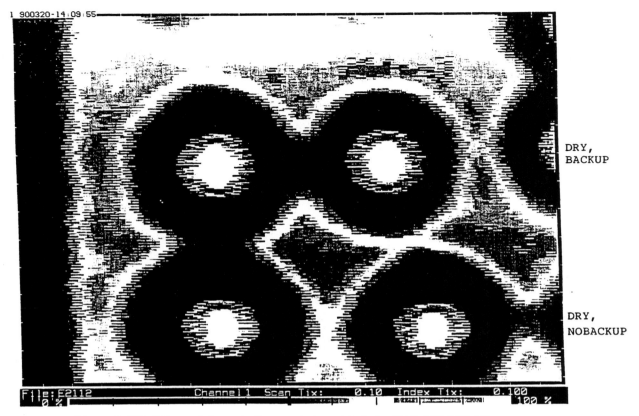

DRY,
BACKUP

DRY,
NOBACKUP

Figure 8. TT C-Scan of Severely Damaged Holes Made by NAS 907 HSS 'J'
Drill at Speed 156 m/min, Feedrate 0.0508 mm/rev, Dry, Without Backup

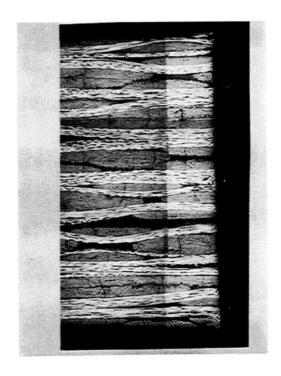

Figure 9. Photomicrograph of Hole Drilled in PMR-15/gr,
Using a Dagger Drill at Optimal Conditions.

Figure 10. Photomicrograph of Hole Drilled in PMR-15/gr,
Showing Severe Panel Damage at Hole Periphery

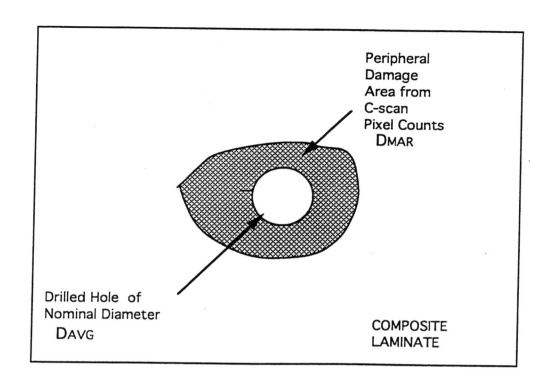

$$\text{D}_{\text{RAT}} = \text{D}_{\text{MAR}} / \text{D}_{\text{AVG}}$$

Figure 11. Proposed Definition of Damage Ratio Parameter for Hole Quality Assessed from TT C-Scans of Drilled Laminate

Table 1. Design of Experiment for Machinability Tests on PMR-15/gr for One Drill Block

Conditions		Dry		Coolant	
Variables		Backup	w/o backup	Backup	w/o backup
Speed	Feed				
78 m/min (250 fpm)	0.025mm/rev (0.0010ipr)				
	0.051mm/rev (0.0020ipr)				
156 m/min (500 fpm)	0.025mm/rev (0.0010ipr)				
	0.051mm/rev (0.0020ipr)				

Table 2. Summary of Machinability Test and Quality Assessment Conditions

ITEM	DESCRIPTION	SPECIFICATION/LEVELS
Workpiece	PMR-15, woven graphite fabric, polyimide resin impregnated flat panel (panel R-7)	Per MIL-U-46187, quasi-isotropic (0,90), 16 ply. Panel dimensions: 12 x 12 x 0.20 in. (300 x 300 x 6 mm), as fabricated
Machine Tool	Tongil CNC Machining Center with automatic tool changer	TNV80, 3-axis, Fanuc controls 6M, 20 HP
Drill Tools	Dagger, 883 grade solid carbide, straight flute	Nominal dia 0.25 in. (6.35 mm) Point angle: 30
	Modified Eight-facet, 883 grade solid carbide	Point angle: 24, 118
	Four-facet Standard Master, 883 grade solid carbide	Point angle: 140
	NAS 907 Split Point, Type J, M42 High Speed Steel	Point angle: 135
Tool Wear Criterion	Localized wear	0.003 in (0.076 mm) for solid carbides 0.01 in (0.254 mm) for HSS
Coolant	Trim-Sol, i.e., water with rust inhibitor, by Master Chemical Corp., where used	Composition: 1:20
Panel Exit Side Backup	Masonite, where used	Thickness: 0.20 in (5 mm)
Hole Quality Measurements	NDE: Ultrasonic C-Scan	Through trans. and Time-of-flight (Damage areas & depth locations)
	Enhanced Radiography Visual Assessment	Slight/Moderate/Severe panel damage
	Metrology: Bowers digital bore gage Talysurf roughness gage	Average diameter and out-of-roundness Arithmetic average finish

150

Table 3. Visual Assessment of Hole Quality in PMR-15/gr, from Machinability Tests on Drills.

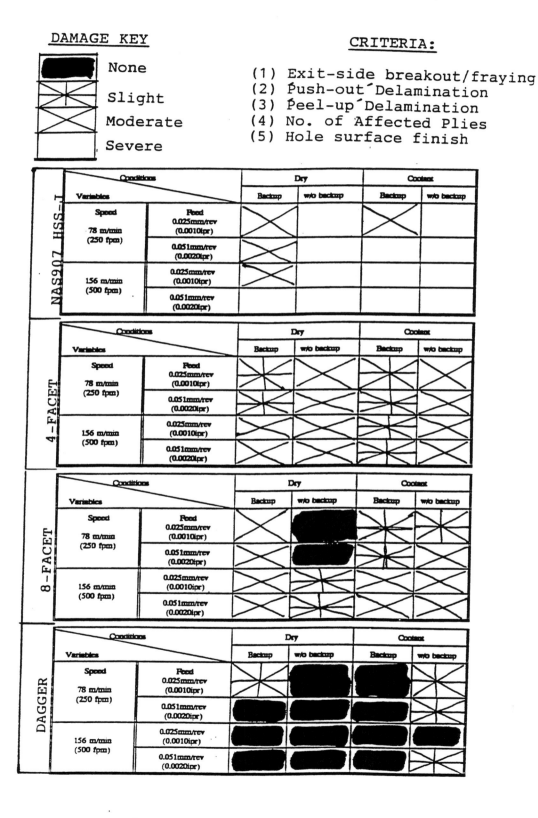

DAMAGE KEY

None
Slight
Moderate
Severe

CRITERIA:

(1) Exit-side breakout/fraying
(2) Push-out Delamination
(3) Peel-up Delamination
(4) No. of Affected Plies
(5) Hole surface finish

Table 4. Summary of Mean Drill Performance Parameters in Machinability Tests on PMR-15/gr:(Maximum recorded values of response parameters are shown in box parentheses [ ].)

Criterion\Drill	Dagger	8-Facet	4-Facet Master	NAS 907-J HSS
Exit breakout (Rank: least = 1)	1	2	3	4
Panel damage, D_{RAT}	1.96 (3.34)	2.37 (3.18)	2.75 (3.62)	3.63 (5.54)
Microcrack density (Rank: lowest = 1)	1	2	3	4
Thrust force, N (lbf)	114 [166] (25.6 [37.4])	201 [378] (45.3 [85.2])	263 [428] (59.3 [96.3])	593 [969] (133.5 [218])
Torque, Nm (ft lbs)	1.29 [2.18] (0.95 [1.61])	1.15 [2.0] (0.85 [1.5])	0.7 [1.64] (0.50 [1.21])	1.53 [2.2] (1.13 [1.61])
Surface finish R_A, um (uin.)	0.4 [1.6] (26 [64])	0.95 [2.2] (38 [88])	1.6 [3.0] (64 [122])	2.4 [4.12] (96 [165])
Hole Diameter, mm (in)	6.354 [6.379] (0.25016 [0.25115])	6.356 [6.369] (0.25022 [0.25075])	6.367 [6.395] (0.25067 [0.25175])	6.375 [6.397] (0.2510 [0.25185])
Hole out-of-roundness, mm (in)	0.0061 [0.025] (0.00024 [0.0010])	0.003 [0.005] (0.00012 [0.0002])	0.0043 [0.018] (0.00017 [0.0007])	0.013 [0.03] (0.00051 [0.0012])
Drill point angle, deg.	30	24, 118	140	135

Table 5. Summary of Mean Static Strengths of PMR-15/gr Coupons in Structural Integrity Tests. (Percentage changes in strength relative to baseline hole quality test coupons are shown in box parentheses [ ]).

Test Type / Hole Condition	Tension	Compression	Residual Compression
Control specimen, GPa (psi)	737 (106990)	396 (57440)	432 (62772)
Baseline Acceptable, GPa (psi)	504 (73216)	285 (41439)	288 (41830)
Severe Delamination, GPa (psi) [% change]	496 [-1.7%] (71967)	256 [-9.7%] (37142)	247 [-14.35%] (35827)
Oversize Hole, GPa (psi) [% change]	511 [+1.3%] (74173)	272 [-4.0%] (39478)	274 [-4.75%] (39844)
Out-of-round Hole, GPa (psi) [% change]	507 [+0.59%] (73653)	253 [-10.8%] (36701)	281 (-2.54%) (40769)

Proceedings of the ASM 1993 Materials Congress, Pittsburgh, Pennsylvania, October 17-21, 1993

Laser Material Processing of Composite Materials

D. Schucker, G. Vees
Technical University of Vienna
Vienna, Austria

Abstract

During the last twenty years lasers have been introduced more and more in manufacturing processes, since they show significant advantages compared to conventional tools as high processing quality, that allows to abandon finishing processes, high flexibility and the absence of tool wear out. For these reasons laser material processing is usually cheaper than conventional processing.

In the past laser material processing has been applied to a large variety of materials, as metals, ceramics, plastics and wood based materials. Since a few years also composite materials have been successfully processed with lasers, whereas the main application is cutting, since composite materials usually consist of substances with largely different mechanical properties and cause thus a fast wear out of mechanical cutting tools. Examples are laser cutting of fiber-reinforced polymeres, plastic covered steel or fiber-reinforced aluminum. An other example for the application of laser material processing to composite materials is laser drilling of composite ceramics and machining of e.g. glass polyester combinations. Even joining of metal matrix composites with lasers has been investigated.

The actual paper mainly gives an overview over laser cutting and welding with special attention to composite materials.

PROCESSING OF METALS, ceramics and other materials with high power lasers has reached a high degree of industrial maturity that shows considerable advantages compared to conventional tools, due to their unique characteristics: thermal processing with minimum heat input, non-contact and flexible processing. So, it can be argued that laser material processing can also be advantageously applied to composite materials as for instance sandwich structures of metals and nonmetalic materials or fibre reinforced plastics. In fact, cutting of these materials with mechanical tools as with knifes and saws is difficult, since a strong wear-out of the tools appears, whereas many of these materials have been cut successfully and economically with lasers. Even welding with lasers has been applied to some special cases of composite materials.

In this paper an overview of recent progress in the field of laser treatment and processing of composite materials is provided.

After a short description of the equipment used for laser processing the mechanisms of laser cutting and welding and the advantages of this technology compared to conventional processes are reviewed with special attention to composite materials. In the third part practical examples for laser processing of composite materials of sandwich-type and for fibre-reinforced materials are as well as for metal matrix materials presented.

Principle layout of a laser processing systems

Since industrial laser systems are expensive, the choice of a laser must be carefully matched to both the machining application and the materials to be processed in order to provide economical operation.

Main parts of a laser processing system are a high power laser with a beam power of several hundred Watts depending on the processing task and the kind of the workpiece. The beam generated by this source is focused by lenses or mirrors and directed on the surface of the workpiece were it is absorbed to a high degree and leads to melting of the material. Furthermore, a gas supply is necassary that produces a gas jet with the help of a nozzle that can easily be used to blow out the material, thus performing cutting or to protect the molten material from oxidation in the case of laser welding. The third main part of a laser processing system is a manipulation unit that moves the workpiece with respect to the focused laser beam and the gas jet along the desired contour, in order to perform cutting or welding. Of course, a CNC-unit controls the operation of all units mentioned before.

Fig.1 shows a typical laser processing system. Usually a CO_2-laser (λ=10,6 μm) is chosen that emits a continuous or pulsed beam with a power around 5 kW that allows to weld aluminium with a thickness up to 6 mm. In the case of cutting, a beam power of 1 - 3 kW is sufficient. Last not least, also Nd:YAG-lasers (λ=1,06 μm) can be used for lower thicknesses. However, estimations of power requirements can be performed by using models of the specific laser machining process to relate the material properties, operating parameters and material removal characteristics such as depth or shape of the cut to the necessary beam power.

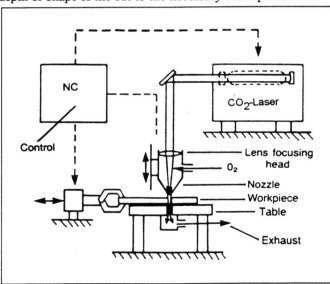

Fig.1. Principal layout of a laser processing system

In general, the highest continuous wave power is obtained from CO_2-lasers, while Nd:YAG lasers provide the highest peak power for pulsed operation. For laser cutting it has been proven to be advantageous to use not only continuous beam power but also pulsed modes. This allows to adjust the beam power to the processing speed, which depends on the curvature of the cut, thus allowing good cut quality even for strongly curved parts of the contour. The amount of laser

power required is determined by the thermal and optical properties of the material to be machined.

An important difference between welding and cutting is the type of processing gas: in the case of laser cutting of metals usually oxygen is choosen since it generates additional heat due to the exothermal reaction. For laser welding usually an inert gas is chosen with much lower pressure than in the case of laser cutting to avoid ejection of liquid material.

Mechanism of laser cutting and welding

Cutting. Fig.2 illustrates the mechanism of laser cutting: the focused laser beam impinges at the momentary end of the cut kerf on a nearly vertical surface and is absorbed there to a large amount. Therefore the material is heated and a thin molten layer is formed. Usually a gas jet, that is coaxial with the laser beam, impinges on the workpiece and acts on the molten material, thus ejecting the latter at the lower side of the workpiece. If the process gas is a reactive one - as oxygen - addional heat is produced and the process is enhanced, but there are some disadvantages as slag adherent to the cut at the bottom side or oxidized cut surfaces. For this reason sometimes an inert gas with high pressure is used, especially for cutting of stainless steel or aluminum.

Due to the movement of the workpiece with respect to the laser beam the erosion front on the surface of the liquid layer moves in the desired direction, thus causing melting of solid material that is then driven out by the mechanical acting of the gas flow as mentioned above, thus performing the cut. If no melting takes place, material removal is carried out by evaporation. This depends on the thermal properties, which can be divided into two basic categories: fixed and loss properties /1/. The first class determines the amount of energy required to melt and to vaporize the material. For example, ceramics require higher laser power to machine than plastics due to their higher latent heats. Loss properties are important because they determine the energy transmitted to the surrounding material during processing.

Usually steel up to a thickness of several mm and isolating materials up to several cm can be cut, whereas the product of thickness of the workpiece and processing speed depends only on the material properties and the beam power. For most industrial materials with workpiece thicknesses up to 10 mm, laser cutting produces a significantly higher material removal rate than mechanical cutting or shearing. Moreover the kerf widthes are much narrower than those achievable with mechanical cutting.

When coupled with a multi-axis system for the workpiece or beam movement, also 3D-workpieces can be cut, whereas with conventional methods only flat workpieces can be treated effectively.

During cutting fibrous materials such as wood, paper, or composites, the laser beam vaporizes the volume of material to be removed, thereby eliminating the residue and debris which remain after mechanical cutting.

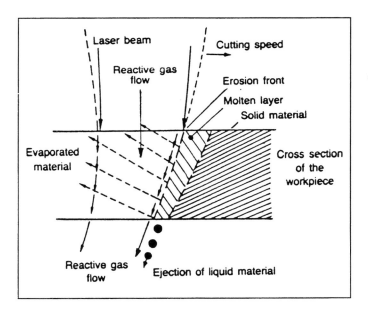

Fig.2 Mechanism of laser cutting /2/

Welding. In this case especially for deep penetration welding a beam with a very high intensity above several 10^6 W/cm^2 is used that causes evaporation of the material. Under the focus a narrow channel extending through the full depth of the workpiece is build up and filled with metal vapor. This channel, the so called "keyhole", allows the beam to penetrate into the workpiece - so, high penetration depths up to few cm can be obtained for steel. Since the wall of the keyhole is at the evaporation point the keyhole is surrounded by a molten pool. Due to the movement of the workpiece with respect to the beam, this molten body together with the keyhole moves in the desired direction, thus melting solid material at the interface between the liquid body and the solid material. The molten material enters the liquid pool, flows around the keyhole, reaccumulates at the backside of the keyhole and resolidifies at the rear side of the liquid pool, thus building up the weld seam. The metal vapour leaving the keyhole at the upper side of the workpiece is mixed with the processing gas. Due to the high intensity of the laser radiation, this mixture is then strongly heated and even ionized, thus forming a plasma above the workpiece. This phenomenom leads to strongly improved absorption, socalled "abnormal absorption", that appears for all metals above a critical intensity of several 10^6 W/cm^2 and leads to nearly 100% absorption, thus providing a very efficient welding process.

Special effects of composite materials. Usually composite materials consist of parts with largely different mechanical properties; examples are metal-plastic structures, wood-plates covered with plastic layers or fibre reinforced polymeres. Strongly varying hardness, anisotropy, inhomogeneous composition, changing elasticity , abrasiveness and tensile strengh cause severe problems for mechanical cutting tools, e.g. saw-plates since the tools are accelerated during cutting the weak parts and then suddenly deaccelerated during cutting the hard parts, thus causing an intermittent and very dangerous change of load. Moreover this change of mechanical forces and also temperature during cutting of the different parts of the composite material can cause strongly varying tensions in the workpiece. So, fiber breaks, debonding, and delamination can occur and lead to reduced quality of the processed workpiece.

Moreover in many cases the thermal properties of the various components of the composite material are quite different. Therefore strongly changing temperatures at the cutting edge of the tool appear, which enhance wear out due to thermal stress. Excessive tool wear out significantly increases the machining time and expenses. Some composite materials even contain constituents that soften due to the heat produced by the cutting process and show thus adhesive affect to the tool.

All these disadvantages can be avoided by using lasers, since in this case no mechanical forces act on the workpiece. Only very little heat is supplied to the material, since heat acts on the workpiece only in a small region with a diameter little more than 0,1 mm. Finally no tool is used that can wear out. Even strongly changing mechanical properties in the composite material do not affect the process of laser cutting. Nevertheless strongly varying thermal and electrical properties may cause problems since they determine the amount of absorption and the temperature obtained during processing. Generally, it can be said, that composite materials composed from materials with similiar thermal and electrical properties but strongly varying mechanical properties can be advantageously cut with lasers without any problems, whereas the effectiveness of laser machining depends primarily on the thermal properties of the material.

A good example is cutting of wood plates covered with plastic surfaces as used for the production of furniture or combinations of plastic and textile materials, that can be processed excellently with lasers.

Examples for successful laser processing of composite materials

Modern fiber-reinforced polymeres for consumer goods are state of the art, since these materials are non-corrosive and have a very small thermal extension. Moreover, complicated workpieces can be produced as a one-piece, whereas using metals many single parts must be mounted.

Cutting of fiber-reinforced polymeres. Laser cutting of different fiber-reinforced polymeres has been performed in several recent investigations. In Table 2 a few examples for CO_2-laser cutting are listed:

Material	Laser Power (W)	Cutting Speed (m/min)	Kerf Depth (mm)	Kerf Width (mm)	Refs
Aramid/Polyester	800	0,5	2	0,6	4
Glass/Epoxy	1000	2	5	0,5	5
Glass/Polyester	800	0,5	2		4
Graphite/Epoxy	1000-2000	0,9 - 7,2	1 - 4		6
Graphite/Epoxy	300	0,3	1	0,1	6
Graphite/Polyester	800	0,5	2	0,5	4
Kevlar/Epoxy	150-950	2	3,2 - 9	0,1	7

One characteristic of laser cutting is the relation between cutting efficiency and beam scanning direction relative to fiber orientation. Due to material anisotropy, the thermal response of a workpiece to the laser beam depends on the cutting direction. This effect is most apparent in graphite-fiber composites, where the thermal properties of the constituents are very different. In cutting experiments with uniaxial laminate, heat losses were found to be large and cutting speed was low when the fibers were orthogonal to the cutting direction - in this orientation, the heat flux takes place along the fiber direction /6/.

Cut quality. Due to the heterogeneous structure of composites some phenomenons appear at the cut surfaces which which are not found for metals or ceramics, as e.g. the thermal decomposition of the base material or protruding fibers. For an evaluation of laser cut composites there must be made a distinction between textural- and milled fiber-reinforced materials, since they show significantly different behaviour in particular at the heat affected zone - mostly the HAZ is visible with the eye.

For evaluating the quality of composite parts cut by a laser beam an international effort on determining cutting quality led to the selection of parameters as there are kerf width, depth of cut, striation drag, stration depth, width of damage and unevenness. Fig.3. shows a much more detailed proposal for an evaluation of a cut kerf:

Independendly from the kind of the texture, textural-reinforced compounds have a large visible HAZ, since fiber bunches form thermal bridges. Due to the high temperatures the matrix-material is evaporated and thermally destroyed partly. Also, the thermal damage zone tends to propagate along the direction of fiber orientation. Since textural-reinforced composites have usually a high density of fibers,

there is no possibility to remove the decomposed matrix-material. So, the heat affected zone consists of a charred layer followed by a thermally destroyed zone. The width of this zone depends on the material used for fibers. As aramid fibers have similar thermal characteristics as polymer materials, material behavior is similar to that of homogeneous materials. In contrast to this, graphite fibers with a thermal conductivity up to two orders of magnitude higher than polymer materials lead to highly directional heat conduction causing a much larger thermal damage zone

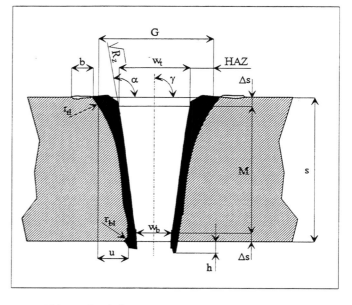

s	thickness of workpiece	r	radius of melted area
Δs	0,1s for s < 2 mm	w	kerf width
Δs	0,2 mm for s > 2 mm	HAZ	heat affected zone
$M = s-2.\Delta s$ ... measuring range for		b	width of deposites
determination of u and α		h	burr heigth
Rz	average roughness	G	total width
u	tolerance for orthogonal	α	angle of flank
	surfaces and slope	γ	angle of cut kerf

Index: t...top, b...bottom, l...left

Fig.3. Evaluation of cut kerf for textural-reinforced compounds/8/

In the case of milled fiber-reinforced composites there is one more parameter: free protruding lenght of the fibers. The cut edge appears completely different. Due to the short fibers, which are surrounded by low heat conducting matrix-material the heat flux to the base material is limited to the lenght of the fibers. For less content of fibers (app.20%) there is much space between the individual fibers, so that evaporated base material can be blown away by a gas jet. The result is not a HAZ as mentioned above but sensitive, free protruding milled fibers, which can be broken off easely.

Chemical decompositions. one problem in laser cutting of composites is the production of chemical decompositions during processing. Gas chromatography analysis and mass spectrometry were conducted on gas samples during laser cutting of graphite/epoxy, aramid/epoxy and glass/epoxy /6/. Mostly fragmented powders of fiber materials were found. CO, CO2 and low molecular organic compounds have been formed by thermal decomposition of the matrix. Cutting of aramid/epoxy produces large quantities of hydrogen cyanide, which causes a considerable health risk.

But in most cases reaction products are unknown, since the produced vapors are a mixture of many different chemical compounds. So, there is a demand for further investigations to improve understanding of the complicated chemical relations. This is one of the requirements for the development of suitable units for waste disposal. There is one conception which suggests a system separated into three parts: a wet type filter (cooling of gases, condensation and reaction with water) is followed by an industrial exhauster including needled felt). Finally, an electrostatical charcoal filter completes the system /8/.

Cutting of metal-plastic composites. Plastic-coated metal composites are one group of those materials with a strongly extending market. The syntetic layer can have different functions as thermal and electrical isolation or wear out protection. Today these composites are used in apparatus engineering or tank construction mainly. So, laser machining of these workpieces has to be considered with the background of 3D-processing.

Optimization of the processing parameters is very difficult on account of large differences in chemical and physical properties. Cut quality of laser cut metal-plastic-composites is determined by thermal damage at the cutting edge.

The damage of polymere layers can be divided into two categories:

      a) partly or complete loss of polymere-layer
      b) visible damage as change of colour or bubbling.

To minimize this thermal damage in particular heat losses and energy per lenght of the processing path have to be considered. So, at a given laser power and for continuous-wave processing the velocity should be near the possible maximum in order to reduce thermal stress. At a rated power of 2 kW (CO_2-laser) a maximum velocity of 8 m/min has been obtained causing a small damage zone of about 0,3-0,4 mm. Using oxygen as processing gas this width is true for low pressures (p=0,2 MPa) /9/. For higher pressures the polymere layer was lifted up to a few millimeters parallel to the edge. The use of inert gas minimizes this effect.

If the polymere layer is a duroplastic, velocities up to 21 m/min have been realized. In comparison to this, for thermoplastic coated sheets the maximum rate is limited to 14 m/min. This is possible due to a special effect of duroplastic polymeres: they do not melt but change from

solid to gaseous state directly, thus avoiding interruptions of the cutting process. Thermoplastic polymeres are melted, enter the cut kerf and are burned. The released carbon combines with oxygen to CO resp. CO2 and leads to hindrance of the cutting process.

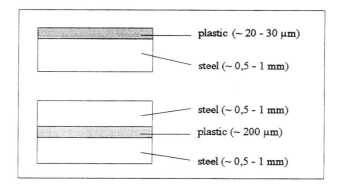

Fig.4 Schematical structure of metal-plastic-composites

For 3D-processing the high velocities desired are not applicable. Temporal modulation of laser power allows to minimize the width of the damage zone for lower velocities. High peak power and short pulses result in low heat losses and thus small damage zones. Considering this parameters for pulsing and the possible use of flexible fiber-optics for beam guiding Nd:YAG-lasers would be the better choice in particular for 3D-processing.

With a pulse duration of t_p=0,5 ms and a pulse frequency of 200 Hz the width of damage could be reduced to 100 µm /9/. If oxygen was used, cuts free of burrs have been obtained. The very small damage zone can be explained by low absorption of the polymeres at the wavelenght of Nd:YAG-lasers, thus reducing the effect of heat accumulation.

Welding of metal matrix composites. For most of the metal matrix composites (MMC) aluminium is the base material, since there is a great demand of new concepts in order to make workpieces light weight . But high reflectivity, high heat conductivity and low viscosity of the aluminum melt cause the difficulties in welding aluminum-alloys and -composites.

In /10/ a study was conducted on laser welding of aluminum reinforced by SiC particles. It was found, that the extent of SiC and A356-Al reaction is proportional to the laser energy input. Aluminum carbide formations as well as SiC particle dissolution increase with increasing power input, whereas physical and chemical changes in SiC particles during laser processing correlate with the amount and mode of energy input. Welds made with pulsed CO_2-laser beams indicate after the tensile tests, that the mechanical properties of the composites were even enhanced for certain laser conditions; therefore pulsed processing appears to be a successful way of joining these MMCs. Similar results were obtained by /13/: the effect of heat input and duration of thermal cycle on the microstructure of SiC particulate reinforced aluminium was investigated. In fact, at low energy inputs only a small region of cellular dentritic eutectic solidification structure was found in the middle of the fusion zone.

The feasibility of laser welding of an alumina reinforced 6061 alloy based composite was investigated in /11/. The presence of alumina particles makes the process more complicated. In contrast, aluminum-alloys containing lithium have proved to be a attractive alternative to traditional high strength Al-alloys and carbon-fiber composites, e.g. for use in aerospace or marine applications /12/. These alloys include high monotonic tensile and yield strengths, decreased densities, increased stiffness, good resistance to the propagation of fatigue cracks with the promise of weight savings.

Summary and Conclusions

Due to the increasing substitution of metals by new materials as fiber reinforced plastics there is a high application potential for laser machining.

As a rule, lasers are used if no applicable conventional process exists, e.g. flexible 2D- or 3D-cutting and welding of structural parts or composites. For that purpose laser sources are necessary with spatial and temporal beam intensity control. But economical using of the possible high processing speeds demand on improvements in the dynamic behaviour of manipulation units. The use of lasers for processing composites is economically since

- wear out of tools is avoided, due to the non-contact processing
- tools must not be changed
- workpieces are processed without any mechanical stress
- high processing velocity is possible, small thermal stress and good reproduceability are obtained

Due to the low thermal stability of plastics, melting temperature of fibers has to be reached as quick as possible in order to reduce the thermal stress. Constituents of the composites and their physical properties mainly affect the results obtained. In contrast to mechanical machining fiber orientation within the laminates is not of great importance for laser cutting. With optimum processing parameters as speed, position of focus, kind of gas or gas pressure aramid and glass fiber reinforced composites can be cut with good quality. The best results concering cut quality could be obtained for aramid fiber reinforced polymeres. Moreover investigations on the determination of pollutant emission during laser cutting of plastics are necassary. Additional measures have to be taken for a carefully waste disposal.

Cutting of plastic-steel-composites causes problems due to their largely different thermophysical properties. Continuous wave processing allows high speeds of machining. This operating methods can be used for mass-produced parts with rough contours. For finishing works pulsed operating must be prefered. Investigations with pulsed Nd:YAG-lasers show satisfactory results concerning cut quality and width of damage, whereas duroplastic polymeres are more suitable for laser cutting than thermoplastic polymeres.

New technologies have enabled industry to manufacture many new types of metal matrix composites. Hand in hand with these new composites also new machining problems come up, one of which is laser welding. As welding of pure aluminum and its alloys is not solved satisfactorily up to now the same is true for aluminum alloy composites. Since there is a large variety of combinations for composites much work is still required to be able to apply laser welding to industrial production.

References

1 - Chryssolouris G., "Laser Machining", Springer-Verlag, N.Y. (1991)

2 - Schuöcker D., The Physical Mechanism and Theory of Laser Cutting, Industrial Laser Annual Handbook (1987)

3 - Haferkamp H., Homburg A., Wendorff H.P., Laserstrahlschneiden von Kunststoff-Stahl-Schichtverbundwerkstoffen, Laser Magazin 2/92

4 - Tagliaferri V., Crivelli Visconti I., A.Di Ilio, Laser Cutting of Fiber-Reinforced Polymeres, Composites, Vol.16, No.4,1985

5 - Koenig W., Wulf C., Grab P. Willerscheid H., Machining of Fiber-Reinforced Plastics, Annals of the CIRP (1985),N2

6 - Flaum M., Karlsson T., Cutting of Fiber-Reinforced Polymers With CW CO_2 Laser, SPIE-High Power Lasers and Their Industrial Applications, Vol.801 (1987)

7 - Van Cleave R.A., Characteristics of Laser Cutting Kevlar Laminates, DOE Rept.No.BDX-613-2075 (1979)

8 - Müller R., "CO_2-Laserstrahlschneiden kurzglasverstärkter Verbund-werkstoffe", Hanser Verlag (1992)

9 - Haferkamp H., Homburg A., Wendorff H.P., Laserstrahlschneiden von Kunststoff-Stahl-Schichtverbundwerkstoffen, Laser Magazin 2 (1992)

10 - Dahotre N.B., McCay M.H., McCay T.D., Gopinathan S., Sharp. C.M., Laser Joining of Metal Matrix Composite, Proceeding: Machining of Composite Materials, Chicago, Illinois, USA (1992)

11 - Kawall S., Viegelahn G.L., Attempts at Laser Welding of an Alumina Reinforced 6061 Aluminum Alloy Composite, Proceeding: Advanced Composite Materials: New Developments and Applications, Detroit, Michigan, USA (1991)

12 - Molian P.A., Srivatsan T.S., Weldability of AlLiCu Alloy 2090-T8E41 using Lasers, Aluminium, Jan. 1990, Vol.:66(1)

Machinability of Resin Impregnated Sintered Steel

Iqbal Shareef
Associate Professor
Department of Manufacturing
Bradley University
Peoria, Illinois

Abstract

Although powder metallurgy process can be effectively used to produced near net shape product, seldom it is used without further processing. Particularly because of the inability of PM process to produce certain intricate internal and external geometry's such as transverse holes, double tapers, threads, etc., secondary machining operations become inevitable. However, it is well known that machining of sintered metals, produced be conventional PM process, posses several problems. As such several attempts have been made to improve the machinability of PM parts by adding additives to metal powder before compaction and then sintering it. In this paper the materials selected for machinability comparison were both PM powder-copper steels and were identical in composition with the exception of one set being impregnated, after sintering, with porosity sealing resin. The resin impregnated specimens were processed by forcing the resin under high pressure to flow through any porosity leaks. Using central composite design, drilling experiments have been conducted on the conventional PM specimens, and plastic impregnated PM specimens. Statistical comparison of Axial force, torque, surface finish of the drilled holes, and the wear of drill bits indicate a significant improvement in the machinability of plastic impregnated PM specimens. Mathematical models for predicting axial forces, and torque are developed. Within the envelope of cutting parameters investigated, the predictor equations in the model for axial force, and torque are found to approximate the behavior of forces with 86.82%, and 95.7% accuracy, respectively.

These results are of significant value for improving the machinability of sintered steels.

ONE OF THE MAJOR ADVANTAGE OF powder metallurgy process compared to other forming processes is its ability to produce parts close to net or near net shape. Unfortunately, parts with complex internal and external geometry's, and parts requiring greater dimensional tolerance cannot be produced by PM process. However, manufacturing processes such as machining extend the capability of PM parts by not only producing complex geometry's, but also by improving the dimensional accuracy and surface finish. As more and more complex shaped steel parts, traditionally produced by forming or machining techniques, are replaced with parts made by PM technique, the need for machining PM parts is rapidly increasing. It is estimated that about 29% of all powder metallurgy automotive parts require some machining operations [1]. As such about 55% of PM part suppliers use machining as a secondary process after sintering. Thus enhancing the machinability of sintered steels is of paramount importance in the production of PM parts.

The major factors affecting the machinability of sintered materials include: manufacturing technique, alloy chemistry, porosity, microstructure, shape, size, distribution of inclusions, and machining parameters [2-3]. Of all these factors, microstructure and alloy chemistry has been characterized as important factors that affect machinability [4-5]. As such numerous efforts have been made to investigate the influence of microstructure [6-8], and alloy chemistry [9-13] on the machinability of sintered steels. However, the work related to porosity of the material appears to be lacking. Porosity in PM parts is an inherent and natural result of the very powder metallurgy processing technique. The porosity in powder metal parts produces an interrupted cutting condition at the chip tool contact. This not only produces undesirable chatter and vibrations, but also shortens tool life. Further, the dimensional accuracy of the machined part is reduced. Presence of pores reduces the thermal conductivity of the material, which in turn results in slower dissipation of heat from the chip tool interface, there by resulting in lower tool life. Due to these problems, impregnation sealing of micro-porosity in PM parts has gained widespread application. Although, impregnation improves the integrity of the part in several respects, its influence on residual stress and machinability of the part is not clearly understood. This paper deals with comparing the machinability of two sets of sintered steel samples. One set is in the as sintered form produced by PM conventional process (PMC), while the other set is impregnated with plastic (PMP) resin by anaerobic wet vacuum/pressure process.

Experimental Techniques

Materials. Standard ASTM E8 dog-bone tensile specimens were made from the powder mix composition given below.

Table 1

Composition	Percentage
Copper	2
Carbon (Graphite)	0.8
Oxygen (Max)	0.2
Lubricant (Atomized Acrawax)	0.75
Atomized Steel	96.25

Sintering was performed in a gas fired, continuous mesh belt furnace using an endothermic atmosphere with a -1° C dewpoint. The specimens were sintered at 1120° C for approximately 30 minutes.

Anaerobic Impregnation Technique. Impregnation is considered as a design and production tool for treatment of high porosity parts such as those made by powder metal technique. At present there are several impregnation technologies available in the market that include but not limited to i) Sodium Silicate also known as Waterglass, ii) Polyester Resins, iii) Low-Viscosity Heat Curable Resins, and iv) Anaerobic Impregnants. Of these technologies, Anaerobic Impregnants are most

commonly used for powder metal parts. Anaerobic mean's *survival in absence of oxygen*, which is opposite of Aerobics, meaning survival in presence of oxygen. In absence of air and oxygen the anaerobic resins automatically cure at room temperature. Although thread lockers have used this technique to fasten threads for a long time, impregnation on engineering parts has found production applications only during the last decade. There are several anaerobic impregnation techniques such as wet vacuum, wet vacuum/pressure, dry vacuum, pressure injection, spray sealing, etc. In this investigation wet vacuum/pressure technique was used for impregnating the PM samples.

The wet vacuum/pressure process essentially consists of submerging the part in a vacuum tank of anaerobic resin. The vacuum cycle removes air from the tank and pores in the part. Then the chamber is first returned to ambient pressure to allow resin to force into the pores, then the chamber is pressurized for a short period of time to further drive resin into the micro pores. This step is followed by rinsing for removal of surplus resin on the surface. Rinsing is followed by immersion of the part in a catalytic activator solution to cure the resin at the surface of each porosity. This creates a hardened plug at the outer portion of the pore, thereby trapping the remaining resin for anaerobic self cure. Finally, the part is rinsed again to remove any activator from the surface. The total cycle time is approximately 20 minutes.

Testing Technique. By far the most common machining operation performed on powder metal parts is drilling. Thus most of the machinability investigations done in the past are based on drilling process [11-14]. There for machinability of the material was determined by conducting drilling tests. All drilling tests were conducted on Bridgeport CNC, series 1 R2E4 machine using a Kistler four component drilling dynamometer type 9273, and a Kistler dual mode amplifier, model number 5004. Different combinations of spindle speed, axial feed, and drill diameter were used in the experiments, and are listed in the next section. The thickness of the sample was 12.5 mm and through holes were drilled in all experiments. Each drilling experiment was conducted with a new drill bit, and in the presence of a mist of light mineral oil, directed towards the drill bit as a lubricant. Subsequently, the three components of drilling force, and a drilling torque were measured. All drills used in the investigation were coated with TiC, and had the same drill bit geometry.

Apparatus. A schematic of the drilling test apparatus is shown in figure 1. The systems consists of a piezoelectric four component drilling dynamometer capable of measuring three forces, and a torque about the drill feed direction. The output from the dynamometer is measured using a strip chart recorder and also a PC based data acquisition system. A Bridgeport CNC Series 1-R2E4 Mill was programmed to obtain the desired spindle speeds, and feeds, while the experiments were conducted with different drill diameters.

Surface roughness measurements of the drilled holes were made by Federal's patented Pocket Surf. A completely portable instrument designed to make surface roughness measurements on a wide variety of surfaces, including small inside diameters.

Experimental Design

Machining Parameters. To obtain a reasonable and efficient level of estimation, it was necessary to restrict the study to few of the most important cutting parameters that influence the response functions in machining. Based on literature search the three cutting parameters that were most frequently investigated are: spindle speed, feed, and drill diameter[15-22]. Torque and axial feed force were measured as a response functions in drilling tests. The other variables such as, workpiece material, lubrication, tool material, and tool geometry were held constant throughout the experimentation.

Statistical Design. Because of the nonlinear nature of the behavior of cutting parameters, selection of a linear model was ruled out, and instead a second order nonlinear model was assumed to be most suitable for this problem. An experimental design for a second order model must have at least three levels of each factor so that the model parameters can be estimated. For this purpose rotatable designs are most preferred. The most widely used design for fitting second order model is the *central composite design* (CCD), which is made rotatable by selection of axial augment points as a=1.6818. Further, by selection of 9 central points the CCD can be made orthogonal [23].

Thus in order to minimize the number of experiments, the experimentation time, the experimentation cost, and at the same time to maximize the validity of the experimental results, a central composite design was used.

The design of experiments matrix is given in the table 2. The choice of CCD not only provided the effect of the independent parameters, but also the second order interactions among the parameters investigated.

Randomization of the experiments was necessary to obtain the data without incorporating systematic errors, which occur due to factors that are difficult to control. This ensured that effect of all the factors that were not considered in the design matrix would remain as close to constant as possible.

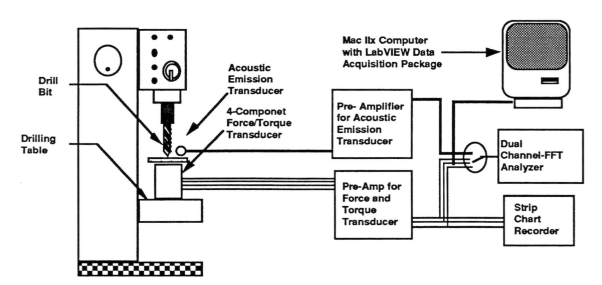

Figure 1. Schematic of the Drilling Test Apparatus.

Table 2a

Cutting Para-meters	Central Composite Design Coded Values				
	-1.68	-1	0	1	1.68
Speed	659	1000	1500	2000	2341
Feed	16	50	100	150	184
Drill Dia	2.636	4	6	8	9.364

Table 2b

Number of Expts.	Speed Rpm "V"	Feed mm/min "f"	Diameter mm "D"
1	-1	-1	-1
2	-1	-1	1
3	-1	1	-1
4	-1	1	1
5	1	-1	-1
6	1	-1	1
7	1	1	-1
8	1	1	1
9	0	0	0
10	0	0	0
11	0	0	0
12	0	0	0
13	0	0	0
14	0	0	0
15	0	0	0
16	0	0	0
17	0	0	0
18	-1.6818	0	0
19	1.6818	0	0
20	0	-1.6818	0
21	0	1.6818	0
22	0	0	-1.6818
23	0	0	1.6818
24	-1.6818	0	0
25	1.6818	0	0
26	0	-1.6818	0
27	0	1.6818	0
28	0	0	-1.6818
29	0	0	1.6818

Table 2c

Torque Expts.			
Code	0	0	0
Actual	1500	100	6

Results

Drilling Experiments. Drilling tests were conducted as per the experiment numbers given in the design of experiments table 2b. Axial force in drilling is compared for PM conventional samples (PMC), and PM plastic impregnated (PMP) samples at twenty nine different cutting conditions, characterized as experiment numbers. The axial force obtained represents an average of the force signal measured from the time when the drill bit was two mm into the material till the drill bit was two mm from the exit surface. Since the thickness of the sample was 12.5 mm, the data was averaged over the remaining 8.5 mm drill travel. The axial force variation is shown in figure 2, and the corresponding torque variation in figure 3.

Roughness Measurements. Using a pocket surf portable surface roughness measuring device, the surface roughness for the drilled holes was measured for all experiments listed in the design of experiments table 2b, and for both PMC and PMP samples. On each drilled hole, the surface profile was scanned over a length of 10 mm. Roughness probe was scanned at least three times along different radial positions of the hole. The value of the surface finish reported is an average of three most consistent readings of Ra. The variation of surface finish measured as Ra in mm, is shown in figure 4 at different experimental conditions, and for both PMC and PMP samples.

Torque Experiments. For tool life measurements, the conventional torque test in drilling was used. In this test the experimental conditions were at the body center of the center composite cube. The cutting parameters: speed, feed, and drill diameter were maintained constant at a coded value of (0,0,0). The actual values of the speed, feed, and drill diameter were 1500 rpm, 100 mm/min, and 6 mm respectively. These experimental conditions are also given in table 2c. The variation of normal force as the number of drilled holes increase from 1 to 100, while all cutting parameters being constant, is shown in figure 5, for both PMC and PMP samples. The corresponding variation of the torque is shown in figure 6.

After the completion of 100 holes on PMC and PMP samples, the surface roughness of only the hole numbers 1, 10, 20, 30, ... 100 were measured. The variation of surface roughness for these sample numbers is shown in figure 7.

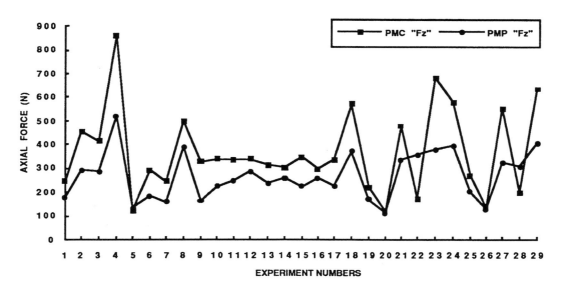

Figure 2. Comparison of Axial Torque in Drilling at Different Cutting Conditions for PM Conventionally Produced Parts (PMC) and PM Plastic Impregnated Parts (PMP)

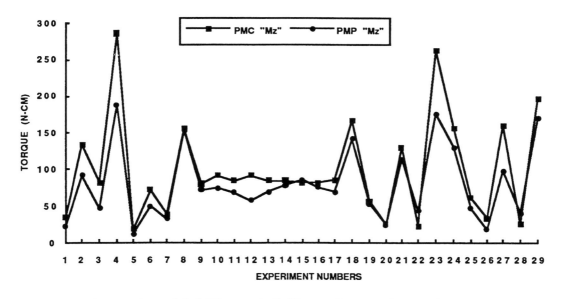

Figure 3. Comparison of Axial Torque in Drilling at Different Cutting Conditions for PM Conventionally Produced Parts (PMC) and PM Plastic Impregnated Parts (PMP)

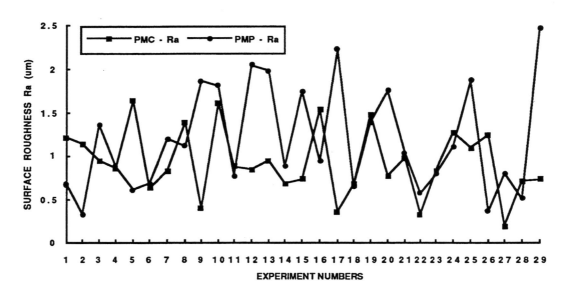

Figure 4. Comparison of Surface Roughness in Drilling at Different Cutting Conditions for PM Conventionally Produced Parts (PMC) and PM Plastic Impregnated Parts (PMP)

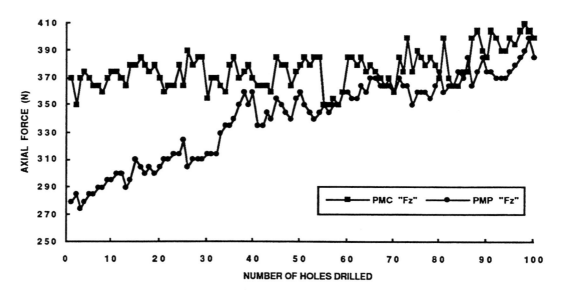

Figure 5. Comparison of Axial Force in Drilling, at Cutting Conditions Defined by Expt. No. 9, for PM Conventionally Produced Parts (PMC) and PM Plastic Impregnated Parts (PMP)

164

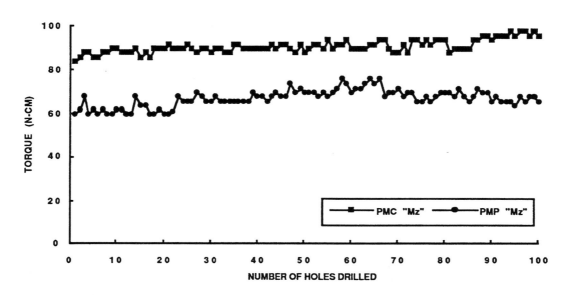

Figure 6. Comparison of Axial Torque in Drilling, at Cutting Conditions Defined by Expt. No. 9, for PM Conventionally Produced Parts (PMC) and PM Plastic Impregnated Parts (PMP)

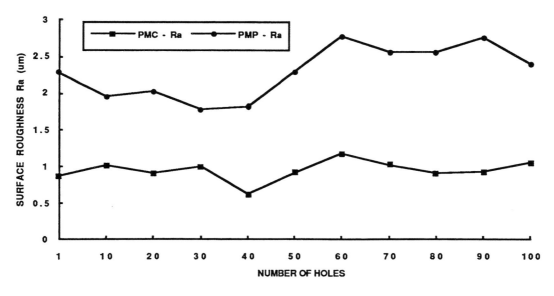

Figure 7. Comparison of Surface Roughness in Drilling, at Cutting Conditions Defined by Expt. No. 9, for PM Conventionally Produced Parts (PMC) and PM Plastic Impregnated Parts (PMP)

Mathematical Models

Mathematical models were developed for both PMC and PMP materials. In the interest of brevity, only the results for parts impregnated with plastic resin (PMP) are reported here.

Axial Force Model. The twenty nine experiments defined in table 2b were statistically analyzed on RS1. From the statistical analysis Bisquare coefficients were found to best fit the data. The ANOVA table is shown below.

Table 3

Bisquare Coefficients for Axial Force				
Term	Coeffi-cients	Std. Error	T-Value	Signi-ficance
1	232.597	11.011	21.12	0.0001
x	-58.272	9.191	-6.34	0.0001
y	62.180	9.197	6.76	0.0001
z	42.264	9.191	4.60	0.0001
yz	45.653	14.282	3.20	0.0042
x^2	15.756	7.880	2.00	0.0581
z^2	40.551	7.880	5.15	0.0001
No. of Cases = 29	R-Square = 0.8682			
Resid. D of F = 22	R-Square-Adj. = 0.8323			

where x, y, and z represent the transformed factors. In terms of the actual cutting parameters, the transformed factors are given by

$$x = \frac{V - 1500}{500}$$

$$y = \frac{F - 100}{50}$$

and

$$z = \frac{D - 6}{2}$$

when these transformations are plugged into the regression equation, we obtain the mathematical model for axial force in drilling, in terms of the real variables speed, feed, and drill diameter as

AF = 936.939 - 0.305615 **V** - 1.49561 **F** - 146.173 **D** + 0.456535 **F D** + 0.0000630234 **V**^{2} + 10.1376 **D**^{2}

Drilling Torque Model. The corresponding ANOVA table for the torque analysis is given below.

Table 4

Bisquare Coefficients for Axial Torq				
Term	Coeffi-cients	Std. Error	T-Value	Signi-ficance
1	73.009	3.805	19.19	0.0001
x	-22.916	2.600	-8.82	0.0001
y	25.598	2.601	9.84	0.0001
z	38.578	2.600	14.84	0.0001
yz	23.574	4.039	5.84	0.0001
x^2	6.062	2.284	2.65	0.0148
y^2	-4.244	2.289	-1.85	0.0778
z^2	11.388	2.824	4.99	0.0001
No. of Cases = 29	R-Square = 0.9570			
Resid. D of F = 22	R-Square-Adj. = 0.9427			

where x, y, and z represent the transformed factors. In terms of the actual cutting parameters, the transformed factors are given by

$$x = \frac{V - 1500}{500}$$

$$y = \frac{F - 100}{50}$$

and

$$z = \frac{D - 6}{2}$$

when these transformations are plugged into the regression equation for axial torque, we obtain the mathematical model, in terms of the real variables speed, feed, and drill diameter as

AT = 256.348 - 0.118578 **V** - 0.562945 **F** - 38.45 **D** + 0.235739 **FD** + 0.0000242487 **V**^{2} - 0.00169769 **F**^{2} + 2.84709 **D**^{2}

Where **AF** is axial force in Newton's,
AT is drill torque in N-cm,
V is drill speed in RPM,
F is drill feed in mm/min, and
D is the drill dia meter in mm.

Discussion

Examination of axial force in figure 2 indicates that the force is somewhat higher during most of the experiments, when machining the conventional PM material (PMC). A similar increase in torque when machining PMC as compared to plastic impregnated PM material (PMP) can be seen in figure 3. However, the question still lingers whether this observed increase in force and torque in figures 2 and 3 is significant or not? In order to answer this question a paired comparison design test was conducted. From this test it was found that during most of the experimental conditions shown in table 2b, the difference was significant.

Although the surface roughness appears to criss-cross for PMC and PMP materials at different experimental conditions in figure 4, a close examination shows that during majority of the cases the surface roughness deteriorated when machining plastic impregnated material. In particular, during cutting conditions defined by the body center of the CCD cube, the roughness was higher for PMP material. Also during all the experimental conditions, when the temperatures generated were larger than certain threshold temperature, the surface roughness deteriorated. It is our conjecture at this time that this threshold temperature was the melting point of the impregnated resin. The actual thermal resistance point of the resin used was 150° C (300° F). Thus whenever, the combination of cutting parameters produced temperatures higher than this critical temperature, it appears that the resin melted and coated helically along the cylindrical surface of the drilled hole. As such when surface rough probe was scanned along this spiral weave of resin, it encountered a systematic set of peaks and valleys. This assumption was confirmed by observation of the surface roughness profile on PMP parts. PMP samples with higher surface roughness showed profiles similar to sinusoidal variation.

In order to compare wear of the drill bit, traditional torque experiments were conducted. One hundred holes were drilled on PMC samples with the same speed, feed, and drill bit described in table 2c. Then this procedure was repeated for PMP samples. From figure 5 it is clear that the axial force is much higher during machining of PMC samples, at least during the beginning of the wear experiments. As the number of holes drilled increases, the axial force for PMP increases, but at the same time remains less than that for PMC material. However, the comparison of torque in figure 6 clearly establishes the fact that PMP samples are relatively easier to machine. Further, comparison of surface roughness in figure 7 once again shows the deterioration of surface finish when machining PMP samples.

After drilling 100 holes, the drill bits were examined under optical microscope for wear. Using the same microscope the wear scar area was measured and found to be 2.3 times higher in the case of PMC drill bit, when compared to the wear scar area of drill bit used for machining PMP samples. The photo micrographs of the drill bits is shown in figure 8.

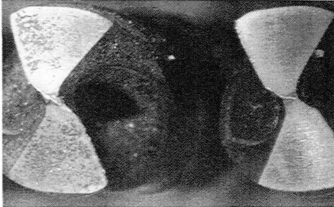
Figure 8a. Left PMC Drill and Right PMP Drill

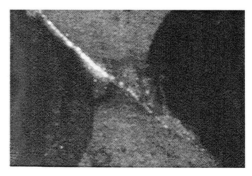
Figure 8b. Magnified Chisel Edge for PMC

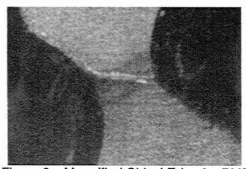
Figure 8c. Magnified Chisel Edge for PMP

From figure 8 it is clear that after drilling 100 holes on PMC material, the wear and gross plastic flow of the drill chisel edge and cutting edges appears to be significantly higher than that on drill bit used for drilling PMP material.

Conclusions

The axial force in drilling plastic impregnated material is lower than when drilling conventional PM parts.

The axial torque in drilling plastic impregnated material is lower than when drilling conventional.

The surface roughness deterioration of plastic impregnated material appears to be due to the melting of impregnated material.

The tool life of the drill is much higher when machining plastic impregnated material.

Relating wear area to tool life, the tool life when machining the conventional powder metal parts is approximately 2.3 times lower than the tool life obtained when machining resin impregnated parts.

From these results, its appears that the machinability of the powder metal parts is enhanced by resin impregnation.

Mathematical models for axial force and axial torque in drilling plastic impregnated material are developed.

Within the envelope of parameters investigated, these equations predict the actual force and torque with accuracy of 87% and 96% respectively.

Acknowledgments

Thanks are due to Mr. Keith Boswell from Powder Metallurgy group at Caterpillar Inc. for supply of the materials and tools for this investigation. The author also wish to thank several of his undergraduate students for conducting parts of the drilling experiments.

References

1. Madan, D.S., "Effect of Manganese Sulfide on Properties of High Performance P/M Alloys and Applications," *Advances in Powder Metallurgy & Particulate Materials,* Vol. 4., pp. 245-267, 1992.

2. Agapiou, J.S., and DeVries, "Machinability of Powder Metallurgy Materials," *Intl. J. of Powder Metallurgy,* Vol. 24, No. 1, pp. 47-57, 1988.

3. Koos, R., Bockstiegel, G., "The Influence of Heat Treatment, Inclusions and Porosity on the Machinability of Powder Forged Steel," *Progress in Powder Metallurgy,* Vol. 37, MPIF, Princeton, NJ, pp. 145-157, 1981.

4. Boyer, H.E., and Gall, T.L., Metals Handbook, Desk Edition, *American Society for Metals,* Chap. 27, pp. 26-27, 1985.

5. Capus, J.M., "Machinability Studies with Sintered Ferrous Alloys," SAE Technical Paper 810246, SAE International Congress and Exposition, Feb., 1981.

6. Fulmer, J.J., and Blanton, J.M., *Advances in Powder Metallurgy & Particulate Materials,* Vol. 4., pp. 283-296, 1992.

7. Johansson, R., "Different Methods to Improve Machinability of High Strength Sintered Steels," *Modern Developments in Powder Metallurgy,* Vol. 21, MPIF, Princeton, NJ, pp. 381-394, 1988.

8. Fletcher, F.B., *Modern Developments in Powder Metallurgy,* Vol. 10, MPIF, Princeton, NJ, pp. 453-456, 1977.

9. Andersen, P.J., and Hirschorn, J.S., *Modern Developments in Powder Metallurgy,* Vol. 10, MPIF, Princeton, NJ, pp. 477-490, 1977.

10. Engstorm, U., "Machinability of Sintered Steel," *Powder Metallurgy,* Vol. 26, No. 3, pp. 137-144, 1983.

11. Roy, L.G., L'Espe´rance, G., Lambert, P., and Pease, L.F., "Prealloyed Manganese Sulfide Powders for Improved Machinability in P/M Parts," *Progress in Powder Metallurgy,* Vol. 43, MPIF, Princeton, NJ, pp. 489-498, 1987.

12. Chopra, K.S., "Manganese Sulfide in Machining Grade Ferrous P/M Alloys," *Modern Developments in Powder Metallurgy,* Vol. 21, MPIF, Princeton, NJ, pp. 361-380, 1988.

13. Nigarura, S., L'Espe'rance, G., Roy, L.G., DeRege, A., and Pease III, L.F., "The Influence of Powder Processing on the Nature of Inclusions and its Relation to the Machinability of MnS Prealloyed P/M Parts," *Advances in Powder Metallurgy & Particulate Materials,* Vol. 4., pp. 223-243, 1992.

14. Chernenkoff, R.A., Hall, D.W., Mocarski, S., and Gagne, M., "Material Characterization of Powder-Forged Copper Steels," SAE Technical Paper 901055, SAE International Congress and Exposition, Detroit, Michigan, March, 1991.

15. Kaldor, S., and Lenz, E. "Investigation of Tool Life of Twist Drills", *Annals of C.I.R.P.,* Vol. 29, (1980), pp. 23-27.

16. Shaw, M.C., and Oxford Jr., C.J., "On the Drilling of Metals 2 - The Torque and Thrust in Drilling", *Am. Soc. Mech. Engrs.,* (1957), pp. 139-147.

17. Williams, R.A., and McGilchrist, C.A., "An Experimental Study of Drill Life", *Int. J. Prod. Res.,* Vol. 10, (1972), pp. 175-191.

18. DeFilippi, A., and Ippolito, R., "Analysis of the Correlation Among Cutting Force Variations, Chip Formation Parameters, and Machinability", *Annals of C.I.R.P.,* Vol. 21, (1972), pp. 29-30.

19. Shareef, I., Wiemken, N., and Lis, J., "Development of a Mathematical Model for Prediction of Forces in Machining", *Advanced Machining Technology III Conference,* SME-IMTS90, Chicago, Illinois, 1990.

20. Jalali, S.A., and Kolarik, W.J., "Tool Life and Machinability Models for Drilling Steels," *International Journal of Machine Tools Manufacturing,* Vol. 31, No. 3, (1991), pp. 273-282.

21. Shareef, I., "Machinability Models for Drilling Cast Iron," Proceedings of the Conference on A Systems Approach to Machining, IAMS, Cincinnati, Ohio, pp. 165-172, May, 1993.

22. Shareef, I., Waheed, M.B., and Durham, K., "Power, Force, and Torque Models for Comparison of Casting Methods," Proceedings of the International Conference on Production Research, Elsevier, pp. 169-172, August, 1993.

23. Montgomery, D.C., "Design and Analysis of Experiments," Third Edition, John Wiley and Sons, New York, NY, (1991).

Proceedings of the ASM 1993 Materials Congress, Pittsburgh, Pennsylvania, October 17-21, 1993

Laser Drilling of Composite Materials

B. Sheehan
HGG Laserfare Inc.
Smithfield, Rhode Island

Laser Drilling of Composite Materials

Composite materials offer the manufacturing engineer a wide range of useful properties on an everyday basis that were only dreamed of decades ago. However, they also represent a host of new challenges when working with them. Laser processing offers a practical solution to many of these fabrication problems.

As soon as the laser made an entry into the world of manufacturing it was accepted as a viable versatile tool; its ability to machine materials which were difficult with conventional techniques and its compatibility with automation, both have allowed the laser to grow in acceptance in, most notably, the aerospace, biomedical, and automotive industries. In some cases, there is no tool that can compete with the laser's capacity for reliability and output.

The two most common types of industrial lasers used in processing composite materials are the solid state Nd:YAG and the carbon dioxide laser. The most prevalent difference between these lasers is the excitation source, but they are more commonly separated by their difference in material processing.

Common operations for both conventional and non-conventional machining of composite materials are trimming, drilling, and boring. Conventional machining is difficult to perform due to the anisotrophy, inhomogeneous composition and hardness and abrasiveness nature of composite materials. Also, excessive tool wear significantly increase machining time and expense. Delamination can occur due to tool friction and is increased with tool wear. Water jet produces cutting forces, but this less than conventional machining causes a host of problems i.e., tooling, tolerances. Also, materials can absorb fluids causing delamination or can become trapped in the fibers. Laser machining offers the advantages of high process rates, no tool wear, no contact force and relatively high precision.

The laser focuses intense energy down to a spot that is only .008" to .010", typically and during processing the material that escapes vaporization is melted and sealed, leaving an unfrayed hole or edge. Reducing delamination, debonding and fiber breakage can lead to higher strength in the finished part.

There are two ways in which a laser drills a hole. The first is known as trepanning, in which the laser essentially cuts a circle into the material. The second is known as percussion or burst drilling, where the beam simply pulses through the material without further manipulation. The size of a burst drill hole is dependent on the diameter of the laser beam. A laser can be fitted with special optics that shrink the typical .008" - .010" beam diameter down to a very minuscule .002" diameter. We will discuss both types of drilling and touch on some related technologies that are continually opening new avenues for laser processing improvements.

Drilling Holes in Kevlar Noise Suppression Panels

Task: To trepan drill 8800 .125" diameter holes in a slightly bowed kevlar panel.

Procedure.
A 1200 watt CO_2 laser was used operating in pulse mode. The overall power output from the beam was 300 watts. The laser beam was held stationary while the part was positioned under the beam.

The use of this method had several drawbacks. One panel was able to be completed in approximately six hours. Costs associated with this cycle time, far exceeded the customer's budget and therefore had to be reduced. There was also a problem caused by inertia. Because the beam was held stationary while the part and the associated tooling were moved, the mass was sufficient enough to cause occasional over-travel resulting in a slightly elliptical hole. Also, higher cutting speeds were not possible due to the physical limitations of the tooling configurations. That is, the equipment has a rather limited range of speed. The goal was to enhance cycle time while enhancing quality. Two devices were instrumental in attaining this goal.

The first step was to find a way to keep the part stationary while manipulating the beam. To do this, a device called an orbital cutting nozzle was attached to the lens focusing assembly. The orbital nozzle rotates the lens which focuses the laser beam onto the work surface (Figure 1). Thus, the beam moves in a circle while the part remains stationary. The orbital nozzle assembly not only solved the problem, it also significantly reduced the time to drill one panel, since the orbital nozzle moves faster than the tooling table.

The second step was to design an auto focus device that would keep the orbital lens assembly the proper focal distance from the work surface. Because conventional auto-focus devices work by utilizing a material's capacitance, they can only be used with conductive materials. Therefore, a new method had to be developed for use on nonconductive materials such as Kevlar. HGG Laser Fare Inc. designed a device that uses an HeNe laser beam to triangulate positions and automatically adjust focal distance when necessary (Figure 2).

The overall result was a significant reduction in cycle and set up time. Under the old method, it took about two seconds to drill a single hole. The orbital nozzle assembly allowed for a hole to be drilled first at .4 seconds and later to .25 seconds. Also, the auto-focus allows more leeway in set up, resulting in a shorter set up time. What once took six hours to do could now to done in two.

The increased cutting speed is doubly advantageous due to the fact that the material is exposed to the beam for a significantly shorter period of time. Therefore, damaging effects of the beam, such as charring are substantially reduced. These effects were also controlled with the auto-focus device. Because focal distance is constantly maintained, the efficiency of the beam is assured because the place of highest energy density is held constant.

Drilling Small Holes for Laminar-Flow Panels

Task: To trepan drill 8800 .125" diameter holes in a slightly bowed kevlar panel

Procedure.
A YAG laser fitted with special optics to keep the beam diameter between .001 - .002 inches is the best choice for this type of application.

This procedure, to be done cost effectively, must be done "on the fly". Basically, it is preferable to have the laser pulse as often as possible while moving the work surface under the beam, with each pulse vaporizing a small hole in the material. The problem this application presents is that if the positioning equipment is not synchronized with the laser controller, then hole patterns cannot be guaranteed for replicable.

The resolution of this obstacle was found in the development of software that could coordinate the speed of the beam pulse (measured as pulses/second) with travel parameters (i.e., speed and distance, measured in inches or centimeters per minute) as well as account for the firing of the laser and assure laser firing.

With this technical advance, material for laminar flow panel (and other applications) can be produced quickly, efficiently and cost-effectively. Quite simply, each pulse will create a single hole and the controller makes it possible to create a specific hole pattern with accurate positioning. Additionally, it is now possible to carry out this task "on the fly" with a reliable degree of repeatability.

Of course, we in the laser industry don't see the laser as a solution for all of the problems presented by new materials and new product designs. The major limitation of using laser to machine composites, as well as other materials, is the fact that the laser beam begins to diverge soon after it is focused. The result of this divergence is an energy dissipation over the area of the divergence (Figure 3). Consequently, cut quality and efficiency decrease proportionately to the distance the beam has to travel through the material. Because of this, material thicknesses of about 3/8 of an inch are about the limit for cutting with systems of less than 1500 watts.

We do, however, see a very bright and focused future for laser processing.

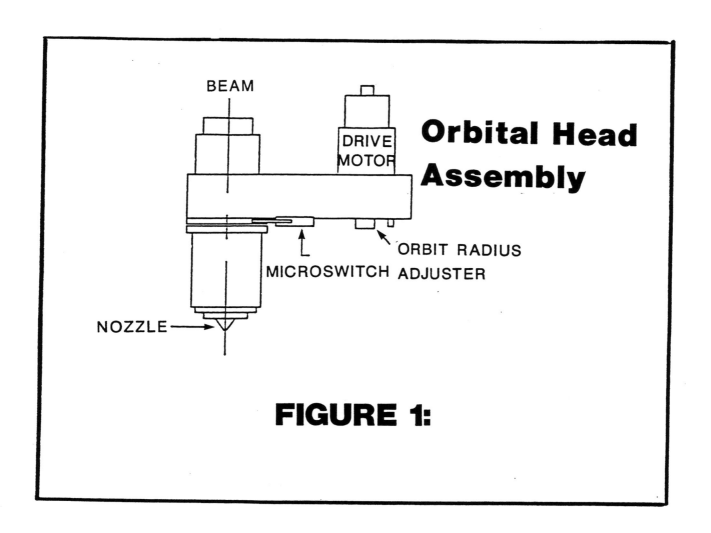

FIGURE 1:

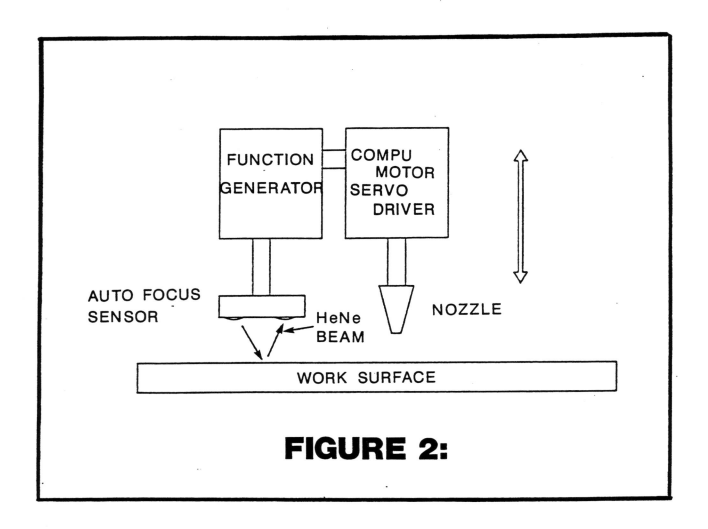

FIGURE 2:

BEAM DIAMETER

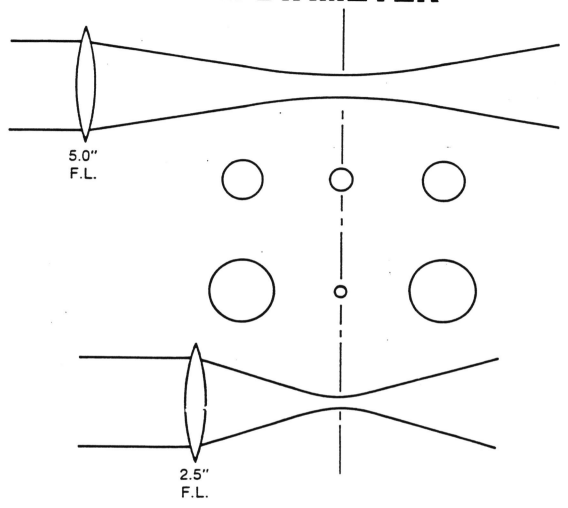

5.0"
F.L.

2.5"
F.L.

Beam diameters at equal distances from focus position for lenses of different focal length

$$\text{Intensity} = \frac{\text{Power}}{\text{Area}} \cong \frac{1.3 \text{ Power}}{(\text{Diameter})^2}$$

FIGURE 3:

Proceedings of the ASM 1993 Materials Congress, Pittsburgh, Pennsylvania, October 17-21, 1993

Procedure Optimization and Hardware Improvements in Abrasive Waterjet Cutting Systems

K. Zaring, G. Erichsen, C. Burnham
Flow International Corporation
Kent, Washington

ABSTRACT

Recent research in abrasive waterjet utilization has generated excellent product enhancements and methods for process optimization. Many hardware enhancements address the five axis, fully automated cutting market. Others minimize the operator intervention when piercing at low pressures with an AWJ system. Still others minimize the "ghosting" that can be seen on the surface of materials cut with an AWJ.

How to use the AWJ efficiently has also been addressed. A database consisting of optimum operating parameters and cut speeds is now available to lessen the learning curve for a new user and to help experienced users cut more efficiently and cost effectively.

ABRASIVE WATERJET (AWJ) CUTTING WORKS BY combining a focused jet of ultra-high pressure (up to 379,212 KPa {55 kpsi}) water with granular abrasives to form an extremely powerful means of cutting and piercing virtually all hard materials, from metals and composites, to glass and ceramics.

AWJ technology has matured considerably over the past 2 years to become a widely used, reliable machining process. However, this relatively young process is still developing. Research and development continues to push the technology toward fully automated systems. The goal is to achieve the highest efficiency with no operator guesswork.

AWJ's offer many advantages over other non-traditional machining methods. These advantages include:

- Omnidirectional cutting capability to cut all types of materials.
- No heat affected zones on the cut materials.
- Low cutting forces; usually less than 2.27 kg (5 lbs) vertically.
- Generally fewer process steps.
- Smaller kerf width than plasma or routing.
- Tight tolerance cutting.
- Very simple or sometimes no tooling required.
- Reliable, repeatable part production.

This paper will give an overview of the components of an abrasivejet cutting system (minus the high pressure pumping system) and explain the function of each. It will then detail the options currently available to fully automate a multi-axis cutting cell. Other system enhancing options will also be detailed, including the FLOWpro cutting database and a dehazing device.

Basic Systems

The basic system components of an AWJ cutting system include the Abrasive Metering System and the Abrasive Cutting Head (Figure 1). Also necessary for an AWJ system is a catcher to confine and dissipate the spent abrasive jet. The components are integrated into any number of motion devices to produce the cut parts required for a variety of applications.

The Abrasive Metering System consists of the abrasive hopper, the abrasive, the abrasive metering valve, and the abrasive delivery line. The reliability and cutting efficiency of AWJ cutting is very dependent on the smooth operation of the metering system. The hopper stores the clean, dry abrasive for use when cutting. High quality, well screened abrasives are needed for consistent AWJ cutting. Wet or poor quality abrasives will have poor flow characteristics. Attached directly to the exit port of the hopper is the abrasive metering valve. Its function is to turn the flow of abrasive on and off, to meter the amount of abrasive used and to purge the abrasive feed line of any transient water when the abrasive waterjet is not in use.

Working in conjunction with the Abrasive Metering System is the Abrasive Cutting System. The Abrasive Cutting System consists of the abrasivejet cutting head, including the high pressure valve actuator, valve body, nozzle body extension tube, waterjet orifice, abrasive mixing chamber and mixing tube. The cutting head is pneumatically operated with its operation tied into that of the abrasive metering valve, i.e. when the cutting head is activated to begin the flow of high pressure water, the abrasive metering valve is opened to begin the flow of abrasive.

When the abrasive cutting head is actuated, high pressure water flows through the orifice into the mixing chamber and out through the mixing tube. As the water enters the mixing chamber, it creates an area of partial vacuum, which draws the metered flow of abrasive particles through the abrasive feed line and into the mixing chamber.

The abrasive combines with the waterjet to create the high energy abrasivejet cutting stream. This stream exits the cutting head through the mixing tube. The mixing chamber assembly includes alignment screws and a gimballed mount. These alignment screws enable the user to quickly align the waterjet stream to the center of the mixing tube. The alignment is necessary to achieve the most powerful cutting stream and to maintain long mixing tube life.

Improvements in the rate of wear of the consumable materials of the abrasivejet cutting head have enhanced its use for continuous cutting and tight tolerance applications. Previous cutting head technology required the replacement of wear parts, particularly the mixing tube, and realignment of the cutting head generally every one to two hours, depending on the application and the cutting accuracy required. This frequent changing of worn mixing tubes required constant operator attention and necessitated much system downtime.

The greatly extended mixing tube life permits parts which are cut at the end of a shift to be within several thousandths of an inch tolerance to those cut at the start of the shift, without any adjustments to the machine tool for kerf compensation or numerous replacements of mixing tubes, as was previously required. This translates to less downtime per shift, higher throughput potential, and tighter cut part tolerances.

CATCHERS

Abrasivejet cutting develops a large amount of energy (up to 67 KW {50 HP}) at the cutting nozzle. As much as 75% of that energy may be retained in the stream after it has passed through a cut. Three basic type of catchers are available to dissipate this energy. They are room catchers, tank catchers and compact catchers. Each catcher dissipates the remaining energy of the abrasivejet stream and collects the spent abrasives and kerf material.

A tank catcher is a large steel container permanently positioned beneath the work surface within the work area of the AWJ motion equipment. Tank catchers are supplied for applications where the work piece is stationary and the end effector is mobile and capable of horizontal or near horizontal cuts, such as with a 2- or 3-axis gantry robot.

Tank catchers are filled with at least 50.8 cm (20 inches) of water to absorb residual energy. Tank catchers can also be filled with other energy absorbing media in addition to the water. The typical energy absorbing media used for these catchers is steel balls. The combinations of energy absorbing media and water is preferred over only water in installations where quieter operation is required. Tank catchers also have material supports which can be as simple as resting the material directly on the steel balls or as elaborate as dedicated palletized fixturing.

When using a standard tank catcher, the spent abrasives and kerf material will settle out and remain in the tank, while the water drains off. The tank must then be cleaned manually as it fills with solids. This clean-out requires that the system be shut down until cleaning is complete. Frequency of cleaning varies based on system usage.

The largest breakthrough in catcher technology has been in the emergence of the self-cleaning catcher. This catcher is used for work envelopes anywhere from 45.72 cm x 45.72 cm (18 inches x 18 inches) to 1.83 m x 3.05 m (6 feet x 10 feet). The system consists of a catcher tank with a properly sloping bottom. This sloped bottom tank is filled with water (and at the discretion of the user, a layer of steel balls). The spent abrasive and kerf materials drain out of the catcher along with the cutting water. These materials then go through a particulate separation device where the abrasive particles settle out and the clean water is drained off. The clean water is pumped back into the catcher to provide a constant supply of flush water, while the solids are dropped into a holding drum. Any excess clean overflow water is directed to drain. When the holding drum becomes full, it is removed and replaced with an empty drum. Drums are changed easily and no system downtime is required.

This catcher technology is very user friendly and useful for all types of cutting applications. It makes the disposal of spent abrasive a much less time consuming and labor intensive job. It also facilitates the disposal of hazardous waste material if what is being cut is considered a hazardous waste.

Compact catchers are small containers filled with energy absorbing media, typically stainless steel balls. These catchers are usually mounted to move with the cutting head via a "C" frame bracket and are used primarily in 3-dimensional machining. After the abrasivejet stream passes through the workpiece, it enters the catcher and strikes the steel balls, sending them into motion. The continuous collision and agitation of the balls effectively absorbs and dissipates residual abrasive waterjet energy. The catcher bodies are not wear items, but the stainless steel balls are. The steel balls are consumed at a predictable rate and are automatically replenished from a small reservoir on the catcher.

The process waste produced by AWJ cutting is a slurry consisting of water and solid sediments, which are minute particles of abrasive grit, kerf material and catcher ball fragments. To prevent the slurry from separating and clogging the outlet drain of compact catchers, a vacuum and waste separation system is supplied to constantly evacuate process waste and transfer it to a waste separation and disposal system.

Compact catcher bodies are designed as small as possible in order to function in tight spaces. Compact catchers are ideally suited for robotic applications where a low profile cutting head is necessary. Following special operating procedures also allows use of compact catchers in non-horizontal cutting applications.

OPTIONS FOR FULL SYSTEM AUTOMATION

When integrating an AWJ onto a robotic system, care must be taken to assure proper operation of both the abrasive metering system and the abrasive cutting head. A number of system options exist that are well suited for multi-axis cutting installations to make them as automated and trouble free as possible.

Currently available is an Automated Metering Valve. Its function is the same as that of the standard manual valve, that is, to turn off and on the abrasive flow and to meter the amount of abrasive used for cutting. This metering valve, however, makes use of a servo motor to position the opening of the valve to flow the proper amount of abrasive for the cutting application. This automatic positioning can be programmed into the cutting program directly on the controller of the robotic system. The operator need never to touch the valve for adjustment, but will adjust the flow as he would another machine axis.

Also available is the Abrasive Loss of Flow Switch. This switch is tied into the abrasive feed system and indicates when abrasive flow has been interrupted for any reason. This interruption can trigger a system shut-down or sound a warning, before any workpiece damage can occur, whichever the user desires. The indication of loss of abrasive flow is invaluable when cutting laminated or brittle parts.

Another system enhancement available is a Bulk Abrasive Transfer System. This system transports abrasive from a large storage hopper to a smaller metering hopper situated relatively close to the abrasivejet cutting head. A bulk transfer system is especially useful when the size of the cutting system is large and the hopper, in order to be near the cutting head, is inaccessible. The system contains sensors to indicate low abrasive levels in both the metering hopper and the storage hopper. When the metering hopper is low, the abrasive is transported from the storage hopper with the use of compressed air. A batch of abrasive drops into the transporter and is pushed through the system piping to the metering hopper with the use of low pressure compressed air.

The low pressure minimizes component wear from the abrasive particles. A hopper close to the cutting head has the advantage of providing consistent abrasive flows for all required cutting parameters.

Finally, the ideal tool for multi-axis cutting systems is the pre-aligned Paser abrasivejet cartridge. This tool has been developed to cut the amount of operator involvement with the cutting system to a minimum and improve part production accuracy. This part is simply attached to the extension tube of the abrasivejet cutting head and cutting can begin. No alignment of jet stream to mixing tube is necessary. The tool center point (TCP) remains consistent from one Paser abrasivejet cartridge to another, thus making it indispensable for 3-dimensional cutting.

PART QUALITY IMPROVEMENTS

For those applications where the surface frosting created during AWJ machining is unacceptable, a new device is now available. It is called the Paser Dehazer. The Dehazer easily attaches to the cutting head and works by surrounding the cutting stream with low pressure water. This minimizes the surface frosting by stripping away the low powered shroud that surrounds the high velocity abrasivejet stream. The Dehazer also has the added benefit of minimizing noise and airborne abrasive grit. The Dehazer is especially useful when cutting glass, brass, marble or any material with a shiny surface.

DATABASE DEVELOPMENT

A large emphasis has been placed on improving the components of the abrasive waterjet system. Equally important is the need to understand the proper way to operate an abrasive waterjet effectively for each application.

There are many variables that affect the performance of an AWJ cutting system. Among the most important are water pressure, abrasive flow rate, abrasive type, waterjet orifice (jewel) size, mixing tube geometry, the type of material being cut and the material thickness. Because these variables may be adjusted over a wide range